Fundamentals of GAS Utilization

Third Edition

John Dutton

Centennial College Press

Editorial: Rhys Griffiths

The author has used his best efforts to ensure that the
contents of this book are accurate, however the book is
sold without warranty of any kind as to the accuracy
of the contents. The user accepts full responsibility for
any consequence arising from the use of this book.

Published by: Centennial College Press
P.O. Box 631
Station A
Scarborough, Ontario
Canada   M1K 5E9

Printed in Canada by Maracle Press

ISBN 0-919852-35-1

Table of Contents

Preface

Fundamentals of Gas Utilization is a basic text book on the principles and application of natural gas handling and usage for residential and light commercial gas systems below 400,000 Btuh (120 kW).

There have been many recent changes in the gas industry in furnace design and control application. The third edition of *Fundamentals of Gas Utilization* addresses these current changes. The book examines the fan assisted furnace in its application as a high efficiency furnace. Hot surface ignition system has also been added to the text as well as the integrated furnace control introduced in *Chapter 11* which deals with automatic ignition systems. The chapters on venting have been substantially changed to deal with the venting requirements for the fan assisted furnace. New venting tables have been added to facilitate the sizing of Category I vented appliances (i.e., natural draft and fan assisted appliances).

Like the first and second editions, this third edition of the text is designed to cover the essentials of trade theory and trade practice in gas fitting at the residential and light commercial level. It can be used as a college text book or a resource manual for self study in the field. For both applications the text will provide the essential material in preparation for provincial certification as a residential, light commercial gas fitter.

Acknowledgements

The material in this third edition of *Fundamentals of Gas Utilization*, as with the first and second, is an accumulation of the contributions of many people. Their cooperation and encouragement has been much appreciated and is gratefully acknowledged.

I extend my sincere thanks to my colleagues and students at George Brown College for their many helpful comments and suggestions in revising the third edition of *Fundamentals of Gas Utilization*.

I would also like to thank the following organizations for their contributions in the form of photographs and illustrations, and for granting permission for reproduction without which this book would not have been possible:

Duomatic Olsen, Inc.
Arkla Industries, Inc.
Emerson Electric (Canada) Ltd.
Lennox Industries (Canada) Ltd.
Borg-Warner (Canada) Ltd.
Grimsby Stove and Furnace Ltd.
Johnson Controls Co.
Essex Group, Inc.
E.J. Walsh and Company Ltd.
Fenwell, Inc.
Mine Safety Appliance Co.
Canadian Meter Co. Ltd.
Dresser Industries Canada Ltd.
Bacharach Instrument Co.
Rockwell International of Canada Ltd.
Maxitrol Co.
Field Control Division
Grinell Co. of Canada
Eclipse Fuel Engineering Co. of Canada Ld.
Robertshaw Controls (Canada) Ltd.

John Dutton
George Brown College
Toronto, Ontario

Properties of Natural Gas 1

The properties of natural gas, like other fuels, are classified into physical and chemical properties.

Physical properties describe the physical aspects of the fuel, its state, weight, colour, odour and composition. Chemical properties describe the characteristics of the fuel's combustion process.

The following is a brief description of the physical and chemical properties of natural gas.

Physical Properties

State: Natural gas has a boiling point of approximately minus 258°F (161°C), therefore, in its application and transmission, natural gas as a substance will always be in a gaseous state. It should be noted that in measuring gases as to volume and flow, we refer to volume in cubic feet (cu. ft. or cf) and flow in cubic feet per hour (cu. ft./hr. or cfh); just as liquids are referred to in volume as gallons and flow as gallons per hour (gph).

Likewise, in the metric system of measurement the volume of a gas is measured in cubic metres (m^3) and flow in cubic metres per hour (m^3/h). Also, liquid volume is measured in litres (L) and liquid flow as litres per hour (L/h).[1]

Colour, Taste, Odour: Natural gas in its pure state is an odourless, colourless and tasteless gas. A safety precaution is that natural gas must be detectable by smell. To achieve this, the local gas company adds an odourant to the natural gas called *Mercaptan.* The amount of odourant added to the gas is very small (approximately one lb. per million cu.ft.). Yet, this is sufficient to give natural gas a noticeable and distinct *gassy* smell.

Composition: The composition of natural gas can vary from place to place throughout North America. The amount of variance in composition however is quite small since the largest component of natural gas is *methane.* Methane represents approximately 85% to 90% of the total substance of natural gas.

---

[1] To assist you in the conversion from the standard or imperial to metric and visa vera, see the conversion tables in Appendix II.

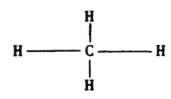

Figure 1-1: The chemical structure of methane (CH₄).

Methane is a simple *hydrocarbon*, a substance consisting of carbon and hydrogen. Methane (CH_4) is composed of one atom of carbon linked with four atoms of hydrogen *(see Figure 1-1)*.

Methane gas is a very light fuel gas (a gas used to supply heat energy). As the number of carbon and hydrogen atoms in a fuel gas is increased, the gas becomes progressively heavier and its heating value as a fuel is increased. *Figures 1-2* illustrates the chemical structure of ethane, propane and butane, all fuel gases that are heavier than methane.

Natural gas, as a fuel gas, will contain methane and other heavier hydrocarbons such as ethane, propane and butane. However, as stated earlier, 85% to 90% of natural gas is methane. It is therefore convenient to regard the properties of natural gas as the properties of methane. A typical analysis of natural gas could be the following:

Methane 89.68%
Ethane.. 4.68%
Propane 1.73%
Butane.. 0.67%
Pentane.. 0.15%
Nitrogen... 2.89%
Carbon Dioxide..................................... 0.20%
And .34 grains of sulfur per 100 cubic feet of natural gas.

Specific Gravity (Relative Density): The specific gravity of a gas is by definition the weight of the gas as compared to the weight of an equal volume of air at standard conditions, in which air is taken at unity (e.g., one).[2] The specific gravity of natural gas is approximately:

0.60

The specific gravity of air is equal to:

1.0

This property is an advantage in the handling of natural gas. Natural gas escaping from a leak will tend to rise and vent itself naturally since the gas is lighter than air. A heavier fuel gas such as propane has a tendency to remain in pockets at ground level creating a hazard if open flames are present. Also, mixing of the natural gas with air in the burner system can be easily accomplished to establish the correct *Flame Characteristics*, which indicate the quality of combustion that is taking place. Flame characteristics are the colour, shape and intensity of the flame.

Ethane (C₂H₆)

Propane (C₃H₈)

Butane (C₄H₁₀)

Figure 1-2: Fuel gases that are heavier than methane.

[2] In the gas industry *Standard Conditions* are an absolute pressure of 14.73 psia and a temperature of 60°F often called standard temperature and pressure S.T.P. In metric, standard conditions are 15°C and 101.325 kPa (absolute) pressure.

Toxicity: Natural gas is nontoxic. There is nothing in the composition of natural gas that is injurious to health in any way. This is in contrast to manufactured or coal gas, which contains carbon monoxide, a very toxic (poisonous) substance.

Chemical Properties

Required Air/Gas Ratio: The required air/gas ratio is the cubic feet or cubic metres of air required to burn one cubic foot or cubic metre of natural gas completely without having any excess air found in the products of combustion.[3] The required air/gas ratio is sometimes called the *theoretical air*. The required air/gas ratio of natural gas is:

$$\boxed{10/1}$$

The following are factors in the *combustion air supply* that must be understood to achieve adequate combustion of natural gas.

i)   The yellow flame (Luminous flame)

A yellow flame is a flame where there is no premixing of the natural gas with the required air for combustion. All the required air for the combustion process is supplied around the flame as it burns at the burner port. The flame will have a slightly blue colour zone at the burner port followed by a much larger area that is bright, luminous and yellow in colour. The blue portion of the flame is where the hydrogen is burning at a greater speed than the carbon that burns at a lower speed in the yellow portion of the flame.

If this flame makes contact with a cold surface, sooting will take place, since the *ignition temperature* of the flame has been lowered. Yellow flames are sometimes found on low input pilot burners used with gas ranges.

ii)   The blue flame (Bunsen flame)

The blue flame is quite different from the yellow flame. It is blue in colour, small, non-luminous and has a higher temperature.

The blue flame is a result of some premixing of the fuel with the required air for combustion. The air required for the combustion process can be broken down into two air supplies: *primary air*, air mixed with the fuel prior to its ignition; and *secondary air*, air mixed with fuel around the flame as in the yellow flame.

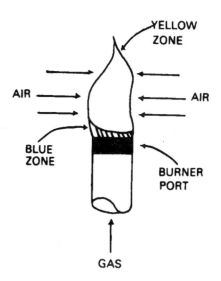

Figure 1-3: The Yellow Flame Burner

---

[3] A rule of thumb—1 cu. ft. of air will release 100 Btu of heat from any fuel. For metric the rule is 3.725 MJ of heat for each M^3 of air supplied.

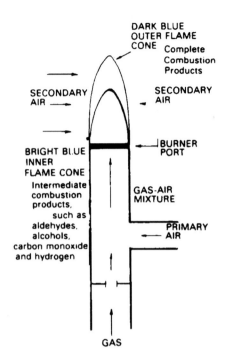

DARK BLUE
OUTER FLAME
CONE Complete
Combustion
Products

SECONDARY
AIR

SECONDARY
AIR

BURNER
PORT

BRIGHT BLUE
INNER
FLAME CONE
Intermediate
combustion
products,
such as
aldehydes,
alcohols,
carbon monoxide
and hydrogen

GAS-AIR
MIXTURE

PRIMARY
AIR

GAS

Figure 1-4: The Blue Flame Burner

The initial combustion takes place on the surface of the inner flame cone as the oxygen from the primary air combines with the gas. Since combustion takes place on the surface of the inner portion, the body of the inner cone is composed of unburned fuel and primary air. Partial combustion takes place in the bright blue area resulting in the release of intermediate products of combustion. In the outer cone, oxygen in the secondary air is mixed with the intermediate products of combustion. This gives the final and complete combustion that takes place on the rim of the outer cone. Complete combustion is achieved by the presence of secondary air.

For the blue flame the outer cone can strike or impinge a cold surface without affecting the combustion as in the yellow flame. However, the inner cone cannot make contact with any cold surface since incomplete combustion will occur, giving *carbon monoxide* and *aldehydes*, which are products of incomplete combustion. Carbon monoxide is a colourless, odourless and extremely toxic gas. While carbon monoxide is an odourless gas, aldehydes have a sharp and penetrating odour. They are also toxic, and tend to irritate the eyes, nose and throat.

iii)   Excess Air

The required air supply is the sum of all primary and secondary air needed to perfectly complete the combustion of the fuel. In practice, additional air must be supplied to ensure the complete combustion of the fuel. This excess air supply above the ideal or theoretical amount is called *Excess Air.*

iv)   Composition of Air

It is the oxygen in the air that supports the combustion of the gas. Since air consists of oxygen and nitrogen, not all the air is involved in the combustion process. Nitrogen is an inert gas and does not participate in the combustion process. The composition of air is approximately:

> 20% Oxygen & 80% Nitrogen

Heating Value or Heat Content: The heating value of a fuel is the amount of heat energy released by a measured amount of the fuel during the combustion process.

The heat energy released is measured in British thermal units (Btu) which is the amount of heat energy that will raise one pound of water through one degree fahrenheit (°F).

The heating value for natural gas is approximately:

> 1000 Btu/cf

4

The gas consumption of an appliance is rated on an hourly basis in terms of:

> The FLOW RATE, in cubic feet per hour (cfh)

or

> HEAT RATE or INPUT RATE, in Btu per hour (Btuh)

The heat rate or, the more commonly used input rate, by definition is simply the amount of heat energy generated by the appliance as it burns the fuel supplied to it during each hour of its operation. Therefore, the input rate of an appliance can be determined by the following:

> INPUT RATE (Btuh)= Heating value of the gas X gas flow rate

Knowing the input rate of an appliance, the flow rate can be determined by the following:

$$\text{The FLOW RATE (cfh)} = \frac{\text{Input rate}}{\text{Heating value of the gas}}$$

Examples:
1. A natural gas appliance has a flow rate of 100 cfh, determine the appliance Btuh input rate.

   Appliance Btuh input rate = 1000 Btu/cf X 100 cfh
    = 100,000 Btuh

2. A natural gas appliance has an input rate of 100,000 Btuh, determine the cfh gas flow rate of the appliance.

   $$\text{Appliance cfh flow rate} = \frac{100,000 \text{ Btuh}}{1000 \text{ Btu/cf}}$$

   $$= 100 \text{ cfh}$$

In the metric system, heat energy is measured in *joules* (J) and the heating value for natural gas as expressed in metric terms is approximately:

> 37.25 MJ/m^3

where: M = mega, a prefix representing 10^6 units
J = joules
m^3 = cubic metres

The hourly rated gas consumption of an appliance, as measured in the metric system, can be expressed as:

> The FLOW RATE in cubic metres per hour (m^3/h)

or

> The INPUT RATE in mega joules per hour (MJ/h)

However, expressing the appliance input rate in MJ/h can be awkward and it is usually expressed in kilowatts (kW) in which:

> 1kW = 3.6MJ/h

Therefore, the usual expression of appliance input rate is:

> The INPUT RATE in kilowatts (kW)

The input rate of an appliance in metric terms can be determined by the following:

$$\text{INPUT RATE (kW)} = \frac{\text{Heating Value of the gas (MJ/}m^3) \times \text{flow rate (}m^3/h)}{3.6 \text{ (MJ/h)}}$$

Knowing the input rate of an appliance, the flow rate, (in metric terms), can be determined by the following:

$$\text{Flow Rate (}m^3/h) = \frac{\text{Input rate (kW)} \times 3.6 \text{ (MJ/h)}}{\text{Heating value of the gas (MJ/}m^3)}$$

In the metric system, heat energy is measured in *joules* and the rate at which the heat energy is used, (i.e., heat rate or power), is measured in *kilowatts*. This makes the conversion from flow rate to input rate and vice versa awkward.

To simplify the process, the heating value or content of a fuel can be expressed as kWh/m^3. Although this appears awkward, it does simplify the method of calculation.

In this respect, the heating value or content of natural gas can be expressed as approximately:

$$10.35 \text{ kWh/m}^3$$

in which $\dfrac{37.25 \text{ MJ/m}^3}{3.6 \text{ MJ/h}} = 10.35 \text{ kWh/m}^3$

The simplified calculations to determine the input rates and flow rates of an appliance are:

INPUT
RATE = Heating value of the gas (kWh/m³) X Flow rate (M³/h)
(kW)

and

FLOW
RATE = $\dfrac{\text{Input rate (kW)}}{\text{Heating value of the gas (kWh/m}^3)}$
(m³/h)

Examples:

1. A natural gas appliance has a flow rate of 5 m³/h, determine the appliance kW input rate.

    Appliance kW input rate   =   10.35 kWh/m³ X 5 m3/h
      =   51.75 kW

2. A natural gas appliance has an input rate of 51.75 kW, determine the m³/h flow rate of the appliance.

    Appliance m³/h flow rate   = $\dfrac{51.75 \text{ kW}}{10.35 \text{ kWh/m}^3}$

      =   5 m³/h

Flame Temperature: The flame temperature for natural gas is approximately:[4]

$$3500°F$$
$$(1954°C)$$

The maximum obtainable flame temperature can only be achieved at perfect combustion where excess air or fuel will not provide the material to absorb the heat of combustion. The highest temperature occurs at a point just above the outer flame cone.

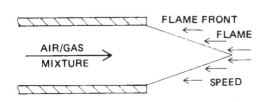

Figure 1-5: Flame Speed or Burning Velocity

Flame Speed: The flame speed is the speed at which the flame front moves towards the air/gas mixture issuing from burner port. The flame front is the dividing line between the air/gas mixture and the combustion products. *(See Figure 1-5.)*

In a stable flame the velocity of the air/gas mixture issuing from the burner port is equal to the burning velocity of the flame, as a result the flame appears stable.

Flame speed depends mostly on the type of gas and the amount of air in the air/gas mixture. Increasing the amount of primary air with constant burner input will increase the flame speed. When the percentage of primary air is increased in a burner, the flame sharpens and the height of the inner cone decreases.

The flame speed for natural gas is approximately:[4]

> 1.0 ft./sec.
> (0.305m/s)

Fuel gases that contain a high amount of hydrogen, such as manufactured or coal gas, have a relatively high flame speed. The higher flame speed allows the burner to achieve a high degree of flame stability under very high air/gas mixture velocities.

Ignition Temperature: Ignition temperature is the temperature at which the combustible mixture of natural gas and air will initiate and maintain the combustion reaction. The ignition temperature for natural gas is approximately:

> 1200° F
> (649° C)

Limits of Flammability: The limits of flammability are the upper and lower percentage of gas in the air/gas mixture that will support combustion. The air/gas mixture can be too fuel lean or too fuel rich to support combustion. The upper and lower limits of flammability can be described as the fuel's range of combustibility in relationship to the percentage of fuel in the air/gas mixture that will support combustion.

The upper and lower limits of flammability of natural gas are approximately:

> Lower Limit = 4%
> Upper Limit = 14%

When the combustion of the fuel is not controlled within the confines of a burner system, the limits of flammability can be called the *Explosive Limits*. There are both the *Lower Explosive Limits* (L.E.L.) and the *Upper Explosive Limits* (U.E.L.). The explosive limits of natural gas are approximately:

$$\boxed{\begin{aligned} L.E.L. &= 4\% \\ U.E.L. &= 14\% \end{aligned}}$$

It is important to understand the operation of portable explosion meters that detect the lower explosion limits of a fuel gas as illustrated in *Figure 1-6*. The principle of operation for various explosion meters is based on the principle of *Catalytic Combustion*.

Using the schematic diagram of the explosion meter *(Figure 1-7)*, an air and gas mixture is drawn into the meter across the filament. The filament consists of a catalytic material that will initiate the combustion of the mixture at a low temperature. The filament, upon the heat of combustion, will change its electrical resistance.

As the filament resistance varies, the balanced electrical bridge, consisting of four resistors, will now be out of balance. A current will flow across the bridge as read by the meter.

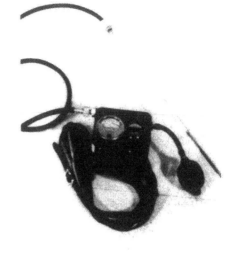

Figure 1-6: Portable Explosion Meter

Figure 1-7: Schematic Flow System and Wiring Diagram of a Portable Explosion Meter

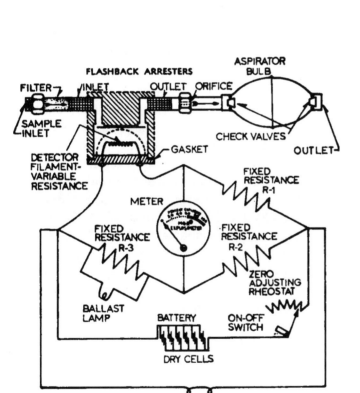

The amount of current flowing across the bridge is a function of the change in filament resistance that is affected by the heat released from the catalytic combustion that in turn is a function of the amount of gas in the combustible mixture being drawn into the instrument. The meter on the instrument is not calibrated in units of current flow, but as a percentage of gas in the mixture leading up to the lower explosive limit marked as 100% on the meter.

The following is an explanation of the various meter readings that can be obtained:

1. Pointer rises slowly, stops between 0 and 100 on the scale. The sample is below the lower explosive limit (L.E.L.) of 4% gas in the air/gas mixture.

2. Pointer moves to the extreme right of the scale and stays there. The sample is above 4% (L.E.L.) and is between 4% and 14% and is explosive.

3. Pointer moves rapidly across the scale and returns to within the scale or below zero. The sample is above 14%, the upper explosive limit (U.E.L.).

Combustion: *Combustion or burning is the rapid combination of a fuel with oxygen resulting in the release of heat.* To achieve the combustion or burning of a fuel, three components of the combustion process must be present as seen in the *combustion triangle (Figure 1-8).*

The presence of the fuel and oxygen are obvious as stated by the opening definition of combustion. However, heat is also an important requirement. Some source of heat (e.g., pilot flame or ignition spark) is needed to elevate the temperature of the air/gas mixture to the required ignition temperature of the fuel. Once the combustion process is started the heat generated in the process will sustain the combustion.

Natural gas is a hydrocarbon consisting of carbon and hydrogen in some combination. The combustion of natural gas can be considered as the combustion of carbon and hydrogen:

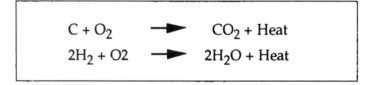

$$C + O_2 \longrightarrow CO_2 + Heat$$
$$2H_2 + O2 \longrightarrow 2H_2O + Heat$$

The combustion of the carbon produces carbon dioxide and heat, and the combustion of the hydrogen produces water (in vapour form) and heat. Combining both carbon and hydrogen as in natural gas, the combustion reaction would be:

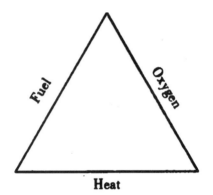

Figure 1-8: The Combustion Triangle

$$CH_4 + 2 O_2 \longrightarrow CO_2 + 2 H_2O + \text{Heat}$$

The Products of Combustion of natural gas and oxygen are carbon dioxide, water (vapor) and heat. The heat generated in the combustion is called the Heat of Combustion and is determined by:

HEAT of COMBUSTION =
Heating value of gas fuel X gas flow rate

However, it is only under certain applications that natural gas is burned using pure oxygen. The source of oxygen for the burning of natural gas utilized in domestic and commercial appliances is air. The composition of air is approximately 20% oxygen and 80% nitrogen, a ratio of 1 oxygen to 4 nitrogen. The combustion of natural gas in which air is the source of oxygen would be:

$$CH_4 + 2 O_2 + 8 N_2 \longrightarrow CO_2 + 2 H_2O + 8 N_2 + \text{Heat}$$

The products of combustion of natural gas and air are carbon dioxide, water vapor, nitrogen and heat.

In the combustion of natural gas, where air is used as the source of oxygen, the nitrogen that is in the air does not enter the combustion reaction. Nitrogen is inert and passes through the combustion process absorbing heat from the combustion reaction.

Tables *T1-1 and T1-2* (on the next page) give the physical and chemical properties of commercial fuel gases used in Canada.

Volume and Heat Energy Unit Conversion Factors for Natural Gas

The following are the conversion factors for natural gas with an approximate heating value of 1000 Btu/cf (37.25 MJ/m3):

MULTIPLY	BY	TO OBTAIN
m^3/h	35.31	cfh
m^3/h	10.35	kW
cfh	1000	Btuh
cfh	0.02832	m^3/h
cfh	0.29299	kW
kW	0.096618	m^3/h
kW	3.413	cfh
m^3/h	35310	Btuh
kW	3413	Btuh
Btuh	0.000293	kW

Table T1-1: Physical and Chemical Properties of Commercial Fuel Gases used in Canada

FUEL GAS	SPECIFIC GRAVITY	HEATING VALUE BTU/CU. FT.	REG'D AIR/GAS RATIO — CU. FT. OF AIR TO CU. FT./FUEL	FLAME TEMP. oF.	FLAME SPEED IN FT/SEC	LIMITS OF FLAMMABILITY
MANUFACTURER	0.5	500	5	3600	2.3	5 — 40
NATURAL GAS	0.6	1000	10	3500	1.0	4 — 14
PROPANE	1.52	2500	25	3650	.95	2 — 10
BUTANE	1.95	3200	32	3660	1.05	2 — 9
ACETYLENE	.91	1448	12	4770	8.75	2.5 — 81

Table T1-2: Physical and Chemical Properties of Commercial Fuel Gases used in Canada

FUEL GAS	RELATIVE DENSITY	HEATING VALUE MJ/m^3	REQ'D AIR/GAS RATIO $-m^3$ OF AIR TO m^3 OF FUEL	FLAME TEMP. °C	FLAME SPEED m/s	LIMITS OF FLAMMABILITY
MANUFACTURED GAS	0.5	18.62	5	1982	0.701	5————40
NATURAL GAS	0.6	37.25	10	1954	0.305	4————14
PROPANE	1.52	93.13	25	2010	0.290	2————10
BUTANE	1.95	119.20	32	2015	0.320	2————9
ACETYLENE	0.91	53.94	12	2632	2.667	2.5————81

Assignment

1. Define the following terms:
   a) Hydrocarbon   e) Blue flame
   b) Specific gravity   f) Primary air
   c) Required air/gas ratio g) Secondary air
   d) Yellow flame   h) Excess air

2. Why is it convenient to consider the properties of natural gas as the properties of methane?

3. List and describe two products of incomplete combustion of natural gas.

4. Give the composition of air.

5. In the practical combustion of natural gas, is all the air utilized? Explain.

6. Define the term heating value of a fuel.

7. Convert 250,000 Btuh into cfh of natural gas.

8. To achieve a stable flame condition the flame speed must equal?

9. Define the terms:
   a) limits of flammability
   b) explosive limits

10. Draw and label the *combustion triangle* and explain its significance.

11. Give the combustion reaction of natural gas with:
    a) Oxygen
    b) Air

12. Describe the needle movement of the explosive meter for:
    a) Reading a natural gas concentration below L.E.L.
    b) Reading a natural gas concentration above the L.E.L. but below the U.E.L.
    c) Reading a natural gas concentration above the U.E.L.

13. How many cubic feet of natural gas would be required to give the equivalent heat produced by 100 cu. ft. of propane gas?

14. Give the following values for natural gas in both standard and metric units:
    a) Specific gravity
    b) Required air/gas ratio
    c) Heating value
    d) Flame temperature
    e) Flame speed
    f) Ignition temperature
    g) Limits of flammability
    h) Explosive limits

15. An appliance has an input rate of 35kW, determine the appliance flow rate in m^3/h.

16. An appliance has a flow rate of $2.5m^3/h$, determine the appliance input rate in:
    i) MJ/h
    ii) kW
    iii) Btuh

2 Gas Physics — Pressure and Flow

One approach to the subject of gas pressure and gas flow can be made by the molecular theory of gases. A gas consists of many molecules and it is the behavior of the gas molecules that determine the properties of a gas. The following are properties of a gas that are important in the understanding of gas pressure and gas flow.

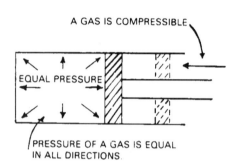

A GAS IS COMPRESSIBLE

EQUAL PRESSURE

PRESSURE OF A GAS IS EQUAL IN ALL DIRECTIONS.

Figure 2-1: Some of the properties of a gas.

1. A gas is able to expand uniformly and indefinitely, expansion being limited only by boundaries of an enclosing container. This property of a gas is called *diffusion*.

2. A gas is highly compressible, because of diffusion; gas molecules can be readily crowded into a smaller space (volume).

3. The pressure of a gas is equal in all directions.

Molecular Theory of Gases

A gas consists of a very large number of very small particles called molecules that are relatively far apart in an empty space. All molecules are identical in each particular gas.

The molecules are in continuous, random and very rapid motion, colliding frequently with each other and with the enclosed walls of a container as illustrated in *Figure 2-2*. The molecules are perfectly elastic so that their collisions with the enclosed walls of the container and each other result in no loss to their total energy. The average speed of the molecules is not reduced due to impact. Think in terms of a rubber ball being thrown against a brick wall. The ball upon impact with the wall will go out of shape; yet, once it has bounced off the wall it soon regains its original shape. The molecules upon collision against the container wall will act in the same fashion. The pressure of a gas is a consequence of this continuous molecular bombardment of the molecules against the enclosing walls of a container.

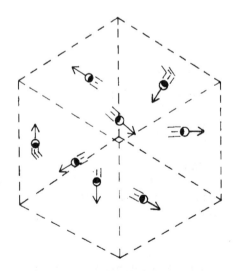

Figure 2-2: Molecules of gas in continuous, random and very rapid motion.

Definition of Pressure

We can describe the pressure of a gas as the force of the molecules being exerted on the walls of a container. Specifically, a gas exerts a pressure, measurable as a force per unit area of the enclosed surface of the container; this pressure is equal in all directions.

Therefore, pressure can be defined as force per unit area:

$$\text{Pressure} = \frac{\text{Force}}{\text{Area}} \quad \text{or} \quad P = \frac{F}{A} \quad \text{or} \quad \frac{\text{lbs}}{\text{sq.in.}} \quad \text{or} \quad \text{psi}$$

And if we consider the metric equivalent:

$$\text{Pressure} = \frac{\text{Force}}{\text{Area}} \text{ or } P = \frac{F}{A} \text{ or } \frac{\text{Newtons}}{\text{sq. metre}} \text{ or } \frac{N}{m^2} \text{ or Pascals (Pa)}$$

Where: N = Newtons, the metric unit of force
m^2 = square metres
Pa = Pascals, the metric unit of pressure

However, since the pascal (Pa) is a relatively small unit of pressure measurement, the *kilopascal* (kPa) is usually used. For example:

$$6895 \text{ Pa} = 1 \text{ psi}$$

and

$$6.895 \text{ kPa} = 1 \text{ psi}$$

The Gas Laws

The pressure of a gas is determined by two significant factors: volume and temperature.

i) Boyle's Law

The pressure of a gas is determined by the number of molecules of the gas within a given container. The more molecules there are per cubic foot or inch of container size, the greater the pressure, simply because there are more molecules to collide with the walls of the container.

Reducing the volume of the container will also increase the pressure of the gas. The force, the number of molecules, has remained the same but the area has been decreased because of the volume reduction of the container causing the pressure of the gas to increase. *Figure 2-3* illustrates this volume pressure relationship.

By compressing the gas to 1/3 of its original volume, you would triple the pressure of the gas, bearing in mind that the number of molecules has remained the same. This variation of gas pressure to volume is known as *Boyle's Law*, which states:[1]

---

[1] Boyle's law can also be stated as: *the volume of the gas varies inversely to the pressure, provided the temperature of the gas remains constant.*

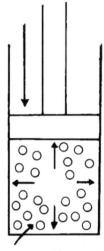

Volume V1
V1= 3V2
Gas molecules are farther apart

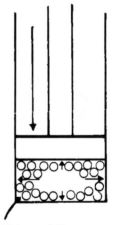

Volume V2
V2 = 1/3V1
Gas molecules are very close

Figure 2-3: Relationship between the volume of a gas and its pressure.

The pressure of a gas varies inversely to the volume provided the temperature of the gas remains constant.

Therefore:

$$P^1V^1 = P^2V^2$$

Where
P_1 = Original Pressure
P_2 = New Pressure
V_1 = Original Volume
V_2 = New Volume

ii)   *Charles' Law I*

The pressure of a gas is also determined by the temperature of the gas. The higher the temperature of the gas, the greater each molecule's velocity will be, since its energy level has been increased. This increase in the molecule's velocity or speed will increase the force that the molecules exert on the walls of the container, which is seen as a higher gas pressure. *Figure 2-4* illustrates this relationship between gas pressure and the temperature of the gas.

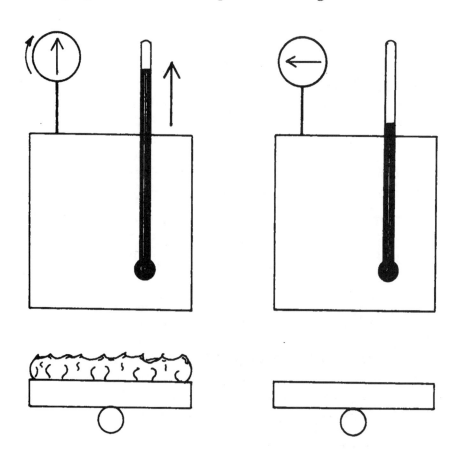

Figure 2-4: Relationship between gas pressure and the temperature of the gas.

The relationship between gas pressure and the temperature of the gas is expressed by *Charles' Law I*.

> The pressure of a gas varies directly with the temperature, provided that the volume of the gas remains constant.

Therefore:

$$\frac{P_1}{P_2} = \frac{T_1}{T_2}$$

Where:
P_1 = Original Pressure
P_2 = New Pressure
T_1 = Original Temperature
T_2 = New Temperature

iii) Charles' Law II

To round out our knowledge of the gas laws, we should look at *Charles' Law II*, which illustrates the relationship between the volume of the gas and its temperature.

As illustrated in *Figure 2-5*, if a gas is heated and allowed to expand at a constant pressure, there will be an increase in the volume of gas relative to its temperature increase. This relationship between volume and temperature of the gas is expressed by *Charles' Law II*.

> The volume of a gas varies directly with the temperature provided that the pressure of the gas remains constant.

Therefore:

$$\frac{T_1}{T_2} = \frac{V_1}{V_2}$$

Where:
T_1 = Original Temperature
T_2 = New Temperature
V_1 = Original Volume
V_2 = New Volume

Figure 2-5: Relationship between the volume of a gas and
the temperature of a gas.

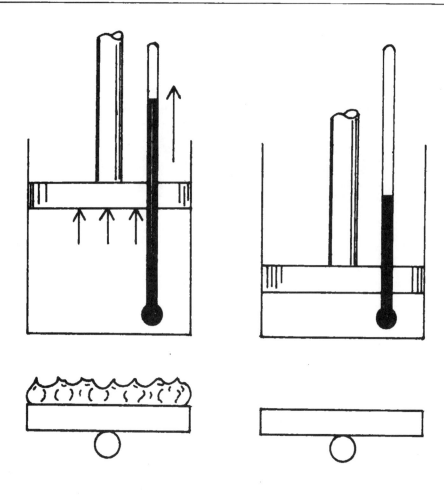

iv) General Gas Law:

The three separate laws, Boyle's Law and Charles' Law I & II, can
be combined to give the *General Gas Law*, which is:

$$\frac{P_1 \, V_1}{T_1} = \frac{P_2 \, V_2}{T_2}$$

Where: P_1 = Original Pressure

P_2 = New Pressure

V_1 = Original Volume

V_2 = New Volume

T_1 = Original Temperature

T_2 = New Temperature

Since both volume and density of a gas are influenced by changes
in temperature and pressure, *absolute conditions* are used for the purpose of comparison and calculation. Absolute conditions are:

T = absolute temperature in degrees *Rankin* (°R)

= 460 + the temperature of the gas in °F

P = absolute pressure in psia

= local atmospheric pressure + the pressure of the gas in psig

Note: 14.73 psia is the atmospheric pressure at sea level at 60°F

For metric, the absolute conditions are:

T = absolute temperature in degrees *Kelvin* (°K)

= 273.15 + the temperature of the gas in °C

P = absolute pressure in kPa absolute

= local atmospheric pressure + the pressure of the gas in kPa gauge

Note: 101.325 kPa absolute is the atmospheric pressure at sea level at 15°C.

Examples:

1. A volume of a certain weight of gas is 100 cu. ft. at 15 psig and a temperature of 40°F. What would be the new volume at a gas pressure of 5 psig and a temperature of 80°F?

$$\frac{P_1 V_1}{T_1} = \frac{P_2 V_2}{T_2}$$

P_1 = 14.73 psia + 15 psig

= 29.73 psia

P_2 = 14.73 psia + 5 psig

= 19.73 psia

T_1 = 460 + 40°F

= 500°R

T_2 = 460 + 80°F

= 540°R

V_1 = 100 cu. ft.

V_2 = ?

Therefore: $V_2 = \dfrac{P_1 V_1 T_2}{T_1 P_2}$

$V_2 = \dfrac{29.73 \times 100 \times 540}{500 \times 19.73}$

V_2 = 162.74 cu. ft.

2. A volume of a certain weight of gas is 50m^3 at 10 kPa gauge and a temperature of 25°C, what would be the new volume at a gas pressure of 20 kPa gauge and a temperature of 10°C?

$$\frac{P_1 V_1}{T_1} = \frac{P_2 V_2}{T_2}$$

P_1 = 101.325 kPa absolute + 10 kPa gauge

= 111.325 kPa absolute

P_2 = 101.325 kPa absolute + 20 kPa gauge

= 121.325 kPa absolute

T_1 = 273.15 + 25°C

= 298.15°K

T_2 = 273.15 + 10°C

= 283.15°K

V_1 = 50m³

V_2 = ?

Therefore: $V_2 = \dfrac{P_1 V_1 T_2}{T_1 P_2}$

$$V_2 = \frac{111.325 \times 50 \times 283.15}{298.15 \times 121.325}$$

$$V_2 = 43.75 \text{ m}^3$$

Definition of Flow

We can think of flow as the movement of a gas from a high pressure area to a low pressure area or the expansion of the gas along the lines of least resistance.

Figure 2-6 is an illustration of two containers of equal volume containing a gas at different pressures. In container "A" the pressure is 100 psi and in container "B" the pressure is 50 psi. If the valve is now open on the pipe connecting the two containers, flow will take place from container "A" to container "B" until the pressure in both containers is 75 psi. The gas pressure has now equalized itself between the two containers.

The flow of a gas is relative to the pressure difference between two areas. The greater the pressure difference, the greater the flow will be. In this example, as illustrated in *Figure 2-6*, the valve is open and maximum gas flow between the two containers takes place. However, as the pressure differential between the two containers gradually diminishes the gas flow will in turn gradually decrease. When the gas pressure has equalized itself across the two containers, the gas flow will stop.

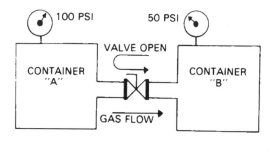

Figure 2-6: The flow of a gas depends upon the pressure difference.

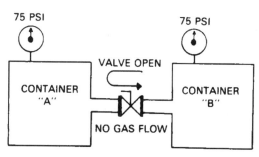

Before we leave flow, we should take into account the idea of *Flow Rate*, or *Rate of Flow*. When the flow of a gas is measured against a time period, we talk of the rate of flow: how much gas has moved past a given point during a specific interval of time. The conventional expression *cubic feet per hour* or *cubic metres per hour* is a measure of the flow rate of gas. This simply means that a certain amount of gas has moved past a given point during one hour.

Definition of Pressure Drop

Flow is defined as the movement of a gas from a high pressure to a low pressure area. However, there is resistance to the flow of a gas, just as there is resistance to the flow of electricity.

According to the molecular theory of gases, as the molecules of the gas move along the lines of least resistance, some of the molecules lose a small amount of their total energy by being rubbed and scrubbed along the sides of the pipe. This partial loss of total energy is realized as *pressure drop*.

Therefore, the resistance to the flow of the gas is measured by the pressure drop in the gas line. The greater the flow rate, the greater will be the resistance to the flow as recorded by a higher pressure drop. The pressure drop, the measurement of resistance to the flow, depends on the following:

i) Length of run of gas pipe:
The greater the distance over which the gas has to flow, the greater will be the overall resistance to it.

ii) The size of the gas pipe (diameter of the pipe):
A larger diameter of pipe will offer less resistance to the flow of gas than one of a smaller diameter.

iii) Number of Fittings:
Fittings, such as tees, elbows and valves, offer resistance to the flow of gas.

iv) The size of the flow rate:
The greater the flow rate, the greater the overall resistance to it.

v) The specific gravity of the gas:
The heavier the gas, the greater will be the resistance to its flow.

Pressure Terminology

An understanding of pressure terminology is essential in order to work with gas firing equipment. Terms such as atmospheric pressure, absolute pressure, gauge pressure, static pressure and working pressure all have a particular meaning as related to the application of gas meters, pressure regulators, pipe sizing and burner performance.

Atmospheric pressure (or barometric pressure) is the pressure the atmosphere exerts on the earth's surface. Atmospheric pressure is measured in pounds per square inch absolute (psia) or in metric measurement, kilopascals absolute, and will vary depending upon the location.

The term *absolute pressure* is a pressure measurement of a gas from a perfect or complete vacuum. For example, the atmospheric pressure at sea level at 60°F is 14.73 psia and at Toronto, Ontario at 60°F it is 14.55 psia. In metric measurement, the atmospheric pressure at sea level at 15°C is 101.325 kPa absolute; Toronto, Ontario at 15°C is 100.32 kPa absolute. The atmospheric pressure is often used as a unit of pressure in which the atmospheric pressure at sea level is taken as one atmosphere of pressure.[2]

Gauge pressure is a pressure measurement taken by a pressure gauge in which zero is calibrated at local atmospheric pressure. *(See Figure 2-7.)* For example, a gauge pressure of 50 psig at sea level would be in absolute pressure 50 + 14.73 psia = 64 psia where 14.73 psia is the atmospheric pressure at sea level at 60°F. This would also apply to kPa giving kPa absolute and a kPa gauge.

Absolute pressure = Gauge pressure + Local atmospheric pressure

Gauge pressure = Absolute pressure − Local atmospheric pressure

---

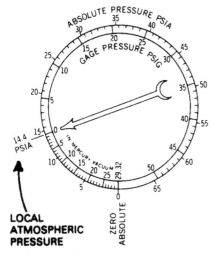

Figure 2-7: A pressure gauge showing the relationship between gauge pressure and absolute pressure.

[2] Actual atmospheric pressure varies with weather, latitude and altitude (i.e., about 1/2 psia or 3.45 kPa less for each 1000 feet above sea level). The normal or standard atmospheric pressure at sea level is 14.7 psia at 32°F (or 101.3 kPa at 15°C) at a latitude of 45°. However, standard temperature condition for the gas industry is 60°F or 15°C giving the atmospheric pressure at sea level at 14.73 psia or 101.325 kPa.

We consider any pressure above one atmosphere, that is the pressure of our atmosphere at ground or sea level depending upon the location, as pressure in a general sense (what we normally consider pressure). Any pressure below one atmosphere is considered a vacuum. Local atmospheric pressure is taken as a reference or datum line in which any absolute pressure below this line is called a vacuum or negative pressure. *Figure 2-8* illustrates the scales for pressure measurement.

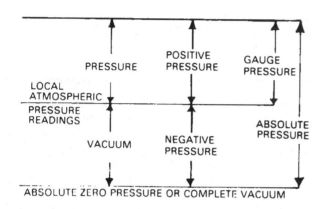

Figure 2-8: Scales for pressure measurement.

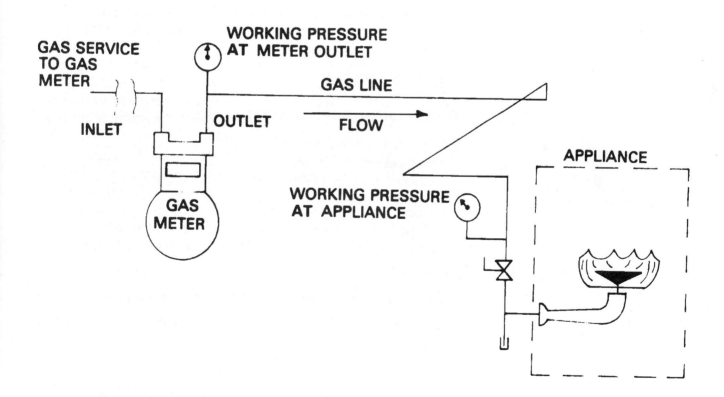

Figure 2-9: Determining the actual pressure drop in a gas line.

The term *static pressure* refers to the pressure in a gas line in which no flow is taking place. The word static conveys the meaning of stationary or anything at a state of rest. Sometimes static pressure can be referred to as *lock up pressure* in which the gas in a gas line is locked up between the gas meter and the burner, which is not firing. However, *working pressure* refers to the pressure in a gas line in which flow is taking place within the gas line. Flow is occurring because the burner is firing and is consuming the gas.

Determining the Actual Pressure Drop in a Gas Line

It is important to determine the actual pressure drop in the gas line. The gas line must be large enough and free of restrictions to adequately supply a sufficient amount of gas to the appliance.

To determine the actual pressure drop in the gas line, take the working pressure at the gas meter outlet and a working pressure at the appliance; the difference will be the pressure drop in the gas line.

Pressure Drop in Gas Line = Working pressure at gas meter outlet minus Working pressure at appliance

Units of Pressure

Pressure can be measured in the following common units:

pounds per square inch ....psi
ounces per square inch..osi
inches of water column.."wc
inches of mercury column ...."Hg
pascals..Pa
kilopascals...kPa

The conversions from one unit of measure to the others are shown below:

1 psi	= 28"wc	1 osi	= 1.75"wc
	= 16 osi		= 0.128"Hg
	= 2.036"Hg		= 0.063 psi
	= 6895 Pa		= 431 Pa
	= 6.895 kPa		= 0.431 kPa

1 "Hg	= 13.6"wc	1 "wc	= 0.57 osi
	= 7.8 osi		= 0.074"Hg
	= 0.49 psi		= 0.036 psi
	= 3386 Pa		= 249 Pa
	= 3.386 kPa		= 0.249 kPa
1 kPa	= 0.145 psi	1 Pa	= 0.000145 psi
	= 0.295"Hg		= 0.000295"Hg
	= 2.32 osi		= 0.00232 osi
	= 4"wc		= 0.004"wc
	= 1000Pa		= 0.001 kPa

Standard Gas Pressure

For domestic gas appliances the average *houseline* or *building line pressure* (that is the pressure at the outlet of the gas meter), is usually 7"wc (1.74 kPa). The average *manifold gas pressure*, the pressure at the gas burner downstream of all control valves and the pressure at which the burner is sized for, is 3.5"wc (.87 kPa). Both 7"wc (1.74 kPa) houseline pressure and 3.5"wc (.87 kPa) manifold pressure are standard pressures in the gas industry for domestic and light commercial application.[3]

Measurement of Gas Pressure

There are two basic instruments used in the gas industry to measure gas pressure, the ordinary *bourdon tube pressure gauge* and the *water filled manometer*. The water filled manometer is usually more accurate since the normal gas pressure being measured in inches of water column is a relatively low pressure. The standard pressure gauge cannot achieve the reliability and accuracy of the manometer; however, it is more convenient in its application.

3 i) For conventional gas systems, the maximum houseline or building line pressure for residential and light commercial gas systems is 14"wc or 1/2 psi (3.5 kPa).
  ii) The gas pressure 1/2 rule:
  Approximately 28"wc = 1 psi
  14"wc   = maximum houseline pressure = 1/2 psi
   7"wc   = standard houseline pressure = 1/4 psi
  3.5"wc = standard manifold pressure = 1/8 psi

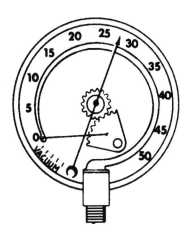

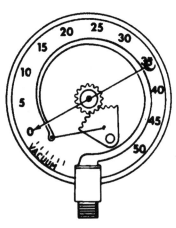

Figure 2-10: Bourdon tube pressure gauge.

The Bourdon Tube Pressure Gauge: When we think of a pressure gauge, the bourdon tube pressure gauge is the instrument that we have in mind. Its operation is quite simple. The pressure of the gas forces the bourdon tube to expand and via a system of gears and linkages the amount of pressure is recorded on the dial face of the instrument. *Figure 2-10* is an illustration of a pressure gauge with a bourdon tube element. *Figure 2-11* is a typical low gas pressure gauge used to measure gas pressure in ounces per square inch (osi) or inches of water column ("wc).

The Water Filled Manometer: The water filled manometer or U tube operates under the principle of pressure displacing a column of water. With one end of the manometer attached to the pressure source and the other open to experience atmospheric pressure, the water column will be forced down on the pressure side and lifted up on the atmospheric side. The total displacement of water column is the sum of the water column lifted on the atmospheric side and the water column forced down on the pressure side. The total displacement of water column is the pressure of the gas measured in inches of water column. *Figure 2-12* illustrates the operation of the simple water filled manometer.

The water column forced down on the pressure side is equal to the water column lifted on the atmospheric side. Having the manometer set at zero on the scale, the total displacement can be obtained by multiplying the displacement on one side by two. This can be seen by a simple formula for reading pressure as determined by the manometer:

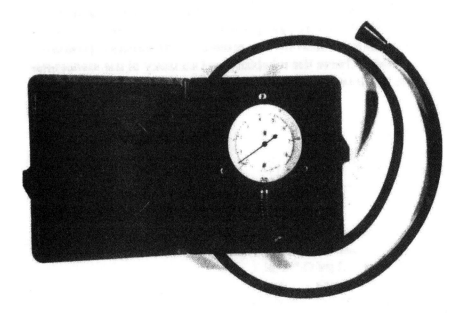

Figure 2-11: A typical low gas pressure gauge measuring pressure in osi or "wc.

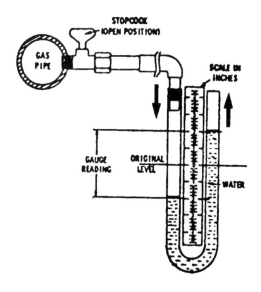

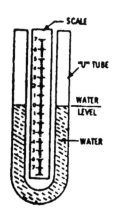

Figure 2-12: A water filled manometer.

$$HT = Hp + Hatm$$
$$HT = 2\ Hp = 2\ Hatm \text{ (with manometer calibrated at zero)}$$

Where: HT = Total column of water displaced in inches of
water column

Hp = Column of water displaced on the pressure side
in inches of water column

Hatm = Column of water displaced on the atmospheric
side in inches of water column

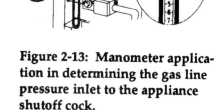

Figure 2-13: Manometer application in determining the gas line pressure inlet to the appliance shutoff cock.

Manometers are available that will read the change in water column in terms of kPa.

Figure 2-13 illustrates the manometer application in determining the gas line pressure inlet to the appliance shut off cock. *Figure 2-14* illustrates the manometer application in determining the appliance manifold pressure at the outlet of the appliance control valve. *Figure 2-15* illustrates the use of the manometer in reading the various points of gas pressure in a typical residential piping system.

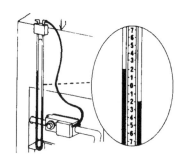

Figure 2-14: Manometer application in determining the appliance manifold pressure at the outlet of the appliance control valve.

27

Figure 2-15: Points of gas pressure in a typical residential piping system.

Points of Gas Pressure

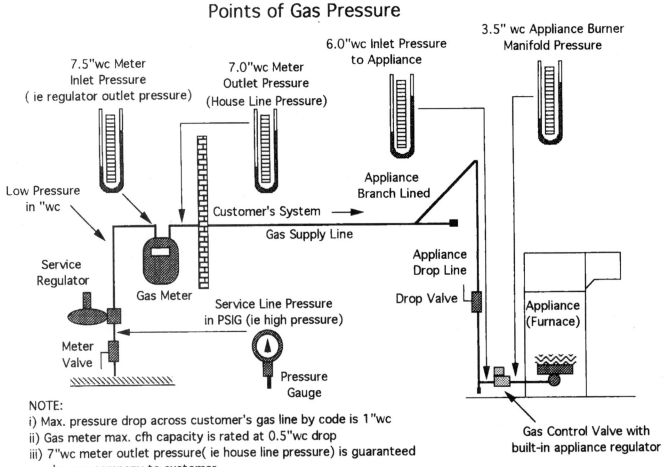

NOTE:
i) Max. pressure drop across customer's gas line by code is 1"wc
ii) Gas meter max. cfh capacity is rated at 0.5"wc drop
iii) 7"wc meter outlet pressure(ie house line pressure) is guaranteed
  by gas company to customer
iv) Any pressure above 1/2 psig or 14"wc is high pressure

Assignment

1. Define pressure in terms of the molecular theory of gases.

2. State the significance of Boyle's Law and Charles' Law I and II
    on the pressure and volume of a gas.

3. A volume of a certain weight of gas is 200 cu. ft. at 10 psig and
    temperature of 60°F. What would the new volume be at a gas
    pressure of 20 psig and a temperature of 120°F ?

4. What is the main factor that determines the rate of flow of a
    gas?

5. List the five factors that determine the pressure drop in a typical
    gas line. Explain how each contributes to the pressure drop.

6. Define the following:

    a)   Absolute pressure
    b)   Atmospheric pressure
    c)   Gauge pressure
    d)   Static pressure
    e)   Lock up pressure
    f)   Working pressure

7. Describe a method of determining the actual pressure drop in a
    gas line.

8. Convert the following:

    a)   2 psi to "wc
    b)   14"wc to psi
    c)   8"Hg to psi
    d)   10"wc to osi
    e)   2 psi to kPa
    f)   14"wc to kPa
    g)   8"Hg to kPa
    h)   7 osi to kPa

9. Define the terms:

    a)   House line pressure
    b)   Building line pressure
    c)   Manifold pressure

10. Give the values for the pressures stated in question No. 9.

11. Give the locations where you would read the pressures stated in question No. 9.

12. Describe the operation of a simple manometer as illustrated in diagram (a) and (b) of *Figure 2-16*.

Figure 2-16: Illustration of a simple manometer.

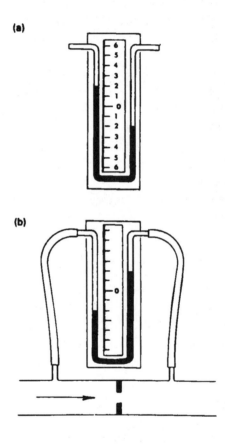

Gas Meters

Gas meters are used to measure and record gas flow in both domestic (residential) and commercial applications. The operation of the gas meter is based on the principle of *positive volumetric displacement* of the gas at conditions (i.e., temperature and pressure) existing in the gas line.

There are basically two types of positive displacement gas meters, the *bellows* or *diaphragm* meter used for both domestic and commercial applications, and the *rotary* meter used only for medium and large commercial applications.

Bellows or diaphragm meters can be further subdivided into tinned steel case meters (usually shortened to tin case meters), and hard case meters. The tin case meter, because of its soft metal construction, can only be installed inside the building. They are gradually being replaced by the hard case meter which can be installed outside of the building.

Figure 3-1 through *Figure 3-5* show the cut away view of a tin case meter, hard case meter, rotary meter, outside installation of a small commercial bellows type hard case meter, and the outside installation of a rotary meter showing the by-pass arrangement. Rotary meter installations will usually have a by-pass arrangement. The by-pass will facilitate continuous gas supply to the commercial or industrial customer during meter removal due to service or meter replacement.

Bellows Gas Meter

Operation: The operation of the bellow type of gas meter will be described with the aid of *Figure 3-6, Figure 3-7* and *Figure 3-8.*

When any of the appliances illustrated in *Figure 3-6* are turned on, the pressure drops slightly in the gas *outlet* line from the meter to the appliance. The outlet line pressure has gone from a static to a working pressure. However, gas pressure in the *inlet* line going into the meter stays high. This causes an *unbalanced pressure* in the meter. The unbalanced pressure pushing on a moveable diaphragm or bellows "A" as illustrated in *Figure 3-7*, makes the bellows expand like an accordion creating a gas flow through the meter.

The flow of gas into and out of the separate chambers in the meter is controlled by sliding valves "B", as illustrated in *Figure 3-7*, so that the gas output is smooth and steady. The control of the gas flow by the sliding valves is illustrated by *Figure 3-8.* In *Figure 3-8* drawing

"A", chamber 1 is emptying, 2 is filling, 3 is empty and 4 has just filled. In drawing "B", chamber 1 is now empty, 2 is full, 3 is filling and 4 is emptying. In drawing "C", chamber 1 is filling, 2 is emptying, 3 has filled and 4 has emptied. In drawing "D", chamber 1 is now completely filled, 2 is empty, 3 is emptying and 4 is filling.

Figure 3-1: A cut-away view of the tin case bellows meter.

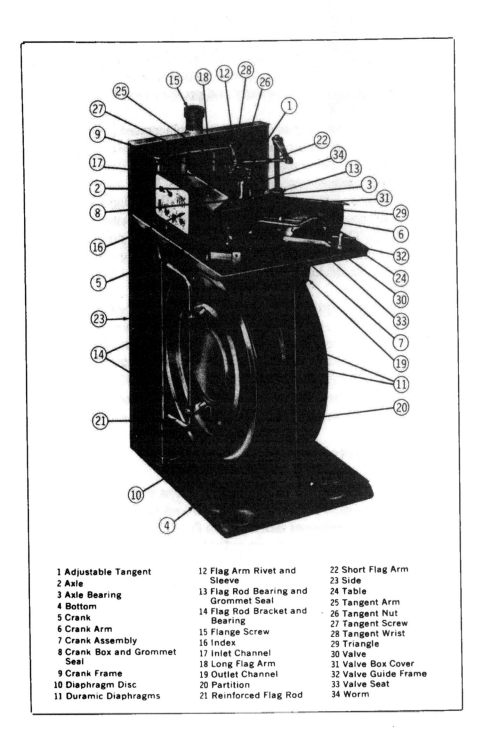

1 Adjustable Tangent	12 Flag Arm Rivet and	22 Short Flag Arm
2 Axle	Sleeve	23 Side
3 Axle Bearing	13 Flag Rod Bearing and	24 Table
4 Bottom	Grommet Seal	25 Tangent Arm
5 Crank	14 Flag Rod Bracket and	26 Tangent Nut
6 Crank Arm	Bearing	27 Tangent Screw
7 Crank Assembly	15 Flange Screw	28 Tangent Wrist
8 Crank Box and Grommet	16 Index	29 Triangle
Seal	17 Inlet Channel	30 Valve
9 Crank Frame	18 Long Flag Arm	31 Valve Box Cover
10 Diaphragm Disc	19 Outlet Channel	32 Valve Guide Frame
11 Duramic Diaphragms	20 Partition	33 Valve Seat
	21 Reinforced Flag Rod	34 Worm

Figure 3-2: A cut-away view of a hard case bellows meter.

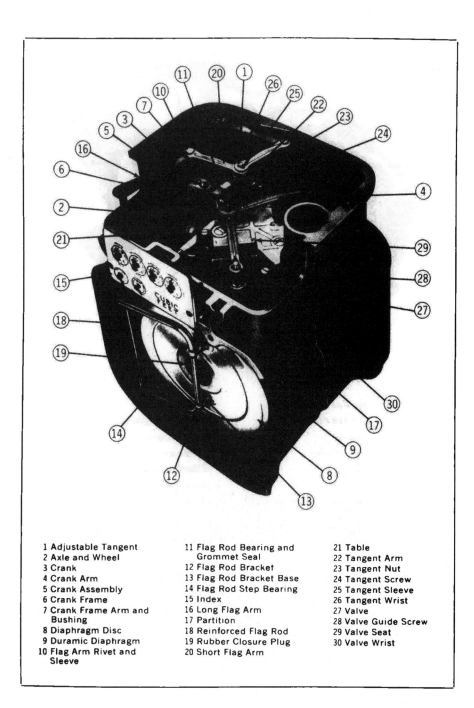

1 Adjustable Tangent
2 Axle and Wheel
3 Crank
4 Crank Arm
5 Crank Assembly
6 Crank Frame
7 Crank Frame Arm and Bushing
8 Diaphragm Disc
9 Duramic Diaphragm
10 Flag Arm Rivet and Sleeve
11 Flag Rod Bearing and Grommet Seal
12 Flag Rod Bracket
13 Flag Rod Bracket Base
14 Flag Rod Step Bearing
15 Index
16 Long Flag Arm
17 Partition
18 Reinforced Flag Rod
19 Rubber Closure Plug
20 Short Flag Arm
21 Table
22 Tangent Arm
23 Tangent Nut
24 Tangent Screw
25 Tangent Sleeve
26 Tangent Wrist
27 Valve
28 Valve Guide Screw
29 Valve Seat
30 Valve Wrist

Figure 3-3: A cut-away view of a rotary meter.

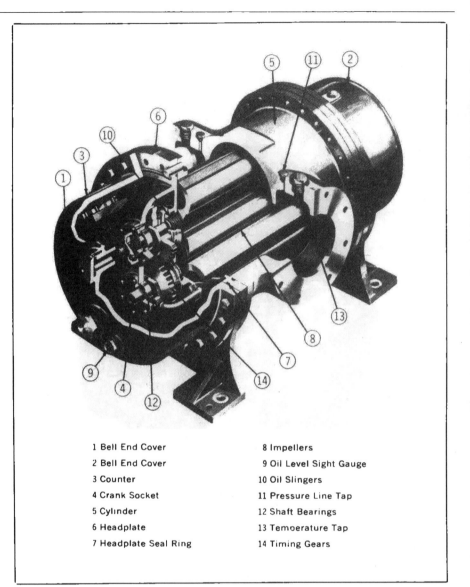

1 Bell End Cover	8 Impellers
2 Bell End Cover	9 Oil Level Sight Gauge
3 Counter	10 Oil Slingers
4 Crank Socket	11 Pressure Line Tap
5 Cylinder	12 Shaft Bearings
6 Headplate	13 Temoerature Tap
7 Headplate Seal Ring	14 Timing Gears

Figure 3-4: Outside installation of a small commercial bellows type, hard-case meter.

Figure 3-5: Outside installation of a rotary type, gas meter (note the by-pass arrangements).

The four drawings in *Figure 3-8* illustrate how each of the chambers are filled with the same volume of gas every time and thereby maintain a consistent flow rate through the meter.

The meter dials "C", as illustrated in *Figure 3-7*, keep count of the number of times the chambers are filled and emptied. Hence, the volume of gas that passes through the meter is recorded. As long as a gas appliance is on, there is an unbalanced pressure in the gas meter and the meter operates.

Meter Dials: There are three types of meter dials found on standard bellows or diaphragm types of meters: Consumption Dials, Indicating Dials and Test Dials.

i) Consumption Dials

Consumption dials record the gas consumption over a period of time for billing purposes. On small domestic meters there are four consumption dials rated at 1000 cu. ft.; 10,000 cu. ft.; 100,000 cu. ft. and 1,000,000 cu. ft. On the larger bellows meters used for commercial application, there are five dials, the first four being the same as the smaller residential meters and the fifth being 10,000,000 cu. ft.

ii) Indicating Dials

The indicating dial is a 100 cu. ft. dial and is only found on some of the larger commercial bellows type of gas meters. Its function is to give accuracy to the first consumption dial. It is not to be read for billing purposes.

iii) Test Dials

Test dials on bellows type of gas meters range from 1/2 cu. ft., 1 cu. ft. and 2 cu. ft. found on domestic gas meters, to 5 cu. ft. and 10 cu. ft. found on the larger commercial meters. The test dial has two functions. First, as a device to determine the appliance input, and second, to test the gas meter and downstream gas line for leaks.

Figure 3-9 shows the three types of dials found on a commercial bellows type of gas meter, consumption, indicating and test dial. Note that the indicating and test dial are not read for billing purposes.

Reading the Gas Meter: The gas meter is an accurate automatic measuring instrument. It keeps track of how much gas flows through it by counting the filling and emptying of the four compartments inside its metal case. Since each compartment fills with the same amount of gas each time, the measuring is very accurate; and because one compartment is being emptied as another is being filled, the flow of gas to the appliance is smooth and uninterrupted.

The following points will help you in reading a gas meter easily and accurately.

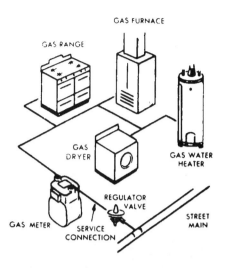

Figure 3-6: Gas meter, metering gas consumption of home appliances.

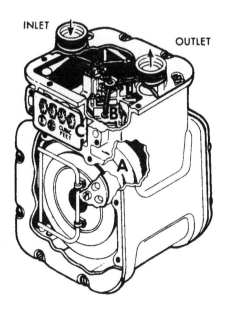

Figure 3-7: Sectional view of a domestic gas meter.

Figure 3-8: Operation of the sliding valves that control gas flow through the meter.

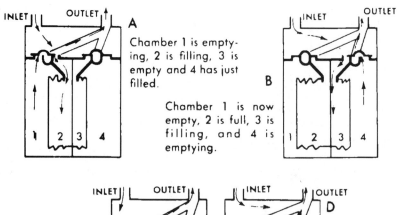

Chamber 1 is emptying, 2 is filling, 3 is empty and 4 has just filled.

Chamber 1 is now empty, 2 is full, 3 is filling, and 4 is emptying.

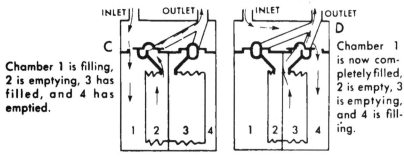

Chamber 1 is filling, 2 is emptying, 3 has filled, and 4 has emptied.

Chamber 1 is now completely filled, 2 is empty, 3 is emptying, and 4 is filling.

These two dials are merely for testing and ARE NOT TO BE READ FOR BILLING PURPOSES.

Figure 3-9: Consumption, indicating, and test dial of a commercial bellows type of gas meter.

1. Always read the meter from right to left (i.e., from the 1000 cf dial to the 1,000,000 cf dial)

2. Note that the dials are divided into tenths, and dials that are next to each other rotate in opposite directions. If the right hand dial goes clockwise, the dial to its left will go counter-clockwise. Always check the figures on the dial to find the direction of rotation.

3. To read the four consumption dials, take the numbers that the dial pointers have just passed and add two zeros. (*See Figure 3-10.*)

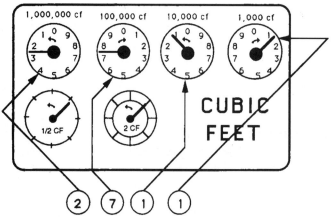

Take the numbers that the pointers have just passed
Add two zeros .... 271 1(00)

271100 is the meter reading in cubic feet of gas

Figure 3-10: Reading the consumption dials of a gas meter.

4. The accuracy of the dial that you are reading is determined by the dial reading of the next lower dial. For example, on reading the 10,000 cf dial in *Figure 3-10*, the dial pointer has just passed 1. This means that approximately 1,000 cf of gas has been recorded by the dial. However, the true or accurate reading is 1,100 cf. The first consumption dial (i.e., the 1,000 cf dial), has a reading of 1 (or 1 x100) giving the true reading of 1,100 cf.

5. To determine how much gas the appliance or appliances have consumed, take readings several days apart. Subtract the first reading from the second to find out how much gas was used during the time between the readings.

Direct Reading Digital Type Gas Meters: At the present time in the gas industry, meters are designed to totalize the cubic feet of gas measured and provide a continuous indication of the gas volume on an *index* or *register*. The *standard index* takes the form shown in *Figure 3-10*, a circle-reading which has a group of circular dials with rotating pointers read by the user to determine gas volume.

The trend today, as illustrated in *Figure 3-11*, is towards a direct-reading digital index, known as an *odometer* type of index. The circular consumption dials are replaced by a direct digital read out as displayed by the odometer index. However, the test dials, because of their function, are still the standard circular type.

Metric Gas Meters: Metric gas meters measure the volume of gas in cubic metres (m^3). As illustrated in *Figure 3-12*, the metric meter is equipped with an odometer type of index to give a direct digital read out of gas consumption in cubic metres.

The test dials on bellows types of gas meters are .01m^3 and .05m^3 for residential or domestic gas meters *(see Figure 3-13)* and 0.1m^3 for larger commercial gas meters.

Function of the Test Dial: The two main functions for the test dial are:

i) Determining the appliance input or what is called *clocking the burner input.*

ii) Testing the meter and downstream gas line for leaks.

Figure 3-11: Gas meters having direct-reading digital index.

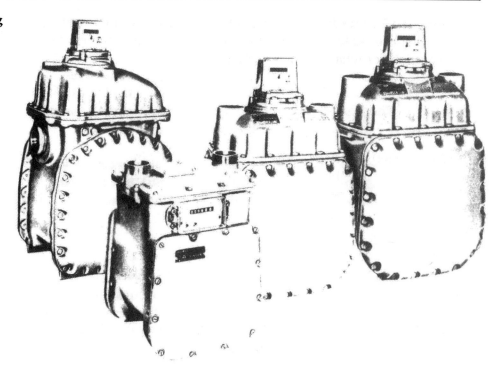

Figure 3-12: Standard index (a) and odometer type of index (b) used on metric gas meters.

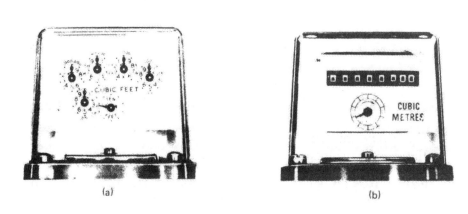

(a)　　　　　　　　　(b)

Figure 3-13: Test dials found on a residential metric type of gas meter.

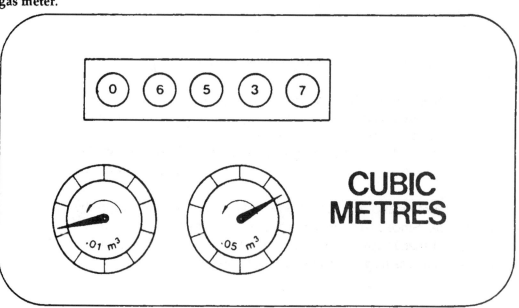

Clocking the Burner Input: The following is a method by which the test dial is used to determine the gas appliance input by timing its revolutions or what is called *clocking.*

$$\frac{3600}{T} \quad X \quad D = Q$$

Where: 3600 = the number of seconds in one hour
  T = the number of seconds for one complete revolution of the test dial
  D = the size of the text dial, i.e., 2 cf or .05 m³
  Q = the gas flow rate, i.e., cfh or m³/h

Examples:

1. Determine the appliance Btuh input rate from a 2 cf test dial that has been clocked at 40 seconds for one complete revolution.

$$\frac{3600}{T} \quad X \quad D \quad = \quad Q$$

$$\frac{3600}{40} \quad X \quad 2 \quad = \quad 180 \text{ cfh}$$

$$180 \quad \text{cfh} \quad X \quad 1000 \text{ Btu/cf} \quad = \quad 180{,}000 \text{ Btuh}$$

2. Determine the appliance kW input rate from a .05 m³ test dial that has been clocked at 40 seconds for one complete revolution.

$$\frac{3600}{T} \quad X \quad D \quad = \quad Q$$

$$\frac{3600}{40} \quad X \quad .05 \quad = \quad 4.5 \text{ m}^3/\text{h}$$

$$4.5 \text{ m}^3/\text{h} \ X \ 10.35 \text{ kWh/m}^3 \quad = \quad 46.57 \text{ kW}$$

When determining the appliance input by clocking the test dial of the meter, make certain there is no gas flowing through the meter other than to the appliance being checked.

Tables T3-1 and *T3-2* allow you to determine appliance cfh or kW rating directly from 1/2 cf, 1 cf, 5 cf, and .01 m³, .05 m³, 0.1 m³ test dials.

Metric meters and appliances will be appearing in the field in the near future. Since metric meters register gas consumption in cubic metres and metric appliances are rated in kilowatts, four possible gas meters to gas appliance combinations are possible.

1. standard meter (cfh) and standard appliance (Btuh)
2. standard meter (cfh) and metric appliance (kW)
3. metric meter (m^3/h) and standard appliance (Btuh)
4. metric meter (m^3/h) and metric appliance (kW)

To facilitate in determining the appliance rated input, the following conversions can be done:
1. standard meter and standard appliance
   cfh X 1000 = Btuh
2. standard meter and metric appliance
   cfh X 0.29299 = kW
3. metric meter and standard appliance
   m^3/h X 35,310 = Btuh
4. metric meter and metric appliance
   m^3/h X 10.35 = kW

Table T3-1: Checking gas input to appliance by meter clocking method for standard gas meters.

SECONDS FOR ONE REVOLUTION	0.5 ft³/REV.		1 ft³/REV.		2 ft³/REV.		5 ft³/REV.	
	ft³/h	kW	ft³/h	kW	ft³/h	kW	ft³/h	kW
10	180	53	360	105	720	211	1800	527
11	164	48	327	96	655	192	1636	479
12	150	44	300	88	600	176	1500	439
13	138	41	277	81	554	162	1385	405
14	129	38	257	75	514	151	1286	377
15	120	35	240	70	480	140	1200	352
16	113	33	225	66	450	132	1125	330
17	106	31	211	62	423	124	1059	310
18	100	29	200	59	400	117	1000	293
19	95	28	189	56	379	110	947	278
20	90	26	180	53	360	105	900	264
21	86	25	171	50	343	100	857	251
22	82	24	164	48	327	96	818	240
23	78	23	156	46	313	92	783	229
24	75	22	150	44	300	88	750	220
25	72	21	144	42	288	84	720	211
26	69	20	138	41	277	81	692	202
27	67	19	133	39	267	78	667	195
28	64		128	38	257	75	643	188
29	62	18	124	36	248	73	621	182
30	60		120	35	240	70	600	176
32	56	16	113	33	225	66	563	165
34	53		105	31	212	62	529	155
36	50	15	100	29	200	59	500	146
38	47	14	95	28	189	56	474	139
40	45	13	90	26	180	52	450	132
42	43		86	25	171	50	429	126
44	41	12	82	24	164	48	409	120
46	39	11	78	23	157	46	391	114
48	38		75	22	150	44	375	110
50	36		72	21	144	42	360	105
52	35	10	69	20	138	41	346	101
54	33		67		133	39	333	98
56	32	9	64	19	129	38	321	94
58	31		62	18	124	36	310	91
60	30		60	18	120	35	300	88
65	28	8	55	16	111	32	277	81
70	26		51	15	103	30	257	75
75	24	7	48	14	96	28	240	70
80	23		45	13	90	26	225	66
90	20	6	40	12	80	23	200	59
100	18	5	36	11	72	21	180	53
110	16		32	10	65	19	164	48
120	15	4	30	9	60	18	150	44
130	14		28	8	55	16	138	40
140	13		26		51	15	129	38
150	12		24	7	48	14	120	35
160	11	3	23		45	13	113	33
170			21	6	42	12	106	31
180	10		20		40	12	100	29

Table T3-2: Checking gas input to appliance by meter clocking method for metric gas meters.

SECONDS FOR ONE REVOLUTION	.01 m³/REV.		.05 m³/REV.		0.1 m³/REV.	
	kW	ft³/h	kW	ft³/h	kW	ft³/h
10	37	127	186	637	372	1271
11	34	115	169	578	339	1156
12	31	106	155	530	310	1059
13	29	98	143	489	286	978
14	27	91	133	454	266	908
15	24	85	124	424	248	848
16	23	79	116	397	233	795
17	22	75	110	374	219	748
18	21	71	103	353	207	706
19	20	67	98	335	196	669
20	19	63	93	318	186	636
21	18	61	89	303	177	605
22	17	58	85	289	169	578
23	16	55	81	276	162	553
24		53	78	265	155	530
25	15	51	74	254	149	509
26	14	49	72	244	143	489
27		47	69	235	138	471
28	13	45	67	227	133	454
29		44	64	219	128	438
30	12	42	62	212	124	424
32		40	58	199	116	397
34	11	37	55	187	110	374
36	10	35	52	177	103	353
38		33	49	167	98	334
40	9	32	47	159	93	318
42		32	44	151	89	303
44	8	29	42	144	84	289
46		28	40	138	81	276
48		26	39	132	78	265
50	7	25	37	127	74	254
52		24	36	122	72	244
54		23	34	118	69	235
56			32	114	66	227
58	6	22	31	110	64	219
60		21		106	62	212
65		20	28	98	57	196
70	5	18	27	91	53	182
75		17	25	85	50	170
80		16	23	79	46	159
90	4	14	21	71	41	141
100		13	19	64	37	127
110	3	12	17	58	34	115
120		11	16	53	31	106
130		10	14	49	29	98
140		9	13	45	27	91
150	2	8	12	42	25	85
160				40	23	79
170			11	37	22	75
180		7	10	35	21	71

Test Meter and Gas Line for Leaks: With the appliance or appliances turned off, turn on the gas meter and mark the position of the test dial hand. If the test dial hand has not moved from its position in 10 minutes, then the gas line can be assumed to be gas tight. However, if the hand has moved, then a gas leak is indicated since the test dial has recorded the flow of gas escaping from the leak.

Temperature Compensated Meters: The preferred meter location is outside. All outside meters are temperature compensated as well as inside meters if the gas is primarily used for heating building space. Temperature variations as experienced between Canadian summers and winters would vary the gas flow through the meter calibrated at standard operating pressures and temperature (60°F and 15°C).[1] To overcome this inaccuracy in meter operation, temperature compensation is designed into the gas meter.

Basically, the compensating mechanism consists of two bi-metallic elements linked into the meter's tangent arms that control the movement of the meter valves, (see *Figure 3-14*). *Figures 3-15* and *3-16* show a bellows type of temperature compensated meter and an outside installation of two bellows type temperature compensated meters.

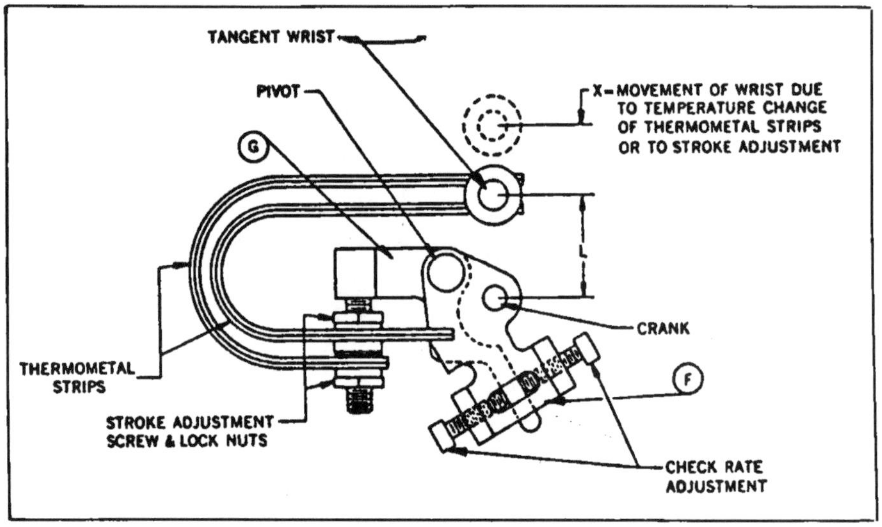

Figure 3-14: Temperature compensating mechanism for a domestic bellows meter.

Figure 3-15: A temperature compensation domestic bellows type of meter.

Classification of Meters by Capacity: Standard or imperial gas meters are classified as to capacity in cu. ft./hr. or cfh having a 0.5"wc pressure differential existing across the meter. *Figure 3-17* illustrates the existing 0.5"wc differential across the meter which occurs at the meter's rated capacity. Metric gas meters are classified as to capacity in m^3/h having a 0.12 kPa pressure differential existing across the meter.

[1] See *Charles' Law II*, Chapter 2

Figure 3-16: Two low capacity temperature compensated meters (maximum capacity of 225 cu.ft./hr. each). The meters are located in a travelled area and are protected by a guard. The installation is off a low pressure header service and is supplying two stores in a shopping plaza.

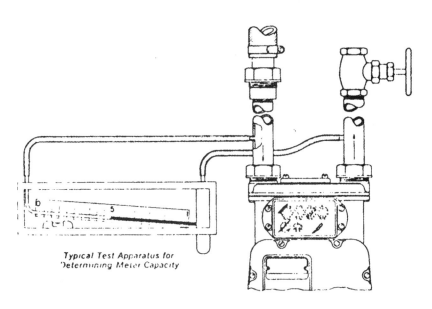

Typical Test Apparatus for Determining Meter Capacity

Figure 3-17: 0.5"wc pressure drop across gas meter at meter's rated capacity.

Rotary Displacement Gas Meters

Rotary displacement gas meters are designed to be rugged yet compact and light in weight: suitable for the many variant installation conditions found in commercial and industrial installations. The smaller rotary meters are supported only by the connected piping and may be mounted either in vertical or horizontal pipe runs. The larger models are foot mounted having side connections only. *Figure 3-18* illustrates the various mountings of rotary displacement meters.

Figure 3-18: Rotary displacement gas meters showing mounting either in the vertical, horizontal and larger foot mounted with side connections only.

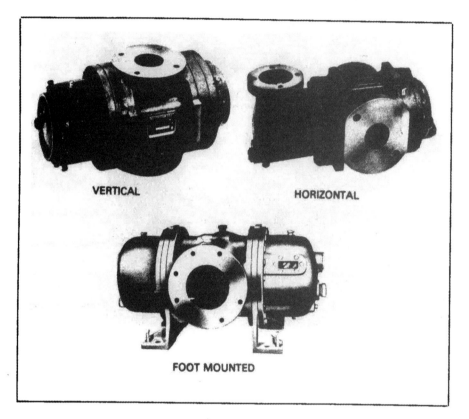

VERTICAL   HORIZONTAL

FOOT MOUNTED

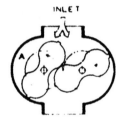

POSITION 1

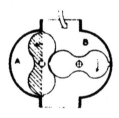

POSITION 2

OUTLET
POSITION 3

Figure 3-19: The principle of gas flow through a rotary displacement meter.

Operation of the Rotary Meter: As shown in *Figure 3-19*, the rotary meter consists basically of two contra-rotating impellers of two-lobe or figure 8 contour, operating within a meter casing. The casing is arranged with inlet and outlet gas connections on opposite sides. Impeller contours are of such form that a continuous seal without contact can be obtained between the impellers at all positions during rotation. A similar seal also exists between the tips of the impeller lobes and the two semi-circular parts of the metal casing.

The gas at the inlet side of the meter is always effectively isolated from the gas at the outlet side by the impellers. The impellers can be caused to rotate by a very small pressure drop across the meter. The rotation is in the direction as indicated in *Figure 3-19*. As each impeller reaches a vertical position, it traps a known specific volume of gas between itself and the semi-circular portion of the meter casing at "A" and "B". In one complete revolution the meter will measure and pass four similar gas volumes, and this total is the *gas displacement of the meter per revolution.*

Reading the Rotary Meter: The counter section of a rotary meter, as illustrated in *Figure 3-20* contains a 7 digit counter; 5 of the digits are visible with the smallest visible digit as the 1000 cu. ft. indicator or index. The counter reading must be multiplied by 100 to obtain the total displacement volume measured by the meter.

The normal pressure drop across rotary meters at rated maximum capacities is 1"wc (.25 kPa).

Figure 3-20: The counter section of a rotary meter—note this is a close up of Figure 3-5.

Test Dial Arrangement for Rotary Meter: *Figure 3-21* illustrates two different arrangements of providing the 10 cu.ft. test dial.

On some rotary meters, the 10 cf test dial is a series of empty frames located on a *test wheel* which is the first of 7 wheels that are located on the counter. The test wheel is marked in ten divisions without numbers, each division or frame representing one cu. ft. of gas. One complete frame, as it moves from the bottom of the counter window to the top of the counter window, represents a flow of 1 cf of gas through the meter.

For other rotary meters, the test dial is located on the counter's end section of the meter. The test dial is a regular 10 cu. cf. test dial as you would find on a bellows type of gas meter. Also, a meter rpm dial is located on the end section next to the 10 cu. ft. test dial.

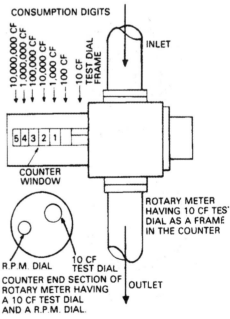

Figure 3-21: Rotary meters illustrating 2 types of test dial arrangement.

Correction Factor For Meter Capacity at Elevated Pressures

Gas meters are simple, but accurate, devices which measure the number of cubic feet of gas passed. The absolute pressure within these meters is equal to the barometric pressure of the atmosphere, plus the pressure in the service line itself. The pressure in the service line, houseline pressure , is usually 4 ounces, 1/4 pound or 7"wc (1.74 kPa). This absolute pressure within the gas meter is called the *base pressure* and the meter's capacity is calibrated at this pressure.

Typical locations in Canada with elevation above sea level, the average barometric or atmospheric pressure experienced, and the total pressure in psia on residential meters in such locations are listed in *Table T3-3.*[2]

Table T3-3: Various barometric pressures throughout Canada.

Location	Elevation Above Sea-Level Feet	Average Barometric Pressure P.S.I.A.	Meter Pressure With 4 Oz. Service P.S.I.A.
Victoria	228	14.62	14.87
Edmonton	2.219	13.56	13.81
Calgary	3.454	12.92	13.17
Winnipeg	786	14.32	14.57
Toronto	374	14.55	14.80
Montreal	98	14.69	14.94
Halifax	83	14.66	14.91

It should be noted that the Canadian Gas Association and American Gas Association recommends that 14.73 psia be adopted as standard pressure base (i.e., base pressure) for all Canadian and American reporting of reserves, production and sale of gas. As a result, most gas companies have adopted 14.73 psia as their standard pressure.

It was pointed out in the section of *Gas Physics: Pressure and Flow,* that the volume of gas is inversely proportional to the absolute pressure (Boyle's Law). Thus any quantity of gas will change its volume as the pressure upon it is changed. A cubic foot of gas will contain different quantities of gas at different pressures. Hence it is necessary to correct flow rates through a gas meter when the pressure of the gas varies from the base pressure.

[2] Local atmospheric pressure or average barometric pressure for Toronto in metric units is 100.32 kPa absolute.

The following is a formula of meter capacity or flow rate correction when the gas pressure has changed from the base pressure.

$$Qa = \frac{Q_r (A+P)}{(P_b)}$$

Where: Qa = Actual flow rate in cfh or m^3/h at base pressure conditions

Qr = Flow rate in cfh or m^3/h as read or recorded at the gas meter

P = Actual gas pressure in psig or kPa gauge

P_b = Base pressure in psia or kPa
(Note: 14.73 psia or 101.325 kPa absolute taken as standard)

A = Atmospheric or barometric pressure at the point of measurement in psia or kPa absolute

Example #1

A gas fired boiler has a flow rate as clocked by the gas meter of 1000 cfh. If the working pressure at the gas meter is 5 psig, what is the actual flow rate at base pressure conditions? The local atmospheric or barometric pressure is 14.40 psia and the local gas company base pressure is 14.73 psia.

Solution:

$$Q_a = \frac{Q_r (A+P)}{(Pb)}$$

Qr = 1000 cfh
P = 5 psig
P_b = 14.73
A = 14.40 psia

Therefore:

$$Q_a = 1000 \ \frac{(14.40 + 5)}{(14.73)}$$

$$Q_a = 1000 \ \frac{(19.40)}{(14.73)}$$

$$Qa = 1,317 \ cfh$$

The actual flow rate through the meter at base pressure conditions is 1,317 cfh.

Example #2

Determine the necessary recorded flow rate by the gas meter required to set the correct firing rate at 1000 kW for a boiler having 14 kPa gauge available gas pressure. Note, the local atmospheric pressure is 100.32 kPa absolute, the base pressure is 101.325 kPa absolute and the heating value of the gas is 10.35 kWh/m³.

Solution:

$$Q_a = Q_r \frac{(A+P)}{(P_b)}$$

$$Q_r = \frac{Q_a}{\frac{(A+P)}{(P_b)}}$$

$$Q_a = \frac{1000 \text{ kW}}{10.35 \text{ kWh/m}^3} = 96.62 \text{ m}^3/\text{h}$$

$$P = 14 \text{ Pa gauge}$$

$$P_b = 101.325 \text{ kPa absolute}$$

$$A = 100.32 \text{ kPa absolute}$$

$$Q_r = \frac{96.62}{\frac{(100.32 + 14)}{101.325}}$$

$$Q_r = 85.64 \text{ m}^3/\text{h}$$

The necessary recorded flow rate by the gas meter is 86.64 m³/h to give the burner firing rate of 1000 kW with an available gas pressure of 14 kPa gauge.

Table T3-4 gives meter correction capacities at elevated pressure from various base pressures and an assumed average atmospheric or barometric pressure of 14.40 psia.

Table T3-4: Pressure corrections factors for natural gas.

Gage Pressure P.S.I.G.	BASE PRESSURE P.S.I.A. 14.65 (4 oz.)	14.73	14.9 (8 oz.)	15.025 (10 oz.)	Gage Pressure P.S.I.G.	BASE PRESSURE P.S.I.A. 14.65 (4 oz.)	14.73	14.9 (8 oz.)	15.025 (10 oz.)
0.0	0.933	0.977	0.966	0.958					
.5	1.017	1.012	1.000	0.992	20.5	2.382	2.369	2.342	2.323
1	1.051	1.045	1.034	1.025	21	2.416	2.403	2.376	2.356
1..5	1.085	1.079	1.067	1.058	21.5	2.451	2.437	2.409	2.389
2	1.119	1.113	1.101	1.092	22	2.485	2.471	2.443	2.423
2.1	1.154	1.147	1.134	1.125	22.5	2.519	2.505	2.477	2.456
3	1.188	1.181	1.168	1.158	23	2.553	2.539	2.510	2.489
3.5	1.222	1.215	1.201	1.191	23.5	2.587	2.573	2.544	2.522
4	1.265	1.249	1.235	1.225	24	2.621	2.607	2.577	2.556
4.5	1.290	1.283	1.268	1.258	24.5	2.655	2.641	2.611	2.589
5.	1.324	1.317	1.302	1.291	25	2.689	2.675	2.644	2.622
5.5	1.358	1.351	1.335	1.324	25.5	2.758	2.743	2.711	2.689
6	1.392	1.385	1.369	1.358	26	2.826	2.811	2.79	2.755
6.5	1.427	1.419	1.403	1.391	26.5	2.894	2.878	2.846	2.822
7	1.461	1.453	1.436	1.424	27	2.962	2.946	2.913	2.889
7.5	1.495	1.487	1.470	1.458	27.5	3.031	3.014	2.980	2.955
8	1.529	1.521	1.503	1.491	28	3.099	3.082	3.047	3.022
8.5	1.563	1.555	1.537	1.524	28.5	3.167	3.150	3.114	3.088
9	1.597	1.589	1.670	1.557	29	3.235	3.218	3.181	3.155
9.5	1.631	1.623	1.604	1.591	29.5	3.204	3.286	3.248	3.221
10	1.666	1.656	1.638	1.624	30	3.372	3.354	3.315	3.288
10.5	1.700	1.690	1.671	1.657	30.5	3.440	3.422	3.383	3.354
11	1.734	1.724	1.705	1.691	31	3.509	3.489	3.450	3.421
11.5	1.768	1.752	1.738	1.724	31.5	3.577	3.557	3.517	3.488
12	1.802	1.798	1.772	1.757	32.	3.645	3.625	3.584	3.554
12.5	1.836	1.826	1.805	1.790	32.5	3.713	3.693	3.651	3.621
13	1.870	1.860	1.839	1.824	33	3.782	3.761	3.718	3.687
13.5	1.904	1.898	1.872	1.857	33.5	3.849	3.829	3.785	3.754
14	1.939	1.922	1.906	1.890	34	3.918	3.897	3.852	3.820
14.4	1.973	1.964	1.940	1.923	34.5	3.986	3.965	3.919	3.887
15	2.007	1.996	1.973	1.957	35	4.055	4.033	3.987	3.953
15.5	2.014	2.030	2.007	1.990	35.5	4.123	4.100	4.054	4.020
16	2.075	2.064	2.040	2.023	36	4.191	4.168	4.121	4.087
16.5	2.109	2.098	2.074	2.057	36.5	4.259	4.236	4.188	4.153
17	2.143	2.132	2.107	2.090	37	4.328	4.304	4.255	4.220
17.5	2.177	2.166	2.141	2.123	37.5	4.396	4.372	4.322	4.286
18	2.212	2.200	2.174	2.156	38	4.464	4.440	4.389	4.353
18.5	2.246	2.234	2.208	2.190	38.5	4.532	4.508	4.456	4.419
19	2.280	2.267	2.242	2.223	39	4.601	4.576	4.523	4.468
19.5	2.314	2.301	2.275	2.256	39.5	4.669	4.644	4.591	4.552
20	2.348	2.335	2.309	2.290	40	4.737	4.711	4.658	4.619

BASED UPON AN ASSUMED AVERAGE ATMOSPHERIC PRESSURE OF 14.4 P.S.I.A.

BASED UPON AN ASSUMED AVERAGE ATMOSPHERIC PRESSURE OF 14.4 P.S.I.A.

Prohibited Meter Locations

The following are inside areas where gas meters should not be located:

i)   Under combustible stairways.
ii) In unventilated or inaccessible locations.
iii) In an area not closer than 3 feet (90 cm) from a source of ignition including furnaces and water heaters.

Also, the gas meter should be located at the same location as the service regulator.

Assignment

1. State the basic principle of operation of both the bellows or diaphragm meters and rotary meters.

2. State the three types of dials found on the standard bellows type of gas meter and give the function of each.

3. Give the reading of the following meters:

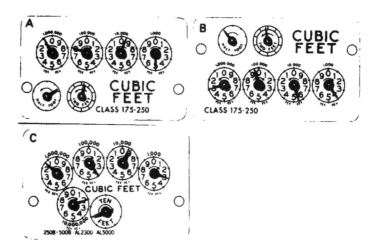

4. Calculate the burner input in Btuh from a 5 cu. ft. test dial making one complete revolution in 70 seconds.

5. Calculate the burner input in kW from a 0.1 m^3 test dial making one complete revolution in 40 seconds.

6. Calculate the burner Btuh input from a 0.05 m^3 test dial making one complete revolution in 30 seconds.

7. What is meant by the term temperature compensated meter?

8. Calculate the actual flow rate through a meter having a working pressure of 2 psig, when the meter has been "clocked" for 1540 cfh. The base pressure is 14.73 psia and the local atmospheric or barometric pressure is 14.40 psia.

9. Determine the necessary recorded flow rate by the gas meter required to set the correct firing rate at 765 kW for a boiler having 15 kPa gauge available pressure. Note: the local atmospheric pressure is 100.32 kPa absolute, the base pressure is 101.325 kPa absolute and the heating value of the gas is 10.35 kWh/m^3.

10. Give the inside locations where a gas meter should not be located.

4 Gas Pressure Regulators

The purpose of the gas pressure regulator is to maintain a constant downstream gas pressure. The pressure regulator will reduce an upstream or inlet pressure to a desired downstream pressure. Within the operating range of the regulator, it will maintain that downstream pressure, regardless of changes in the gas flow and changes in the upstream pressure condition.

The Three Operating Elements of a Regulator

Gas pressure regulators have three main operating elements that work together in providing the pressure control action of the regulator. As shown in *Figure 4-1*, the three elements are:

The Loading Element
The loading element usually takes the form of a regulator spring. The amount of spring pressure acting down upon the diaphragm determines the amount of downstream pressure. A greater spring pressure takes a higher downstream pressure acting underneath across the diaphragm surface to counterbalance it.

The Measuring Element
The measuring element is usually a neopreme diaphragm. The diaphragm measures the changes in the downstream condition and responds to position the valve (the restricting element) to a position which counteracts the change, thus returning the downstream pressure to its original level.

The Restricting Element
The restricting element is the valve part of the regulator. It is actuated by the measuring element (the diaphragm) and upon whether there has been an increase or decrease in the downstream pressure, the valve will either close off, creating a higher pressure drop, or open up, creating less of a pressure drop. In any event, the resulting pressure drop due to the valve's new position acts to offset the changes in the downstream pressure condition and bring it back to its original level.

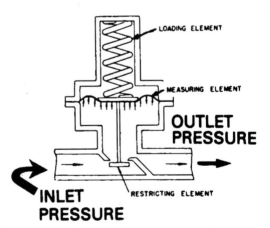

Figure 4-1: The three operating elements of a regulator.

Analysis of Operation

An analysis of the operation of a gas pressure regulator can be made by looking at how the downstream pressure is controlled or maintained.

Referring to *Figure 4-2*, the valve stem is in a state of equilibrium caused by the force of the downstream pressure acting up across the bottom of the diaphragm surface, and the force of the spring pressure acting down on the top surface of the diaphragm. The control action of the regulator is quite simple. If the downstream pressure drops below the set level, as adjusted by the spring pressure, the diaphragm becomes unbalanced and moves the valve to a more open position. As the valve takes a more open position, the pressure drop across the valve is reduced and the downstream pressure is restored to its original level. However, if the downstream pressure is too great, the reverse action takes place and the valve opening is reduced. A higher pressure drop is created across the valve and the downstream pressure is brought back to its original level.

The *vent*, located on the regulator body above the diaphragm allows the upper chamber above the diaphragm to *breathe*. The only force acting down upon the diaphragm must be the spring pressure. Without the vent, air could be compressed with the upward movement of the diaphragm, adding its force of compression to that of the spring's, causing sluggish or delaying action in the regulator's response.

The downstream pressure is set by adjusting spring pressure. If a higher downstream pressure is required, then more spring pressure is required and is accomplished by screwing the spring adjustment screw in. The opposite action would be taken if a lower downstream pressure is required. When the downstream pressure is to be set a manometer or pressure gauge must be placed on the downstream side to indicate the level of pressure reached.

Types of Regulators

There are basically two types of pressure regulators involved in the utilization of natural gas. From the standpoint of function they are the appliance regulator and the service regulator.

Appliance Regulator
The appliance regulator reduces the upstream houseline pressure of 7"wc (1.74 kPa) to the required downstream manifold pressure of 3.5"wc (.87 kPa) at the burner.

The appliance regulator is located at the start of the burner valve train assembly ahead of the burner or appliance control valves, as illustrated in *Figure 4-3* of a valve train assembly of a residential conversion burner.

Figure 4-2: The gas pressure regulator.

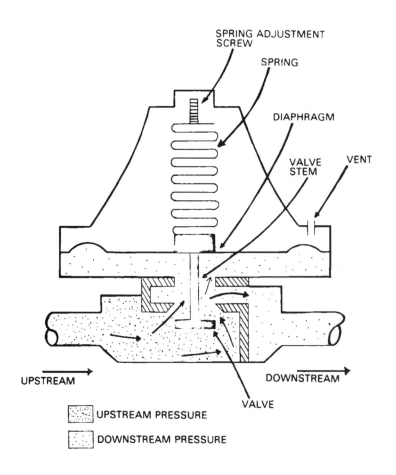

SPRING ADJUSTMENT SCREW

SPRING

DIAPHRAGM

VALVE STEM

VENT

UPSTREAM

DOWNSTREAM

VALVE

UPSTREAM PRESSURE

DOWNSTREAM PRESSURE

Figure 4-3: Low capacity appliance regulator used on a residential conversion burner. Note the pilot take off downstream of regulator.

Type of Appliance Regulators:

i) Low Capacity Type

Low capacity type appliance regulators, as illustrated in *Figure 4-4*, are designed to provide safe and uniform gas pressure to residential gas appliances. These regulators can have both main burner load and main burner and pilot burner load application.

Low capacity type appliance regulators that have a main burner and pilot load application are designed with a "P" stamping on the regulator body to indicate pilot load capacity. They are specifically designed to give pressure control to tiny pilot flows that are an essential operating requirement for the appliance.

ii) High Capacity Type

High capacity type of appliance regulators are used on larger residential and commercial appliances. Usually these appliance regulators are of the *straight-thru-flow design*, as illustrated in *Figure 4-5*. Straight-thru-flow regulators have been widely accepted in the industry because of their low frictional flow resistance that results in greater capacities for a given size of regulator.

iii) As a Component of a Gas Control Valve

The appliance regulator is often used as a component of a combustion control valve, as illustrated in *Figure 4-6*. It provides the same function as a low capacity type of appliance regulator. The only difference is that it is physically a part of a combination control valve.

Outlet Pressure Adjustment: Appliance regulators can be either the *limited* or *variable* adjustment type. Limited adjustment type appliance regulators are usually factory set at an outlet pressure of 3.5"wc (.87 kPa) and are adjustable ± .5"wc (.12 kPa) from the factory setting.

Variable adjustment type appliance regulators are equipped with regulator springs that can give an adjustment to outlet pressure of 3" – 6"wc or 2" – 5"wc (.75 – 1.5 kPa or .5 – 1.25 kPa) depending upon the spring range of the regulator.

However, outlet pressure adjustment can only be attempted when there is sufficient inlet pressure. The minimum required inlet pressure for outlet pressure adjustment is 1"wc (.25 kPa) above the maximum adjustment range of the spring. For example, with an outlet pressure spring range of 2"-5"wc (.5 - 1.25 kPa) the minimum inlet pressure requirement would be 6"wc (1.5 kPa). Adjusting the outlet pressure when there is insufficient inlet pressure available could overfire the appliance if the inlet pressure was to increase some time after the adjustment was made.

Appliance Regulator Accessories: Appliance regulator accessories, as illustrated in *Figure 4-7*, are used to improve the operating characteristics of the regulator.

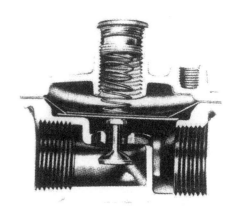

Figure 4-4: Low capacity appliance regulator that can be used for main burner or main burner & pilot load application.

Figure 4-5: High capacity appliance regulator—straight-thru-flow type.

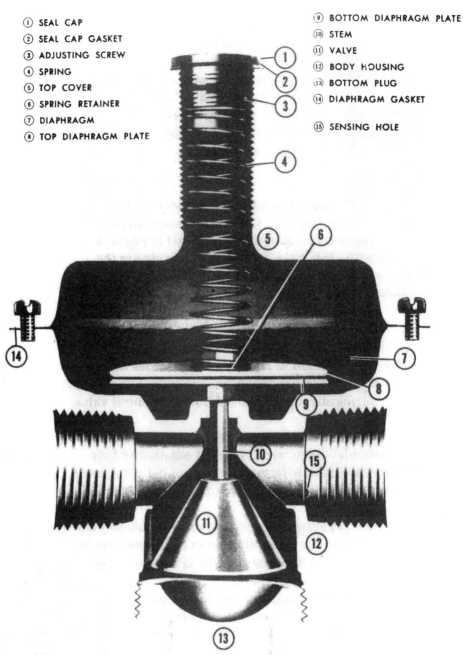

① SEAL CAP
② SEAL CAP GASKET
③ ADJUSTING SCREW
④ SPRING
⑤ TOP COVER
⑥ SPRING RETAINER
⑦ DIAPHRAGM
⑧ TOP DIAPHRAGM PLATE

⑨ BOTTOM DIAPHRAGM PLATE
⑩ STEM
⑪ VALVE
⑫ BODY HOUSING
⑬ BOTTOM PLUG
⑭ DIAPHRAGM GASKET

⑮ SENSING HOLE

Figure 4-6: Appliance regulator as a component of a gas control valve.

Figure 4-7: Appliance regulator accessories.

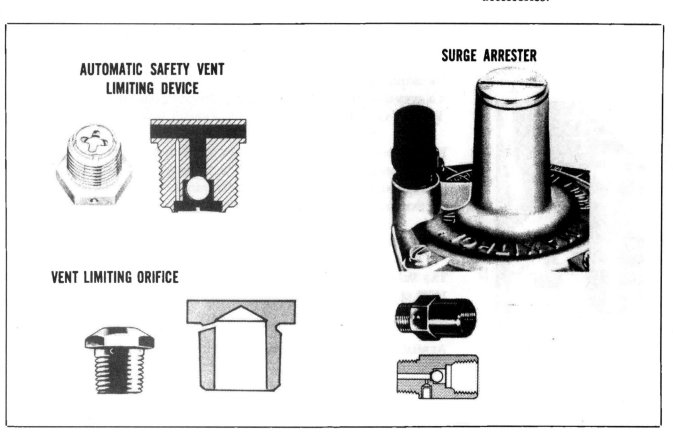

AUTOMATIC SAFETY VENT
LIMITING DEVICE

SURGE ARRESTER

VENT LIMITING ORIFICE

Surge Arrester: The surge arrester induces soft lighting, controls flame roll out and maintains pilot flame stability. The surge arrester is mounted in the regulator vent boss and causes the regulator to open slowly and close normally.

Vent Limiting Orifice: The vent limiting orifice is usually machined from brass. Its purpose is to allow equal limits of inhalation and escape of air from the upper diaphragm chamber. In the event that the diaphragm does rupture, the leakage is limited to less than 1 cfh ($0.02832 \text{ m}^3/\text{h}$) at 7"wc (1.74 kPa) gas pressure.

Automatic Safety Vent Limiting Device: A ball check permits free inhalation of the regulator for fast regulator-diaphragm response, but automatically limits gas escape to safe limits should a diaphragm rupture. This device gives sensitive response even at low inlet pressure.

Service Regulators

The service regulator, as illustrated in *Figure 4-8* is located at the gas meter inlet and reduces the upstream gas service line pressure in pounds per square inch to 7"wc (1.74 kPa) houseline pressure at the gas meter outlet.

Operating Components of a Service Regulator: The operating components of a service regulator are illustrated in *Figure 4-9*.

The Linkage: The linkage provides the connection between the diaphragm and the valve. Movement of the linkage, as actuated by the diaphragm, will open and close the valve. Basically, the linkage is a system of levers that will multiply the diaphragm movement to close the valve tightly.

The Orifice: The orifice restricts the gas flow through the regulator; and in conjunction with the valve, controls the flow of gas through the regulator. The orifice is sized according to the customer's total cfh demand, upstream and downstream pressure conditions.

The Vent: The vent allows the regulator to breathe.

The Valve Seat: The valve seat is made of soft material providing a 100% shut-off when the valve is closed preventing any gas flow through the orifice.

Available Features: Some service regulators can have the following available features:

Figure 4-8: Outside service regulator and meter installation.

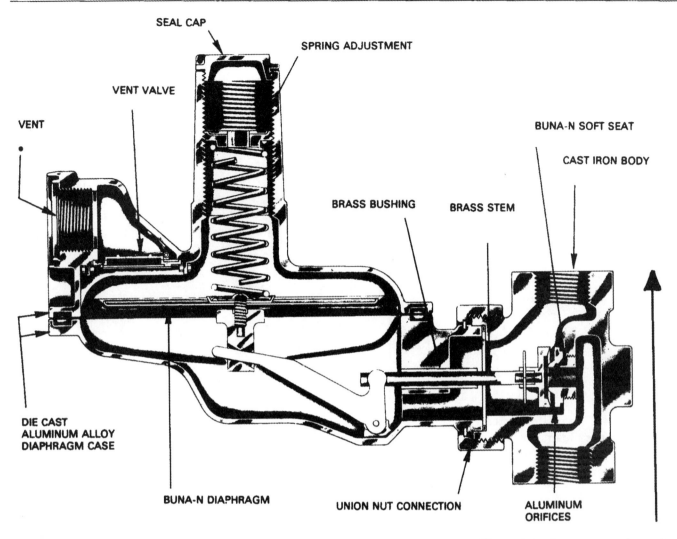

Figure 4-9: A cut-away view of a standard service regulator.

Labels on figure:
- SEAL CAP
- SPRING ADJUSTMENT
- VENT VALVE
- VENT
- BUNA-N SOFT SEAT
- CAST IRON BODY
- BRASS BUSHING
- BRASS STEM
- DIE CAST ALUMINUM ALLOY DIAPHRAGM CASE
- BUNA-N DIAPHRAGM
- UNION NUT CONNECTION
- ALUMINUM ORIFICES

i) Internal Safety Relief (IRV)

Service regulators that have this feature are equipped with special seats located at the diaphragm and linkage connection. The seat will open allowing gas to pass out of the regulator through the vent, in the event that the downstream pressure exceeds allowable pressure conditions. *(See Figure 4-10.)*

ii) Lock-off Mechanism

Service regulators that have this feature are equipped with an additional seat design to close, shutting off the flow of gas through the regulator, if the outlet pressure is too high or too low. If the regulator locks off under the above conditions it must be manually reset.

Positive Shut-off: Service regulators provide a positive shut-off when no flow is occurring in the line to the appliances. The service regulator will usually *lock-up* to within 10% of the original outlet pressure setting. *(See Figure 4-11.)*

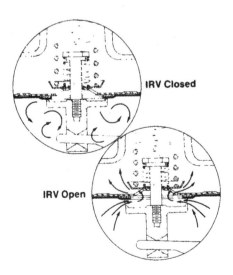

IRV Closed

IRV Open

Figure 4-10: Internal relief valve (IRV) mechanism employed by a service regulator.

Sizing the Gas Pressure Regulator

Gas pressure regulators, whether a service regulator or an appliance regulator, are sized according to:

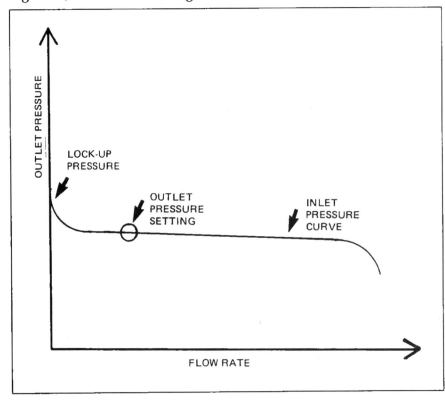

Figure 4-11: Regulator performance curve illustrating outlet pressure setting and lock-up pressure.

1. Inlet pressure available
2. Required outlet pressure
3. Flow rate required by the appliance or appliances.

Field Servicing of Regulators

Table T 4-1 outlines symptoms, possible causes, field test and remedies for appliance regulator problems that may be encountered in the field.

Assignment

1. State the function of a gas pressure regulator.

2. List the three main operating elements of a gas pressure regulator and state the purpose of each.

3. Briefly analyze the action of a gas pressure regulator in its attempt to maintain a constant downstream gas pressure.

FIELD SERVICE CHECK LIST FOR APPLIANCE REGULATORS

A. SYMPTOM (See Footnote A)*	B. POSSIBLE CAUSES (See Footnote B)*	C. FIELD TEST	D. REMEDY
OUTLET PRESSURE TOO HIGH (See Footnote D)*	1) Incorrect spring adjustment. 2) Ruptured diaphragm. 3) Flow rate too low on main burner load regulators. 4) Gas is turned on upstream with control valve open. 5) Stretched spring.	1) Remove seal cap. 2) Apply soap solution to vent outlet- bubbles indicate leaky diaphragm. 3) Check orifice size to determine flow. Should not be less than 5% minimum main burner regulation capacity. 4) Close control valve before opening manual valve upstream. Wait 30 seconds, then open control valve. 5) Manually turn off gas. Remove seal cap and adjusting screw. If spacings between spring turns are not uniform, spring has probably been stretched.	1) Adjust for proper tension. 2) Replace diaphragm. 3) Replace regulator with one of smaller size. 4) This is a temporary condition and will rectify itself in less than 30 seconds. 5) Replace with new spring.
OUTLET PRESSURE TOO LOW	6) Incorrect spring adjustment. 7) Inlet pressure too low. 8) Regulator improperly installed. 9) Wrong spring. 10) Inlet pressure too high.	6) Remove seal cap. 7) Remove spring-hold diaphragm down with screwdriver - no rise in outlet pressure indicates inlet pressure too low. 8) See that arrow on bottom side of regulator points in direction of gas flow. 9) Remove spring. Hold diaphragm down with screwdriver. Rise to correct outlet pressure indicates stronger spring is required. 10) Regulators for domestic service are not expected to perform accurately if inlet pressure is greater than 28"wc (7kPa).	6) Adjust spring to proper tension. 7) Check for obstructions in system upstream of regulator. 8) If incorrect, install regulator properly. 9) Replace with correct spring. 10) If inlet pressure is greater than 28"wc (7kPa) consult manufacturer for special applications.
REGULATOR RESPONDS BUT ACTION SLOW OR SLUGGISH	11) Obstruction in vent causing limited diaphragm movement. 12) Regulator equipped with Surge Arrester for purposes of improving combustion characteristics. 13) Sensing hole at base of threads on outlet side of valve chamber blocked by excessive pipe dope.	11) Inspect vent opening on top cover of regulator. (See Footnote C)* 12) Remove Surge Arrester from vent to see if regulator response is restored. 13) This condition occurs very rarely but when it does exist will always be detected at time of original installation.	11) free vent hole with small wire, being careful not to puncture diaphragm. 12) Be sure orifices in Surge Arrester are clean and not blocked. Double check with manufacturer to determine if Surge Arrester is properly sized for application. 13) Remove regulator from line, clean sensing hole, and re-install.
REGULATOR FORMERLY OPERATING SATISFACTORILY, WILL NO LONGER MAINTAIN OUTLET PRESSURE	14) Change inlet pressure conditions 15) Loss of flexibility of diaphragm.	14) Check pressure as suggested in C-7 and C-10.	15) Follow remedies in D-7 and D-10 16) Replace diaphragm.

* FOOTNOTES

(A) Before making the tests listed above, make sure that the regulator is installed in the line properly and that the pressure conditions and flow rates are within design limitations of the regulator.

(B) The possible cause for any of the symptoms outlined above could be misalignment or damage to any of the regulator parts due to excessively rough, handling or faulty field servicing. To check on freedom of movements of the working parts, remove bottom plug and work valve mechanism up and down with finger. The valve should work freely and without binding.

(C) In the event the regulator is vented to the combustion chamber or some other remote location, be sure that the connecting tube is free of dirt, ice or other obstructions.

(D) In order to check outlet pressure, the appliance must be operating. Under conditions of no flow, pressure on the outlet side of the straight-through-flow models, will be equal to the pressure on the inlet side.

Table T4-1: Field Service Check List for Appliance Regulators

4. Give the function of:
   a) Appliance regulator
   b) Service regulator
   c) Vent
   d) Surge arrester
   e) Vent limiting orifice
   f) Automatic safety vent limiting device
   g) The service regulator linkage
   h) The service regulator orifice
   i) The service regulator valve seat

5. What is meant by the term:
   a) Limited adjustment type of appliance regulator
   b) Variable adjustment type of appliance regulator
   c) Minimum required inlet pressure

6. Briefly describe the following features that may be found on some types of service regulators:
   a) Internal safety relief (IRV)
   b) Lock-off mechanism

7. Identify the components of a gas pressure regulator as shown in *Figure 4-12*.

Figure 4-12: Gas Pressure Regulator

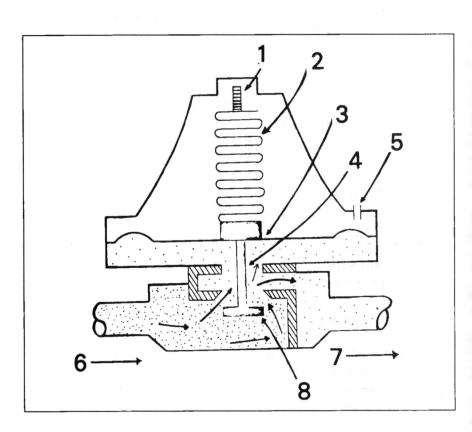

Gas Piping

In this section we are concerned with the practical application and standards of gas piping. The areas that are covered are the local gas company's distribution system, piping terminology, gas piping practice and gas pipe and tube sizing.

Local Gas Company's Distribution System

The flow of the gas from the gas well to the customer's appliance can be illustrated by looking at a local gas company's distribution system as shown schematically in *Figure 5-1*.

The following are the various points where the gas is handled, treated and its pressure reduced in the local gas company's distribution system:

Gas Well: Here the gas flows out of the gas well, which belongs to a gas producing company, and into a network of field or gathering lines that convey the gas to a central transmission line. The network of field or gathering lines is controlled by a gathering company, which delivers the gas to a transmission company.

Compressor Station: At the transmission company's compressor station, the gas is compressed, purified, measured and then fed into the transmission line under very high pressure (1000 psig or 7000 kPa) since the gas will usually be transported over a long distance.

City Gate Station: At the city gate station, the gas is measured, odourized and regulated as the transmission company feeds the gas into the local gas company's distribution system.

Extra High Pressure Distribution Mains: Extra high pressure distribution mains supply gas from the city gate station to lower pressure distribution mains or directly to customer services, usually very large commercial or industrial customers. The pressure in these lines varies from 100–653 psig (700–4500 kPa).

District Regulating Station: Before the gas is supplied to lower pressure distribution mains, it must be regulated down from extra high pressure to lower levels of pressure. This occurs at the district regulator station.

From the district regulator station, gas is supplied to the distribution system at four levels of pressure:

i)   High pressure: 65–174 psig (450–1200 kPa)
ii) Intermediate pressure: 10–64 psig (70–440 kPa)
iii) Medium pressure: 3–12 psig (20–80 kPa)
iv) Low pressure: 5–14"wc (1.2–3.5 kPa)

Figure 5-1: Local gas company's distribution system showing points of pressure reduction.

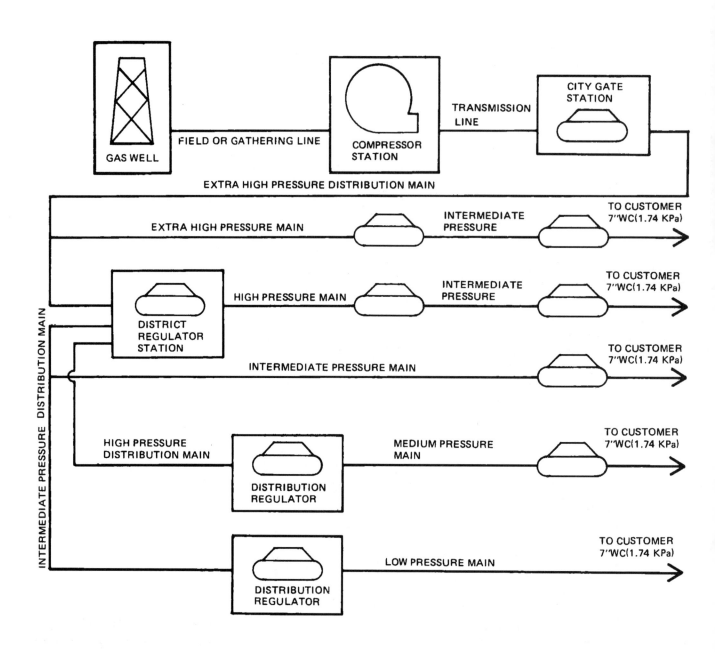

Locations at Which the Gas Pressure is Reduced

The following are the various locations in the gas company's distribution system where the gas pressure is reduced:

Local Gas Company:
- city gate station
- district regulator station
- distribution regulators
- service regulators

Customer
- appliance regulator

Note: The outlet pressure at the service regulator *(see Figure 4-8)* is usually set at 7.5"wc giving approximately 7"wc at the meter outlet as supply or building line pressure since some pressure is lost across the gas meter

Terminology

Referring to *Figure 5-5* — this figure illustrates the following terms associated with gas piping.

Gas Main: The gas main is the main gas line supplying gas under pressure to customers along a city street. The gas pressure falls into five categories as previously explained: extra high pressure, high pressure, intermediate, medium and low pressure.

Figure 5-2 illustrates the gas main and the gas service being taken off from it, together with a curb box (valve) location. The *curb valve* is a gas stop which enables the gas supply to the customer's service to be discontinued. It is usually below ground level at the point where the service line is connected to the gas main.

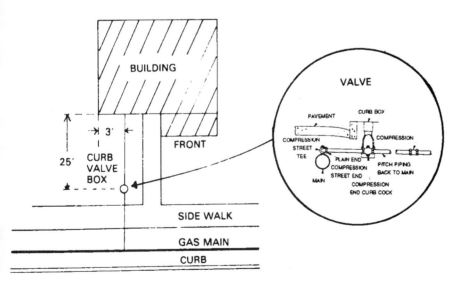

Figure 5-2: Gas service being taken off gas main and entrance at front of building below ground level. Note the enlarged view of curb box and valve.

Gas Service: The gas service is the gas line that conveys the gas from the main to the customer's premises. The gas pressure in the service line is the same pressure as that in the gas main.

Upon entering the building the service regulator will reduce this pressure to the required houseline pressure within the building line. *Figure 5-3* illustrates a gas service entering the building above ground level. The *service stop* (valve) enables the gas supply to be discontinued at a point ahead of the meter and service regulator at the customer's premises. It is usually located above ground level at the inlet to the service regulator. (*See Figures 3-4, 3-5 and 4-8.*)

Figure 5-3: Gas service entering the building above ground level.

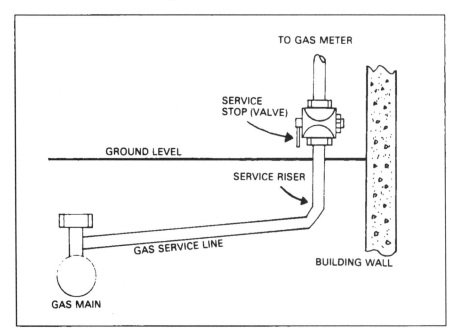

Gas Supply Line or Building Line: This is the main interior building line that supplies gas to the various appliances within the building.

Branch Line: The branch line is the gas line running from the supply line over to an individual appliance.

Drop Line: The drop line is considered a part of the branch line. It is that part of the branch line which drops down to the appliance as fed by an overhead supply line.

Riser: Same as a drop line except it conveys the gas up to an appliance.

Drip or Dirt Pocket: As illustrated in *Figure 5-4*, the drip or dirt pocket consists of a tee, nipple and cap located at the bottom of a drop line. Its function is to trap moisture and dirt in the gas line. A drip is required on every drop line and its diameter is the same as that of the drop line it services or 2" diameter, whichever is less. The length of the drip is usually not less than 3 inches (75 mm) or not less than the internal diameter of the drop line, whichever is greater.

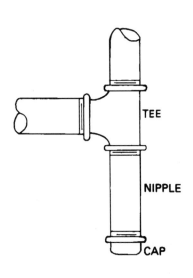

Figure 5-4: The pipe drip.

Piping Extension: The piping extension is a slight continuation of the supply line and it consists of a tee, nipple and cap located at the end of the supply line. Its function is to provide for future extension of the supply line in the event that additional appliances are added to the system.

Concealed Piping: Any piping, other than that passing directly through walls and partitions, that is concealed, for example, behind a false wall, is differentiated from exposed piping, for example, piping that is in plain view.

It should be noted, as illustrated in *Figure 5-5*, what constitutes the gas company's system and what constitutes the customer's. Generally, everything downstream of the gas meter belongs to the customer and everything upstream of the meter, including the meter, is the gas company's. This can be illustrated by the fact that only gas company personnel can adjust the service regulator that determines the building's gas supply pressure.

Figure 5-5: Illustrating piping terminology.

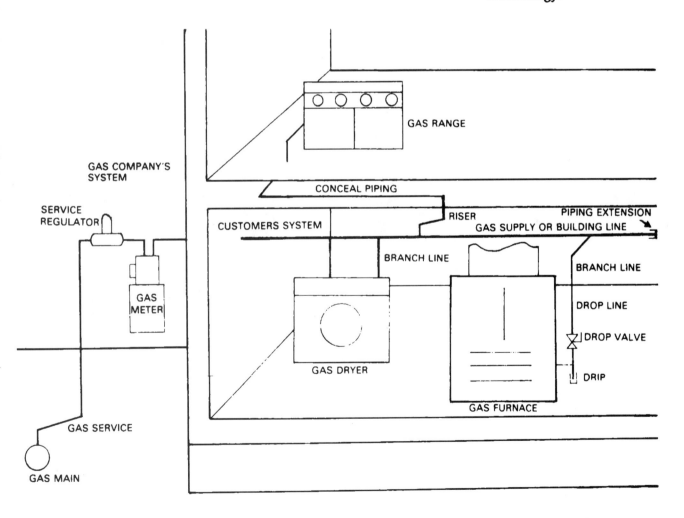

Figure 5-6: Pipe fittings.

90° ELBOW   90° REDUCING ELBOW   45° ELBOW

90° STREET ELBOW   45° STREET ELBOW   TEE

REDUCING TEE   COUPLING   REDUCING COUPLING

CAP   PLUG   UNION

BUSHING   CLOSE NIPPLE   SHORT AND LONG NIPPLES

1 Depending upon local and national code requirements, all or some of these fittings are not allowed on gas piping systems.

Gas Piping Practice

The following is a summary of requirements and standards that constitute good gas piping practice using conventional black pipe and fittings and seamless copper, brass and steel tubing using flare or brazed connections.

Acceptable Material: Steel gas pipe must be black and piping fittings must be malleable iron or steel. Copper tubing used above ground must be type K or L up to and including 1 1/4 inch nominal size or type GP of not less than 3/8 inch nominal size. For underground service, the copper tubing must be type K.[2]

Copper tubing is connected by either 45° brass *flare connectors (see Figure 5-7)* or by brazing with a material having a melting point exceeding 1000°F (525°C).

Figure 5-7: 45° brass flare connectors.

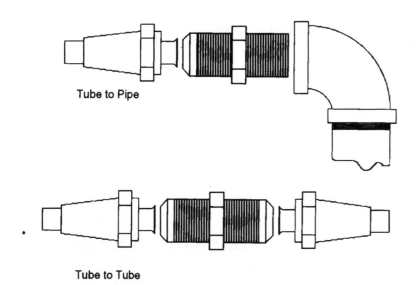

Tube to Pipe

Tube to Tube

Plastic pipe or tubing may be used to convey gas underground to outdoor appliances. However, its application must conform to local and national code requirements.

Piping, tubing or fittings previously used with other gases may be reused provided it is ascertained that the piping, tubing or fittings to be used are equivalent to new material. This piping, tubing or fittings to be reused must be cleansed, inspected and tested.

Figure 5-6 illustrates the types of pipe fittings that are used in gas piping systems.

[2] Depending upon local and national code requirements, type L tubing can be used underground if externally coated with extruded PVC resin at the time of manufacture.

Appliances such as gas ranges and dryers can be connected to the gas supply by *flexible connectors*. *Figure 5-8* illustrates the use of a flexible connector connecting a gas range to the gas supply. Flexible connectors allow the gas appliance to be moved for cleaning and servicing without interruption to the gas supply. Flexible connectors must be connected to rigid pipe with a shut-off valve located in the same room as the appliance. Also, they cannot go through any wall, floor, ceiling or partition, or be used in a concealed location. The maximum length of a flexible connector is 6 feet (2 meters).

Figure 5-8: Application of a flexible connector connecting a gas range to gas supply line.

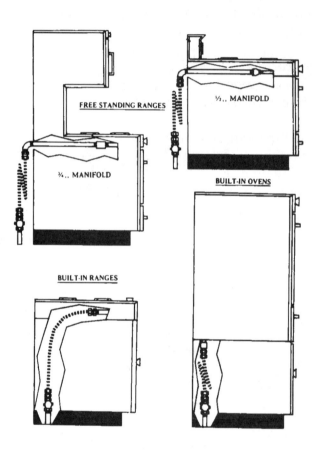

FREE STANDING RANGES

½., MANIFOLD

¾.. MANIFOLD

BUILT-IN OVENS

BUILT-IN RANGES

Appliances such as gas ranges, dryers, gas refrigerators and counter equipment usually employ flexible connectors for the gas hook-up. Other appliances, such as gas furnaces, hot water heaters and space heaters (i.e., vented appliances), may also use flexible connectors for the gas connection if recommended by the appliance manufacturer.

Pipe Coating: If the pipe and fittings are in contact with a material exerting a corrosive action, they should be coated with an approved corrosive resistant material.

Joint Compounds: Pipe dope and pipe tape, of an approved type, will act as a joining sealant for gas piping. Pipe dope and pipe tape are applied only to the male thread of the fitting. If applied to the female thread of the fitting, there is the possibility that the sealant will be forced into the pipe itself, causing an obstruction. When using pipe tape, the tape is stretched and applied in a clockwise direction having a 50% overlap. Note, when using pipe dope or tape the first two threads are left free of any dope or tape.

Reaming: The ends of all gas piping shall be reamed.

Gasket Material: Gasket material for regulators and control valves, etc., must be made of some synthetic rubber material, since natural gas will corrode natural rubber.

Building Structure: No building structure used as a building support should support any gas piping or tubing if by doing so that structure is weakened in any way.

Supporting Pipe and Tubing: Gas piping and tubing cannot be supported by any other pipe, or by any other arrangement other than approved pipe supports. *Table T5-1* lists the distances between supports for the diameter of the pipe or tubing used.

Table T5-1: Pipe and Tubing Support Spacings

Piping Support Spacing

Iron Pipe Size in Inches	Position	Maximum Spacing of Support - Feet(Metres)
1/2 or less	Horizontal	6 (2.0)
3/4 -1	Horizontal	8 (2.5)
1 1/4 - 2 1/2	Horizontal	10 (3.0)
3 -4	Horizontal	15 (5.0)
5 - 8	Horizontal	20 (6.0)
10 or larger	Horizontal	25 (8.0)
1 1/4 or larger	Vertical	Every floor but not less than 125% of horizontal spacings
Tubing - all sizes	Horizontal & Vertical	6 (2)

Prohibited Practice: Depending on local and national code requirements, the following are not usually allowed for gas piping:

i) Bending gas pipe
ii) Bushings, thread protectors or running threads
iii) Street elbows and tees
iv) Close nipples
v) Right and left hand threaded fittings
vi) Gas lines to be used as an electrical ground, or using pipe or tubing in lieu of wiring, except for low voltage control or ignition circuits or electronic flame detection devices circuits incorporated as a part of an appliance.

Limitations on the Location of Gas Piping and Tubing: Gas piping and tubing cannot be located in any area where, in the event of a gas leak, the gas would be diffused throughout the building; such areas are:

i) Chimneys
ii) Coal chutes
iii) Warm air and ventilating ducts[3]
iv) Elevator shafts
v) Dumb waiters
vi) Stairwells of other than a one or two family dwelling

Gas piping and tubing cannot be located in a concealed position where large quantities of corrosive chemicals are used, i.e., battery shops. Also, it cannot be located in areas in which the piping or tubing is in contact with cinders that may corrode the piping or tubing.

Gas Outlets: A gas outlet is the termination of the gas piping near or at the location of an appliance or a proposed appliance. Gas outlets that terminate a gas supply shall be made gas tight by a plugged valve or a cap or a plug that is compatible with the piping or tubing.

The unthreaded portion of the threaded piping outlet should extend at least 2 inches (50 mm) through floors and at least 1 inch (25 mm) through finished ceilings and walls. Also, the outlet should be located as close as is practical to the appliance being serviced by the outlet.

Branch Outlet Pipes: To prevent moisture or dirt from entering the branch line, a branch line must be taken from either the side or the top of the supply line. However, it can be taken from the bottom of the supply line if it is a drop line and is provided with a drip or dirt pocket. *Figure 5-9* illustrates the three methods of taking a branch line from a gas supply line.

When a branch outlet is placed on a main supply line before its size is known, then the outlet will be of the same size as the supply line which supplies it.

Pipe Sizes That Require Welding: Pipe of a size 2 1/2 inches or over must be welded.

---

[3] Depending upon local and national code requirements, piping and tubing may be installed in a false ceiling space, including one used as a return air plenum of a central warm air or air conditioning system.

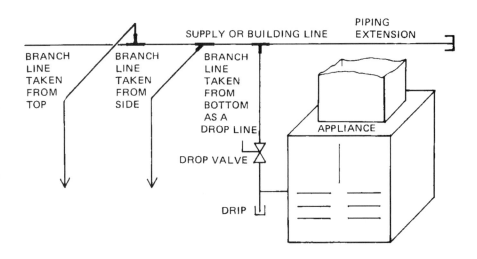

Figure 5-9: Methods of taking branch lines from a gas supply line.

Piping and Tubing Between Buildings: All gas piping running from one building to another will have a shut-off valve at the point of exit from the first building and one at the point of entry to the adjoining building.

Concealed Piping and Tubing: All concealed piping and tubing must be tested and inspected in its final position prior to being concealed; and, the concealed location must not be one in which an undetected leak could accumulate. Gas piping of a size less than 1/2 inch cannot be concealed. Also, unions or swing joints, made by a combination of fittings, should not be used where piping is concealed.

Piping and Tubing in Floors: Gas piping and tubing installed in concrete or other solid types of floors will be laid in a channel in the floor and covered for protection, while permitting access to the piping. Alternately, the pipe or tubing can run in a ventilated *sleeve* under the floor.

Vertical Pipe Chase: A vertical pipe chase should have an opening at each end having a minimum area equivalent to that of 1" diameter (25 mm) round opening.

Underground Piping and Tubing: Underground gas piping and tubing must meet the following requirements:

i)   All pipe joints must be welded
ii)   All joints or connections in copper tubing must be brazed
iii) The piping cannot be smaller than 1/2 inch
iv)   Must be laid 15 inches (44 mm) below ground level or 24 inches (60 mm) if running below commercial driveways or parking lots
v)   Cannot pass below foundations, walls or under buildings
vi)   Must be wrapped with a corrosion resistant material.

Gas Shut-off Valves: Manual gas shut-off valves shall be either the plug, ball or eccentric type and should not be subjected to pressures greater than their certified pressure rating. *Figure 5-10* is a cut-away view of a taper plug spring load gas shut-off valve.

Figure 5-10: Taper plug spring load gas shut-off valve. Note, when valve plug is turned in the barrel, the taper valve opening is aligned to gas inlet allowing gas to pass through the valve.

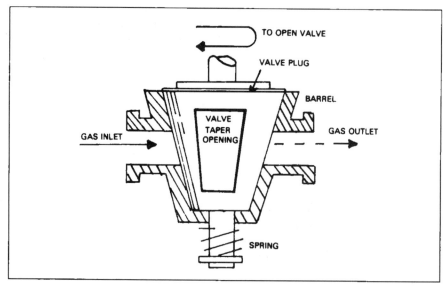

Figure 5-11: Lubricated plug valves.

A manual valve, known as the *drop valve,* must be installed in every drop line or riser; for lines greater than 1 inch diameter or having gas pressures greater than 1/2 psig (3.5 kPa), the drop valve must be of the ball, eccentric or *lubricated plug cock* type as illustrated in *Figure 5-11.*[4]

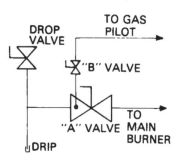

Figure 5-12: "A" & "B" valve arrangement.

[4] A manually operated 1/4 turn valve of the plug and barrel type designed so that the lapped bearing surfaces can be lubricated and the lubricant level maintained without removing the valve from service.

Some older heating units have a manual type of valve, which is located downstream of the drop valve. These valves have a pilot valve incorporated in their valve body ahead of the valve's shut-off plug. This valve arrangement is called an *A & B valve,* as illustrated in *Figure 5-12.*

The "A" part of the valve is the main gas line shut-off and the "B" part is a pilot shut-off. *Figure 5-13* illustrates a plug valve having a pilot take-off plug in its valve body, while *Figure 5-14* illustrates a variety of pilot valves. *Figure 4-3* illustrating the low capacity type of appliance regulator, also illustrates the application of the "A" & "B" valve.

Figure 5-13: Lubricated plug valves that have a pilot valve take off on the valve body - known as an "A" valve when used in conjunction with a pilot valve.

Gas Supply Pipe Identification: In commercial and industrial buildings the gas supply line is differentiated from other systems by being painted with a coat of highly visible yellow-orange paint.

Pressure Inside Buildings: *Table T 5-2* illustrates maximum building line pressures for various types of residential, commercial and industrial buildings. For one or two family dwellings and row housing, 2 psig (14 kPa) is given as the maximum permissible pressure. This allows the incorporation of the special 2 psig (14 kPa) copper tube system that is described in Appendix V. Normally, for conventional piping and tubing systems, 14"wc (3.5 kPa) is considered the maximum permissible pressure.

Minimum Pipe Size: The smallest size of pipe that can be used indoors is 1/2 inch in diameter: however, 3/8 inch piping may be used as a branch line not exceeding 25 feet (7.5 m) in length and not supplying more than 15,000 Btuh (4.5 kW).

Table T5-2: Pressures Inside Buildings

Type of Building	Maximum pressure, psig (kPa)	
	Other than Central Boiler or Mechanical Room	Central Boiler or Mechanical Room
One & two family dwellings row housing	2 (14)	—
Hotels & Motels	5 (35)	20 (140)
Residential, other than one and two family dwellings and row housing	5 (35)	20 (140)
Institutional and Assembly	5 (35)	20 (140)
Commercial	20 (140)	20* (140)
Industrial	60 (410)	60 (410)
Central Heating Plants	—	60 (410)

* 60 psig (410 kPa) is permissible in boiler or mechanical rooms located on the roof of commercial buildings.

Figure 5-14: Series of pilot gas valves - known as "B" valves when used in conjunction with a main shut-off valve.

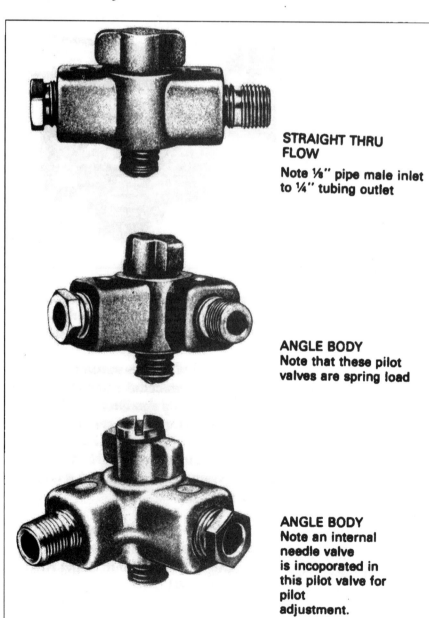

STRAIGHT THRU FLOW
Note ⅛" pipe male inlet to ¼" tubing outlet

ANGLE BODY
Note that these pilot valves are spring load

ANGLE BODY
Note an internal needle valve is incoporated in this pilot valve for pilot adjustment.

Testing Gas Lines

Gas lines must be tested upon being installed and the testing should be made:

i)   Before the appliances are connected
ii) After the appliances are connected, and
iii) After gas has been turned on into the system.

Before the Appliances are Connected

Before the appliances are connected, the gas line is isolated and is tested with air or inert gas (carbon dioxide or nitrogen) at pressures shown in *Table T 5-3*. The pressure should be measured with a mercury manometer or pressure gauge calibrated in increments not greater than 2 pounds (14 kPa), or 2% of the maximum dial reading of the pressure gauge, whichever is greater. The duration of the test is shown in *Table T 5-3*. All manual gas valves, as well as control valves and other components having a pressure rating below the test pressure, are isolated from the gas line being tested. The high test pressure may damage them, creating a hazardous condition in the future. *Figure 5-14* illustrates the testing of the gas line before the appliance is connected.

Table T 5-3: Test Pressure Table

Pressure Test Requirements for Gas Lines

Working Pressure		Diameter of			Length of Pipe/Tubing		Test Pressure		Test Time
psig	(kPa)	Pipe	or	Tubing	feet	(m)	psig	(kPa)	Minutes
0-2*	(0-14)	All Sizes			200 or less	(60)	15	(100)	15
0-2*	(0-14)	All Sizes			more than 200	(60)	15	(100)	60
2-33**	(14-230)	All Sizes			200 or less	(60)	50	(340)	60
2-33**	(14-230)	All Sizes			more than 200	(60)	50	(340)	180
over 33	(230)	All Sizes			all lengths		1.5 X the maximum operating pressure		180
all welded pipe		All Sizes			all lengths		50 psig (340 kPa) or 1.5 X the maximum operating pressure		180

* up to and including 2 psig(14 kPa)
** over 2 psig(14kPa) but not more than 33 psig(230 kPa)

After the Appliances are Connected

Before conducting the following test, a visual check should be made to ensure that gas could not escape from an opening in the piping system. Also, immediately after allowing gas into the piping system, a check should be made to ascertain that no gas is escaping by carefully watching the gas meter test dial.

Having the appliances shut off and a manometer placed in the supply line at the meter outlet (*see Figure 5-16*), gas is introduced into the supply line. The valve at the meter is now turned off and

Figure 5-15: Testing the gas line before the appliance is connected.

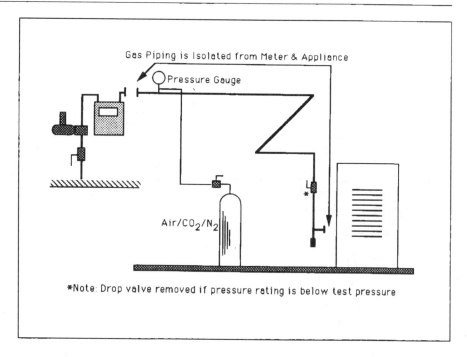

Gas Piping is Isolated from Meter & Appliance

Pressure Gauge

Air/CO$_2$/N$_2$

*Note: Drop valve removed if pressure rating is below test pressure

gas under pressure is *locked-up* in the supply line. The gas pressure, as read from the manometer, must hold for at least ten minutes. The manometer or pressure gauge used for the test must be calibrated in increments not greater than 1" wc (250 Pa).[5] Once the test is completed, all appliance connections, control valves and other appliance piping components must be soap tested under normal operating pressure to ensure that they are gas tight.

Before conducting the above test, it may be necessary to check the shut-off valve at the gas meter *(see Figure 5-3)* for *valve seepage.* The valve may be seeping gas as a result of dried and hardened valve grease.

Once the gas line is brought to a static pressure condition, release a small amount of locked-in gas pressure by quickly removing and then replacing the manometer tubing. This will open the service regulator, allowing the gas line to be tested back to the shut-off valve at the gas meter. If gas pressure creeps back up, then the gas valve is passing gas, which would invalidate the test.

This test should be done before the gas line is tested to ensure that a gas line leak is not masked by gas seeping through the gas valve at the gas meter.

---

[5] i) For systems where the working pressure exceeds 0.5 psig (3.5 kPa) but does not exceed 5 psig (17.5 kPa), the pressure gauge or equivalent device shall be calibrated to read in increments of not greater than 1 ounce of pressure (0.5 kPa).

ii) For systems where the working pressure exceeds 5 psig (17.5 kPa), the pressure gauge or equivalent device shall be calibrated to read in increments of not greater than 2 psig (14 kPa) or 2% of the maximum dial reading of the gauge, whichever is greater.

Figure 5-16: Testing the gas line
after the appliance is connected.

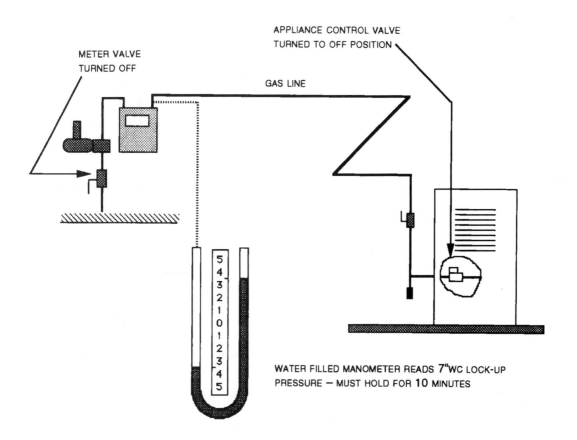

APPLIANCE CONTROL VALVE
TURNED TO OFF POSITION

METER VALVE
TURNED OFF

GAS LINE

5
4
3
2
1
0
1
2
3
4
5

WATER FILLED MANOMETER READS 7"WC LOCK-UP
PRESSURE — MUST HOLD FOR 10 MINUTES

After Gas has been Turned On Into the System

This test is applied to the gas line whenever gas is turned on in the
system after a period of shut-down or when gas is going to be left
turned on for a new installation.

Having appliances shut off, the gas is turned on at the meter and
the meter's test dial hand is marked as to its position. The position
of the test dial hand must hold for at least 10 minutes.

If a gas leak is indicated by any of the above tests, then the leak
can be found using a soap and water solution, wiping each fitting
or joint in the section of line that has been tested. The formation of
bubbles would indicate that gas is leaking at that fitting or joint.

Purging of Gas Lines

After the gas line has been tested, it must be purged. Purging the gas line means getting the air out of the line by having the gas force the air out under pressure.

When purging a gas supply line, the line is always purged at the farthest appliance to ensure that the complete supply line is purged. Branch lines are then purged individually as close as possible to the end farthest from where the gas is introduced into the branch line.

Gas lines 4" in diameter or larger, that were air tested, cannot safely be purged unless an inert gas such as carbon dioxide or nitrogen is used to separate the air from the gas. Also, the system must be purged directly to the outdoors.

Methods of Purging

Piping and Tubing Systems Supplying an Appliance Having an Input Over 400,000 Btuh (120 kW):

i)   Must be purged directly to the outside using a purging line and practicing the following controls:

   • The purging line should be no closer than 10 feet (3 m) to any building air intake.

   • The purging point should be under constant supervision and controlled by a 1/4 turn lever handle gas cock within 5 feet (1.5 m) of the purge point. This is the only valve that will control the purging.

   • No smoking should be permitted during the purging operation and all sources of ignition must be removed.

ii) By using an approved purge burner, illustrated in *Figure 5-17*.

Figure 5-17: Typical purge burner assembly.

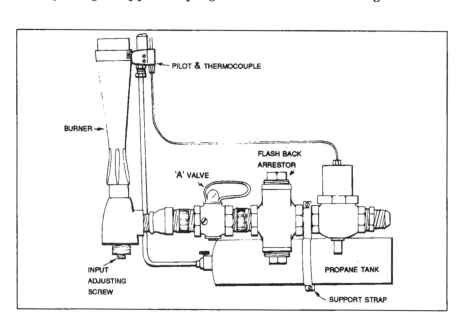

Piping and Tubing Systems Supplying an Appliance Having an Input Under 400,000 Btuh (120 kW):

i)   The purging can be done at a readily accessible burner such as an open top burner of a gas range.[6]
     Having the primary air shutter closed, a lighted taper is applied to the burner where it will safely ignite the gas at the burner port. The air/gas mixture is flared off at the burner until a stable gas flame, having yellow tips, is established. The primary air shutter is readjusted to give the correct flame characteristics to the burner flame after the purging has been completed.

ii) For an appliance having a combustion chamber the purging can be done at the pilot outlet of the appliance control valve. The pilot tubing is disconnected and the gas is purged at the pilot outlet at the control valve of the pilot outlet.

General Light-up Procedure

Once the gas piping or tubing has been tested and the piping or tubing system has been completely purged, the appliance can be started or *lighted up*. The following is a general light-up procedure that can be applied to the majority of residential or domestic gas appliances.

1. Check position of main and pilot burners.
2. Turn thermostat and other controls to *off* position (if applicable).
3. Turn gas control valve to *off* position or assure that it is in the off position.
4. Ventilate the combustion chamber (if applicable).
5. Apply lighted taper, match, etc., to pilot burner port, ignition tube or port, etc., or prepare for ignition in the appropriate manner for the particular piece of equipment.
6. Turn gas control valve to *pilot* position (if applicable).
7. Depress the gas control valve's reset *button.*
8. Light pilot flame while holding in the control reset button for approximately 1 minute until pilot flame is established.
9. Release button.
10. Ensure pilot remains lit and flame has proper characteristics and size.
11. Turn gas control valve to *on* position (slowly).
12. Activate thermostat and other controls (if applicable).
13. Main flame ignition should occur quickly and smoothly.

---

[6] A burner located in the combustion chamber of an appliance is not deemed an accessible burner.

Pipe and Tube Sizing

The gas piping or tubing installation must supply the maximum demand of the appliance without undue pressure loss. The factors that determine the correct pipe or tube size that will give a minimum pressure loss or drop for the piping or tubing installation are the following:

Length of Run
The longer the length of run of the piping or tubing, the greater will be the pressure drop of the system. Larger diameter pipes and tubing are, therefore, needed for systems that have long runs to ensure a minimum pressure drop.

Allowable Pressure Drop
National and local codes establish maximum allowable pressure drops which are used to determine piping and tubing systems. The maximum allowable pressure drops for which piping and tubing systems are sized are given in *Table T5-4. Tables T5-5, T5-6, T5-7* and *T5-8* give the maximum capacity of pipe and tubing in cubic feet per hour (m^3/h) of natural gas for available supply pressure of less than 7"wc (1.75 kPa) and available supply pressure of 7"wc (1.75 kPa) up to and including 14"wc (3.5 kPa).

Capacity in cfh (m^3/h)
The higher the maximum demand capacity of the system in cfh (m^3/h), the greater will be the pressure drop; and systems with higher capacities require larger diameter pipe or tubing.

Specific Gravity of the Gas (Relative Density)
Specific gravity (relative density) is a factor in pipe and tube size. Fuel gases that have a lower specific gravity can, for comparable systems (same capacity in cfh [m^3/h], length of run and allowable pressure drop), have a smaller diameter of pipe and tubing.

Number of Fittings
Sizing piping systems for large commercial and industrial applications must take into account pressure lost through the pipe fittings. The loss through each fitting is equated to an *equivalent length of pipe* of the same diameter as the fitting. Therefore the *total length of run*, which consists of the length of pipe plus the equivalent length of the fittings, is used when sizing the system. Local and national codes have tables that give the equivalent resistance of bends, fittings and valves in length of straight pipe in feet and metres. However, no allowance need be made for a reasonable number of fittings and is required only for the larger commercial and industrial piping systems.

MAXIMUM ALLOWABLE PRESSURE DROP FOR PIPING & TUBING SYSTEMS

SUPPLY PRESSURE	MAXIMUM ALLOWABLE PRESSURE DROP
Less than 7"wc (1.75 kPa)	0.5"wc (0.125 kPa)
7"wc (1.75kPa) up to 14" wc (3.5 kPa)	1.0"wc (0.25 kPa)
2 psig (14 kPa) and over	75% of supply pressure

Tables T5-5 to T5-8: Piping/Tube Sizing Tables

Table T5-5 (a)

Maximum Capacity of Schedule 40 Pipe Including a Reasonable Number of Fittings In cfh for a Gas Supply Pressure of Less than 7 inches Water Column and a Maximum Loss In Pressure of 0.5 - inches Water Column (Based on a 0.60 Relative Density Gas)

Length of Pipe (Feet)	Nominal Pipe Size in inches											
	1/2	3/4	1	1 1/4	1 1/2	2	2 1/2	3	4	5	6	8
10	120	271	545	1201	1862	3766	6165	10500	22020	38690	61240	124700
20	85	192	385	848	1316	2663	4358	7426	15580	27360	43310	88210
30	70	156	315	693	1074	2174	3559	6063	12720	22330	35360	72020
40	59	136	272	600	931	1884	3082	5250	11010	19340	30620	62370
50	54	121	244	537	833	1685	2756	4697	9852	17300	27390	55780
60	49	111	222	489	759	1538	2516	4287	8993	15790	25000	50930
70	45	102	205	453	704	1424	2330	3969	8326	14630	23150	47150
80	43	96	192	425	658	1331	2179	3713	7789	13670	21650	44100
90	40	90	182	400	620	1255	2055	3500	7343	12900	20410	41580
100	37	86	172	380	589	1192	1949	3320	6966	12230	19360	39450
125	34	76	154	340	527	1065	1743	2971	6230	10940	17330	35280
150	31	70	141	310	480	972	1592	2711	5688	9987	15810	32200
175		65	130	287	445	900	1473	2510	5266	9247	14640	29820
200		61	121	269	416	842	1379	2348	4925	8652	13700	27900
250		54	108	240	372	753	1233	2100	4406	7738	12250	24950
300		49	99	219	340	688	1126	1917	4021	7063	11180	22770
350		46	92	203	315	636	1042	1775	3723	6539	10350	21080
400		43	86	190	294	595	975	1660	3483	6117	9684	19730
450		40	81	179	278	562	919	1566	3284	5768	9131	18600
500		36	77	169	263	533	871	1485	3115	5471	8661	17630
550		36	74	161	250	507	831	1416	2971	5217	8258	16820
600		35	70	155	240	487	795	1356	2844	4996	7909	16110

Table T5-5 (b)

Maximum Capacity of Schedule 40 Pipe Including a Reasonable Number of Fittings In m3/h for a Gas Supply Pressure of Less than 1.75 kPa and a Maximum Loss In Pressure of 0.125 kPa (Based on a 0.60 Relative Density Gas)

Length of Pipe (Metres)	Normal Pipe Size (NPS)											
	1/2	3/4	1	1 1/4	1 1/2	2	2 1/2	3	4	5	6	8
3.0	3.4	7.7	15.4	34.0	52.7	107	175	297	624	1096	1734	3532
6.0	2.4	5.4	10.9	24.0	37.3	75	123	210	441	775	1227	2498
9.0	2.0	4.4	8.9	19.6	30.4	62	101	172	360	632	1001	2040
12.0	1.7	3.9	7.7	17.0	26.4	53	87	149	312	548	867	1766
15.0	1.5	3.4	6.9	15.2	23.6	48	78	133	279	490	776	1580
18.0	1.4	3.1	6.3	13.9	21.5	44	71	121	255	447	708	1442
21.0	1.3	2.9	5.8	12.8	19.9	40	66	112	236	414	656	1335
24.0	1.2	2.7	5.4	12.0	18.6	38	62	105	221	387	613	1249
27.0	1.1	2.6	5.2	11.3	17.6	36	58	99	208	365	578	1178
30.0	1.1	2.4	4.9	10.8	16.7	34	55	94	197	346	548	1117
37.5	1.0	2.2	4.4	9.6	14.9	30	49	84	176	310	491	999
45.0	0.9	2.0	4.0	8.8	13.6	28	45	77	161	283	448	912
52.5		1.8	3.7	8.1	12.6	25	42	71	149	262	415	845
60.0		1.7	3.4	7.6	11.8	24	39	67	139	245	388	790
75.0		1.5	3.1	6.8	10.5	21	35	59	125	219	347	707
90.0		1.4	2.8	6.2	9.6	19	32	54	114	200	317	645
105.0		1.3	2.6	5.8	8.9	18	30	50	105	185	293	597
120.0		1.2	2.4	5.4	8.3	17	28	47	97	173	274	559
135.0		1.1	2.3	5.1	7.9	16	26	44	93	163	259	527
150.0		1.1	2.2	4.8	7.5	15	25	42	88	155	245	499
165.0		1.0	2.1	4.6	7.1	14	24	40	84	148	234	476
180.0			2.0	4.4	6.8	14	23	38	80	141	224	456

Table T5-6 (a)

Maximum Capacity of Schedule 40 Pipe Including a Reasonable Number of Fittings In cfh for a Gas Supply Pressure of 7 inches Water Column up to and including 14 inches Water Column and a Maximum Loss in Pressure of 1.0 inch Water Column (Based on a 0.60 Relative Density Gas)

Length of Pipe (Feet)	Nominal Pipe Size in inches											
	1/2	3/4	1	1 1/4	1 1/2	2	2 1/2	3	4	5	6	8
10	227	474	894	1835	2749	5295	8439	14919	30429	55051	89140	183148
20	156	326	614	1261	1890	3639	5800	10253	20914	37836	61265	125877
30	125	262	493	1013	1517	2922	4658	8234	16795	30384	49198	101083
40	107	224	422	867	1299	2501	3986	7047	14374	26004	42107	86514
50	95	199	374	768	1151	2217	3533	6246	12739	23047	37319	76676
60	86	180	339	696	1043	2008	3201	5659	11543	20883	33814	69474
70	79	166	312	640	959	1848	2945	5206	10619	19212	31108	63915
80	74	154	290	596	893	1719	2740	4843	9879	17873	28940	59461
90	69	145	272	559	837	1613	2571	4544	9269	16769	27154	55790
100	65	137	257	528	791	1524	2428	4293	8756	15840	25649	52699
125	58	121	228	468	701	1350	2152	3805	7760	14039	22732	46706
150	52	110	207	424	635	1223	1950	3447	7031	12720	20597	42319
175	48	101	190	390	584	1126	1794	3171	6469	11703	18949	38933
200	45	94	177	363	544	1047	1669	2950	6018	10887	17628	36220
250	40	83	157	322	482	928	1479	2615	5333	9649	15624	32101
300	36	75	142	291	437	841	1340	2369	4832	8743	14156	29086
350	33	69	131	268	402	774	1233	2180	4446	8043	13024	26759
400	31	64	121	249	374	720	1147	2028	4136	7483	12116	24894
450	29	61	114	234	351	675	1076	1903	3881	7021	11368	23357
500	27	57	108	221	331	638	1017	1797	3666	6632	10738	22063
550	26	54	102	210	315	606	966	1707	3481	6298	10198	20954
600	25	52	98	200	300	578	921	1628	3321	6009	9730	19990

Maximum Capacity of Schedule 40 Pipe Including a Reasonable Number of Fittings In m3/h for a Gas Supply Pressure of 1.75 kPa up to and including 3.5 kPa and a Maximum Loss in Pressure of 0.25 kPa (Based on a 0.60 Relative Density Gas)

Length of Pipe (Metres)	Normal Pipe Size (NPS)											
	1/2	3/4	1	1 1/4	1 1/2	2	2 1/2	3	4	5	6	8
3.0	6.4	13.5	25.4	52.1	78.1	150.5	239.8	423.9	864.7	1564.3	2533.0	5204.4
6.0	4.4	9.3	17.5	35.8	53.7	103.4	164.8	291.4	594.3	1075.2	1740.9	3576.9
9.0	3.6	7.4	14.0	28.8	43.1	83.0	132.4	234.0	477.2	863.4	1398.0	2872.4
12.0	3.0	6.4	12.0	24.6	36.9	71.1	113.3	200.3	408.5	738.9	1196.5	2458.4
15.0	2.7	5.6	10.6	21.8	32.7	63.0	100.4	177.5	362.0	654.9	1060.5	2178.8
18.0	2.4	5.1	9.6	19.8	29.6	57.1	91.0	160.8	328.0	593.4	960.9	1974.2
21.0	2.3	4.7	8.9	18.2	27.3	52.5	83.7	147.9	301.8	545.9	884.0	1816.2
24.0	2.1	4.4	8.2	16.9	25.4	48.8	77.9	137.6	280.7	507.9	822.4	1689.7
30.0	1.9	3.9	7.3	15.0	22.5	43.3	69.0	122.0	248.8	450.1	728.8	1497.5
37.5	1.6	3.4	6.5	13.3	19.9	38.4	61.2	108.1	220.5	398.9	646.0	1327.2
45.0	1.5	3.1	5.9	12.0	18.1	34.8	55.4	98.0	199.8	361.5	585.3	1202.6
52.5	1.4	2.9	5.4	11.1	16.6	32.0	51.0	90.1	183.8	332.5	538.5	1106.3
60.0	1.3	2.7	5.0	10.3	15.4	29.8	47.4	83.8	171.0	309.4	500.9	1029.2
75.0	1.1	2.4	4.5	9.1	13.7	26.4	42.0	74.3	151.6	274.2	444.0	912.2
90.0	1.0	2.1	4.0	8.3	12.4	23.9	38.1	67.3	137.3	248.4	402.3	826.5
105.0	0.9	2.0	3.7	7.6	11.4	22.0	35.0	61.9	126.3	228.6	370.1	760.4
120.0	0.9	1.8	3.5	7.1	10.6	20.5	32.6	57.6	117.5	212.6	344.3	707.4
135.0	0.8	1.7	3.2	6.6	10.0	19.2	30.6	54.1	110.3	199.5	323.0	663.7
150.0	0.8	1.6	3.1	6.3	9.4	18.1	28.9	51.1	104.2	188.4	305.1	626.9
165.0	0.7	1.5	2.9	6.0	8.9	17.2	27.4	48.5	98.9	179.0	289.8	595.4
180.0	0.7	1.5	2.8	5.7	8.5	16.4	26.2	46.3	94.4	170.7	276.5	568.1

Maximum Capacity of Type L Copper Tubing including a Factor of 20% for Fittings in cfh for a Gas Supply Pressure of Less than 7 inches Water Column and a Maximum Loss in Pressure of 0.5 inch Water Column (Based on a 0.60 Relative Density Gas)

Outside Diameter (Inch)	Length of Tubing, Feet													
	10	20	30	40	50	60	70	80	90	100	125	150	175	200
3/8	26	18	14	12	11	10	9	8	8	8	7	6	6	5
1/2	59	41	33	28	25	22	21	19	18	17	15	14	13	12
5/8	110	76	61	52	46	42	38	36	34	32	28	25	23	22
3/4	187	128	103	88	78	71	65	61	57	54	48	43	40	37
7/8	287	197	158	136	120	109	100	93	87	83	73	66	61	57
1 1/8	578	397	319	273	242	219	202	188	176	166	147	134	123	114

Maximum Capacity of Type L Copper Tubing including a Factor of 20% for Fittings in m3/h for a Gas Supply Pressure of Less than 1.75 kPa and a Maximum Loss in Pressure of 0.125 kPa (Based on a 0.60 Relative Density Gas)

Outside Diameter (Inch)	Length of Tubing, metres													
	3	6	9	12	15	18	21	24	27	30	38	45	53	61
3/8	0.75	0.51	0.41	0.35	0.31	0.28	0.26	0.24	0.23	0.22	0.19	0.17	0.16	0.15
1/2	1.69	1.16	0.93	0.80	0.71	0.64	0.59	0.55	0.52	0.49	0.43	0.39	0.36	0.33
5/8	3.15	2.16	1.74	1.49	1.32	1.19	1.10	1.02	0.96	0.91	0.80	0.73	0.67	0.62
3/4	5.33	3.66	2.94	2.52	2.23	2.02	1.86	1.73	1.62	1.53	1.35	1.23	1.13	1.04
7/8	8.20	5.64	4.53	3.87	3.43	3.11	2.86	2.66	2.50	2.36	2.08	1.90	1.73	1.61
1 1/8	16.51	11.35	9.11	7.80	6.91	6.26	5.76	5.36	5.03	4.75	4.18	3.82	3.49	3.24

Table T5-8(a)

Maximum Capacity of Type L Copper Tubing Including a Factor of 20% for Fittings in cfh for a Gas Supply Pressure of 7 inches Water Column up to and including 14 inches Water Column and a Maximum Loss in Pressure of 1.0 inch Water Column (Based on a 0.60 Relative Density Gas)

Outside Diameter (Inch)	Length of Tubing, Feet													
	10	20	30	40	50	60	70	80	90	100	125	150	175	200
3/8	38	26	21	18	16	14	13	12	12	11	10	9	8	8
1/2	86	59	48	41	36	33	30	28	26	25	22	20	18	17
5/8	160	110	89	76	67	61	56	52	49	46	41	37	34	32
3/4	271	187	150	128	114	103	95	88	83	78	69	63	58	54
7/8	418	287	231	197	175	158	146	136	127	120	107	97	89	83
1 1/8	841	578	464	397	352	319	294	273	256	242	214	194	179	166

Table T5-8(b)

Maximum Capacity of Type L Copper Tubing including a Factor of 20% for Fittings in m3/h for a Gas Supply Pressure 1.75 kPa up to and including 3.5 kPa and a Maximum Loss in Pressure of 0.25 kPa (Based on a 0.60 Relative Density Gas)

Outside Diameter (Inch)	Length of Tubing, metres													
	3	6	9	12	15	18	21	24	27	30	38	45	53	61
3/8	1.09	0.75	0.60	0.51	0.46	0.41	0.38	0.35	0.33	0.31	0.28	0.25	0.23	0.21
1/2	2.46	1.69	1.36	1.16	1.03	0.93	0.86	0.80	0.75	0.71	0.62	0.57	0.52	0.48
5/8	4.58	3.15	2.53	2.16	1.92	1.74	1.60	1.49	1.40	1.32	1.16	1.06	0.97	0.90
3/4	7.75	5.33	4.28	3.66	3.25	2.94	2.71	2.52	2.36	2.23	1.96	1.79	1.64	1.52
7/8	11.93	8.20	6.59	5.64	5.00	4.53	4.16	3.87	3.64	3.43	3.02	2.76	2.52	2.34
1 1/8	24.03	16.51	13.26	11.35	10.06	9.11	8.38	7.80	7.32	6.91	6.08	5.55	5.08	4.71

Pipe and Tube Sizing for a Single Appliance:

In sizing the piping or tubing for a single appliance, the following steps are taken:

1. Determine the maximum capacity in cfh (m^3/h).

2. Measure the length of piping or tubing from the gas meter to the appliance.

3. Using the appropriate table (i.e., allowable pressure drop according to the available pressure) find the cfh (m^3/h) capacity at, or just over, the required cfh (m^3/h) capacity of the system for the length of run of the piping/tubing system. From here move to the side or top of the table and the required pipe/tube size will be given.

Figure 5-18 is an example of a pipe sizing exercise for a single appliance installation.

Figure 5-18: Example

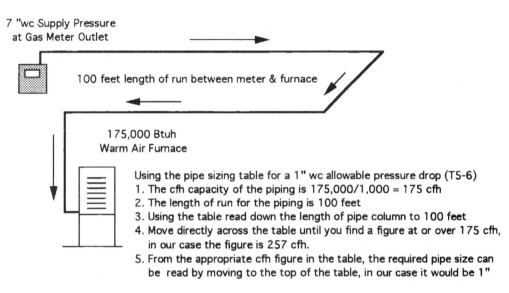

EXAMPLE

Determine the pipe size for the single appliance installation shown below

7 "wc Supply Pressure
at Gas Meter Outlet

100 feet length of run between meter & furnace

175,000 Btuh
Warm Air Furnace

Using the pipe sizing table for a 1" wc allowable pressure drop (T5-6)
1. The cfh capacity of the piping is 175,000/1,000 = 175 cfh
2. The length of run for the piping is 100 feet
3. Using the table read down the length of pipe column to 100 feet
4. Move directly across the table until you find a figure at or over 175 cfh, in our case the figure is 257 cfh.
5. From the appropriate cfh figure in the table, the required pipe size can be read by moving to the top of the table, in our case it would be 1"

Note: When sizing pipe, always take from the table, the figure at or over the length of run and cfh capacity of the system piping. This will insure that you will not under size the piping system .

Pipe and Tube Sizing for a Multiple Appliance Piping System:

Determining the correct pipe and tube size for a piping system that has more than one appliance requires an empirical technique. The following are the steps by which a multiple appliance piping and tubing system can be solved:

1. Determine the total capacity of the system in cfh (m³/h).

2. Determine the longest length of run in piping/tubing system (usually from the meter to the end appliance). *Note:* this is the only length of run that will be used when sizing the system.

3. Break up the supply line into sections and size the individual sections using:
   a) amount of cfh (m3/h) in that section;
   b) the appropriate pipe/tube sizing table as to available supply pressure;
   c) longest length of run in the system.

4. Size each individual branch line in the system by the same method used in sizing the various sections of the supply pipe:
   a) amount of cfh (m3/h) in that branch line;
   b) the appropriate pipe/tube sizing table as to the available supply pressure;
   c) longest length of run in the system.

Figure 5-19: Example

Figure 5-19 is an example of a pipe sizing exercise for a multiple appliance installation.

EXAMPLE
Determine the pipe size for the multiple appliance installation shown below

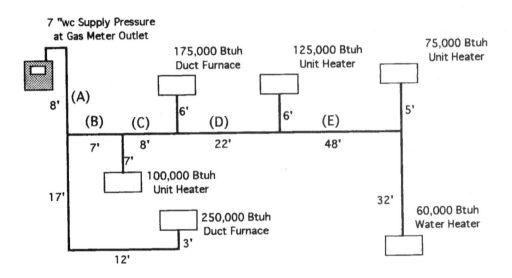

Using the pipe sizing table for 1"wc allowable pressure drop (T5-6)
1. Total cfh capacity of system is 785 cfh
2. Longest length of run is 125' (from gas meter to water heater)
3. Sizing supply line by sections:
    (A) 785 cfh @ 125' ------------------------------------ 2"
    (B) 535 cfh @ 125' ------------------------------- 11/2"
    (C) 435 cfh @ 125' ------------------------------- 11/4"
    (D) 260 cfh @ 125' ------------------------------- 11/4"
    (E) 135 cfh @ 125' ------------------------------- 1"
4. Sizing the branch lines:
    250 cfh Duct Furnace @ 125' --------------------- 11/4"
    175 cfh Duct Furnace @ 125' --------------------- 1"
    125 cfh Unit Heater @ 125' --------------------- 1"
    100 cfh Unit Heater @ 125' --------------------- 3/4 "
    75 cfh Unit Heater @ 125' --------------------- 3/4"
    60 cfh water Heater @ 125' --------------------- 3/4"

Gas Piping Assignment

1. Define the following terms:

    a) supply line
    b) branch line
    c) drop line
    d) piping extension
    e) gas main and service

2. State the limitation on the usage of flexible connectors.

3. State the main limitations on the location of gas piping and tubing. Give four examples.

4. State the six requirements in the installation of underground piping and tubing.

5. Describe the following:

    a) A test for gas lines before the appliances have been connected.
    b) A test for gas lines after the appliances have been connected.
    c) A test for gas lines after the gas has been turned on into the system.

6. What is meant by the term purging?

7. At what point is a gas supply line usually purged?

8. Describe the methods by which a gas line can be purged for systems:

    a) over 400,000 Btuh (120 kW)
    b) under 400,000 Btuh (120 kW)

9. State the factors that determine gas pipe and tube size.

10. Size the following piping systems:

    a) A package boiler having a maximum firing rate of 500,000 Btuh, being fed by a gas supply line 100 feet long under 7"wc gas pressure.
    b) The piping system illustrated in *Figure 5-20*.

Figure 5-20: Question 10-b

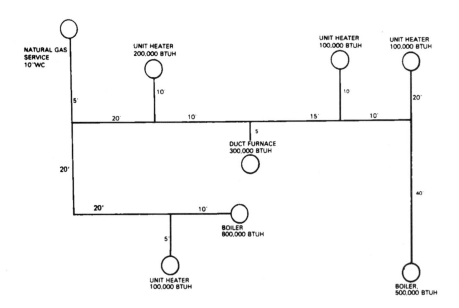

Gas Venting—Part 1— Venting Fundamentals and Air Supply

6

The Natural Draft Gas Appliance

Gas appliances that rely on the buoyancy of warm flue gases for venting (i.e., gravity venting) are called natural draft appliances. Until the recent arrival of high efficiency appliances, with induced draft firing and power venting *(see Chapters 14 and 15)* most residential gas appliances were natural draft appliances. This and the next chapter on venting, will be mainly concerned with conventional venting systems that apply to the natural draft appliance and the fan assisted appliance described in *Chapter 7*.

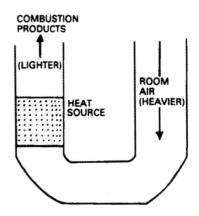

Figure 6-1: Vent draft action.

The Purpose of Venting

The purpose of venting a gas appliance is to remove the products of combustion.

For gravity or natural draft venting, the sole energy source is the heat above room temperature in the combustion products or *flue gases* that are delivered to the vent collar or draft hood outlet of an appliance. As illustrated in *Figure 6-1*, the cooler, heavier room air, forces the lighter combustion products upward. The difference in weight (buoyancy) between the hot flue gases and the surrounding cooler room air causes the *draft* which makes the venting system function.

However, if this energy source is insufficient, then problems will occur in the venting process or action such as:

i)   spillage of the flue gases at the appliance drafthood (or diverter)
ii) condensation of the water vapour within the flue gases.

Therefore, the overall purpose of venting is the *removal of the products of combustion without spillage taking place at the draft diverter and condensation of water vapour occurring within the vent.*

The Combustion Process

Since the purpose of venting is the removal of the products of combustion, a review of the combustion process and the identification of the products of combustion is necessary. As stated, in *Properties of Natural Gas*, combustion is defined as the *rapid combination of a fuel with oxygen resulting in the release of heat.*

The combustion of natural gas would be the following:

Natural Gas + Oxygen → Carbon Dioxide + Water Vapour + Heat

$$CH_4 + 2O_2 \rightarrow CO_2 + 2H_2O + Heat$$

The source of oxygen used in the combustion process is air, and the composition of air is approximately 20% oxygen (O_2) and 80% nitrogen (N_2), a ratio of 1 to 4 (1 oxygen to 4 nitrogen). Therefore, we can rewrite the combustion equation for natural gas as:

Natural Gas + Air → Carbon Dioxide + Water + Nitrogen + Heat

$$CH_4 + 2O_2 + 8N_2 \rightarrow CO_2 + 2H_2O + 8N_2 + Heat$$

Approximately 10 cu. ft. or cu. metres of air is required for the combustion of 1 cu. ft. or cu. metre of natural gas. Approximately 11 cu. ft. or cu. metres of products of combustion is formed by the combustion of 1 cu. ft. or cu. metre of natural gas and all of this must be removed by the gas vent. Of the 11 cu. ft. or cu. metres, approximately 2 cu. ft. or cu. metres is water in vapour form, which is a source of condensation if the flue gas temperature falls below its *Dew Point temperature.*[1]

The products of combustion of natural gas in which air is the source of oxygen are:

Carbon Dioxide	CO_2
Water Vapour	H_2O
Nitrogen	N_2
Heat	

However, the above description is that of *Perfect Combustion.* Normally, more air is supplied to the combustion process than what is required for perfect combustion This will ensure that all of the fuel will be completely burned. This additional amount of air is called *Excess Air (See Properties of Natural Gas).* Therefore, the products of combustion for natural gas in which excess air is utilized to ensure the *complete combustion* of the fuel are:

1 The temperature at which water vapour would begin to condense out of the flue gases if they should be cooled to that temperature. The dew point temperature is approximately 127°F (53°C).

Carbon Dioxide
Water Vapour
Nitrogen
Excess Air
Heat

Carbon Monoxide

One gas that must not be found in the product of combustion is carbon monoxide (CO). Finding carbon monoxide in the flue gases is a sign of incomplete combustion as a result of insufficient air supplied to the combustion process to completely burn the fuel.

As described in *Properties of Natural Gas*, carbon monoxide is an intermediate combustion product and if given sufficient air will burn to completion giving carbon dioxide and heat.

$$CO + 1/2 \, O_2 \rightarrow CO_2 + Heat$$

A major concern about carbon monoxide is its toxicity. Carbon monoxide can be absorbed into the blood. It combines with hemoglobin in the blood and acts to reduce the oxygen carrying function of the blood. A person exposed to carbon monoxide can die because of a lack of oxygen.

Various instruments are available to test for carbon monoxide. *(see Figure 13-17)* and should be used to check for it in the air should there be any concern as to its presence. The following areas should be tested for carbon monoxide:

1. In the atmosphere, at head height.
2. Near gas appliances.
3. Close to heating ducts.
4. Near appliance draft diverters and fire doors, on appliances in basements or utility rooms.

Also, the sequence of testing should be:

1. In the air before the appliance is started;
2. Just after the appliance is turned on;
3. After the appliance has operated for about 15 minutes.

Because of the possibility that carbon monoxide may be formed, the design and installation of gas vents becomes very important to ensure the safe and effective operation of the gas appliance.

Venting Action of the Natural Draft Appliance

The natural draft gas appliance is fired by a burner that is not equipped with a mechanical device, such as a burner fan, for supplying the air for combustion. The burner is defined as a *natural draft burner*. The main exponent of the natural draft burner is the *atmospheric burner* shown in *Figure 8-1*. In an atmospheric burner, the air for combustion is mixed non-mechanically with the gas under room or atmospheric conditions, hence the term atmospheric burner.

For the natural draft appliance the atmospheric burner (natural draft burner) is designed to fire with a *zero or neutral overfire draft condition* in the combustion chamber of the appliance. This is required in order to maintain a consistent air supply to the burner flame. A variable draft condition over the fire would vary the amount of air supplied to the burner flame and hence effect the operating efficiency of the appliance.

The neutral overfire draft condition is achieved by the application of a fixed *draft diverter* or *draft hood*. By drawing in *dilution air* through its *relief opening*, the fixed draft diverter *breaks* the natural draft created by the venting action of the appliance venting system to give a neutral draft condition over the fire. A consistent air supply to the burner flame is assured regardless of variations (i.e., outside wind conditions) in natural draft produced by the appliance venting system.

As the hot flue gases rise through the heat exchanger of the appliance and out through the appliance vent, the relief opening of the draft diverter allows room air to be induced into the appliance vent. This chills the flue gases breaking the venting action developed by the appliance venting system. The flue gas temperature inlet to the draft diverter is approximately 480°F (249°C) and its outlet temperature is approximately 300–350°F (149–177°C). This outlet temperature is sufficient to allow gravity or natural draft venting of the flue gases to overcome the lateral resistance of the vent connector. Also, sufficient heat is maintained within the flue gases to prevent condensation that can occur if the flue gas temperature drops below the dew point temperature.

Figure 6-2 is a cut-away of a typical *Hi-Boy* gas fired warm air furnace. Return air from the heated rooms is filtered as it is drawn into the blower compartment of the furnace. The blower pressurizes the return air and the air is heated as it passes over the outer surface of the heat exchanger. The heat of combustion generated by the burner flame draws in the required amount of combustion air to sustain the combustion of the burner flame. The combustion products rise through the interior of the heat exchanger and are vented by the chimney to the outside. Dilution air is drawn through the draft diverter relief opening, breaking the venting action to maintain a neutral condition over the burner flame.

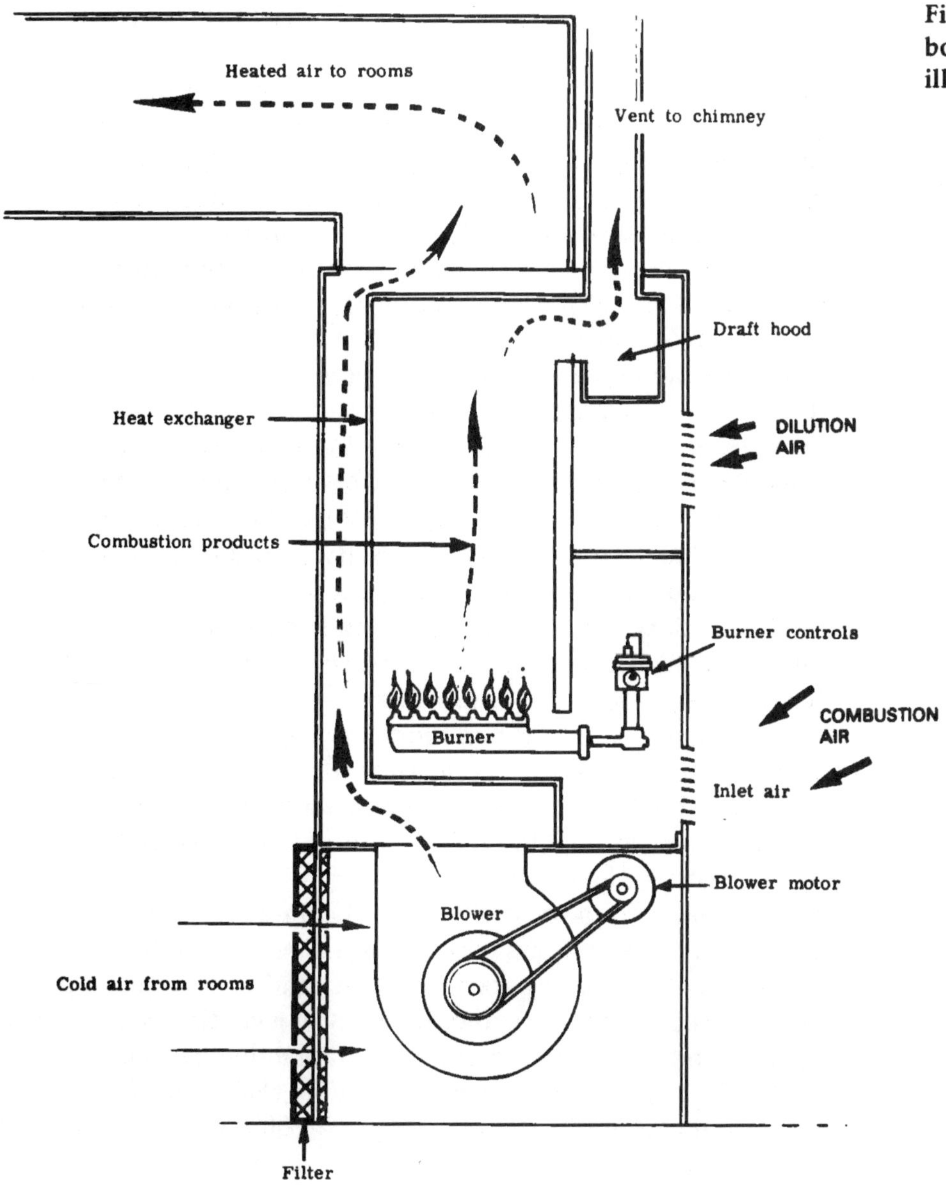

Figure 6-2: A cut-away of a "Hi-boy" gas fired warm air furnace illustrating the venting action.

Heated air to rooms

Vent to chimney

Draft hood

DILUTION AIR

Heat exchanger

Combustion products

Burner controls

COMBUSTION AIR

Burner

Inlet air

Blower motor

Blower

Cold air from rooms

Filter

Venting Problems

There are two main problems that can occur in gas venting systems: *spillage* of the flue gases at the appliance draft diverter relief opening and *condensation* of water vapour on the inside walls of the appliance vent and flue outlet collar.

Spillage: Spillage is a result of the venting system either being overloaded or having a *down-draft* opposing the flow of the flue gases in the appliance venting system.

A venting system can be overloaded by having:

1. The appliance overfiring;
2. Appliance venting system restricted or blocked;

3. Appliance venting system too small;
4. Appliance venting system poorly designed.

A down-draft is caused by a lack of make up air or by the outside chimney or vent location. If an appliance within a fairly tight room does not receive sufficient air for the combustion process, the pressure condition in the room becomes *negative*. More air is being used up in the combustion process than is being supplied by natural infiltration through the building. Since flow takes place across a pressure differential, the atmospheric pressure outside and the negative pressure inside the building causes a flow of outside air down through the appliance venting system. The appliance flue gases must generate sufficient buoyancy in the venting system to over come the down draft condition. If the down draft condition is too severe, then the flue gases cannot move up through the appliance vent and therefore spill out at the draft diverter relief opening.[2] Outside chimney or vent location is another cause of down-draft. *Figure 6-3* illustrates this condition of wind funneling outside air into the appliance venting system causing a down-draft condition.

Whether the spillage is caused by overloading the appliance venting system or by a down-draft condition, the room in which the appliance is located will develop humidity and a flue gas odour. Spillage of the flue gases at the draft diverter relief opening can be checked, as illustrated in *Figure 6-4*, by putting smoke or a flame from a match or lighter near the bottom of the draft hood at the relief opening. If the smoke or flame is drawn upward into the draft hood, then no spillage is occurring and the appliance is experiencing normal venting action or draft conditions. However, if the smoke or flame is forced downward away from the relief opening then spillage is taking place. Also, as illustrated in *Figure 6-5*, the cause of the spillage can be determined by checking the venting action at the draft diverter relief opening during the appliance's on and off periods.

New natural draft appliances are equipped with a *spill* or *vent safety switch (see Figure 6-6)*. The switch is a thermally activated manual reset safety limit switch that is wired into the safety limit circuit of the appliance. If the appliance is experiencing spillage, then the switch will sense the additional heat at the draft hood relief opening and shut the appliance down. The appliance can only be restarted once the spill switch has been manually reset.

---

[2] Natural draft appliances become spillage susceptible with a negative building pressure greater than 0.02"wc (5 Pa).

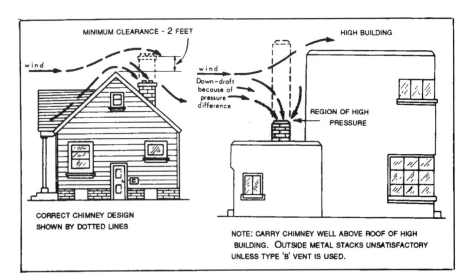

Figure 6-3: Typical chimney location apt to cause a down-draft condition.

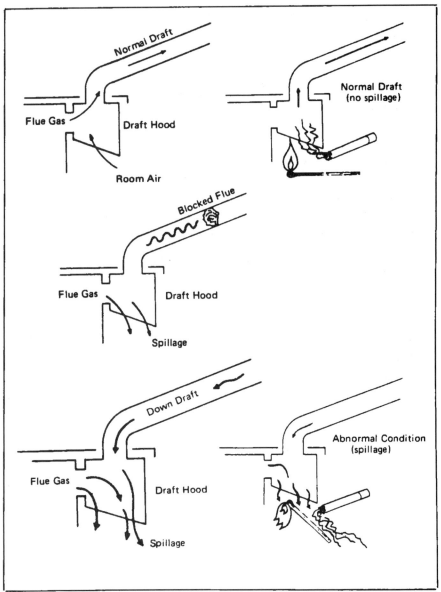

Figure 6-4: Testing for spillage at the draft diverter relief opening.

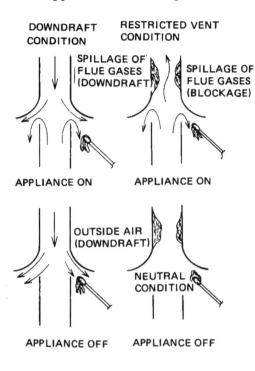

Figure 6-5: Determining a downdraft condition by checking the venting action at the draft diverter relief opening during the appliance on and off periods.

DOWNDRAFT CONDITION   RESTRICTED VENT CONDITION

SPILLAGE OF FLUE GASES (DOWNDRAFT)

SPILLAGE OF FLUE GASES (BLOCKAGE)

APPLIANCE ON   APPLIANCE ON

OUTSIDE AIR (DOWNDRAFT)

NEUTRAL CONDITION

APPLIANCE OFF   APPLIANCE OFF

Condensation: Condensation is caused by the flue gases being excessively cooled after their exit from the draft diverter. Long lateral vent runs through unheated areas as well as venting into an outside masonry chimney are two conditions that could contribute to condensation due to excessive cooling of the flue gases. In both cases, insulated venting would be required to maintain sufficient flue gas temperature.

Condensation may also be caused by having the chimney or appliance vent too large (i.e., its cross section area) or having the appliance underfired. In either case, the appliance venting system is underloaded. The flue gases travel through the appliance vent very slowly, allowing sufficient heat transfer to take place reducing the flue gas temperature to the critical level. To correct this condition of an oversized chimney, a chimney liner consisting of a metal vent can be inserted to reduce the chimney's cross sectional area.

The possible effect of condensation is corrosion which may occur inside the appliance heat exchanger, flue passages and vent pipes where the water condenses.

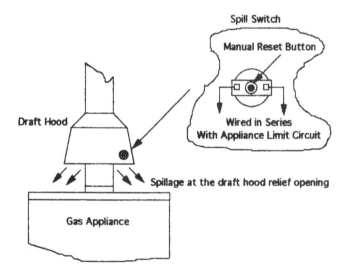

Spill Switch

Manual Reset Button

Wired in Series With Appliance Limit Circuit

Draft Hood

Spillage at the draft hood relief opening

Gas Appliance

Figure 6-6: Spill or vent safety switch that protects the appliance against spillage.

Combustion Air

As illustrated in *Figure 6-7* air required for the combustion process of the appliance must meet the following three requirements:

1. Air for combustion (required air/gas ratio of 10 cu. ft. or cu. metres of air to 1 cu. ft. or cu. metres of natural gas plus additional excess air to ensure the complete combustion of the fuel).
2. Air for draft diverter dilution.
3. Air for ventilation.

To meet the above requirements each cu. ft. or cu. metre of gas burned may require up to 30 cu. ft. or cu. metres of air. Also, range hoods and exhaust fans may further increase the need for air to prevent a negative pressure condition in the building as a result of air starvation.

The amount of air supply required to maintain adequate appliance operation within a building or structure is a function of:

i) Total Btuh input of gas appliances;
ii) Appliance design (appliances equipped with draft diverters require air for draft diverter operation);
iii) Tightness of the building or structure construction. Given a structure of relatively normal construction and of sufficient size, the air supply can be maintained by natural infiltration through the building. However, with smaller structures or structures having a tight construction, air supply can only be maintained by providing an air supply opening or duct allowing outside air to communicate directly with appliance(s) within the structure or building (see Figure 6-8).

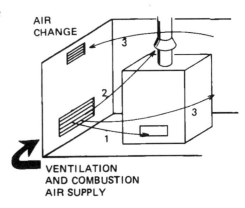

VENTILATION
AND COMBUSTION
AIR SUPPLY

Figure 6-7: The three requirements of combustion air:
1. **Air for combustion.**
2. **Air for draft diverter dilution.**
3. **Air for ventilation.**

Figure 6-8: Outside air supply required to maintain adequate appliance (s) operation within a structure or building.

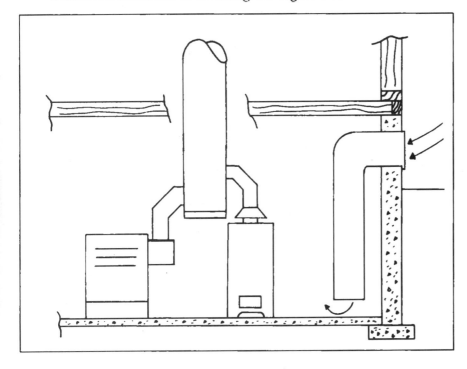

Sizing Combustion Air Supply

The following will ensure sufficient combustion air supply to an appliance or appliances located within a structure or enclosure having individual or combined inputs not in excess of 400,000 Btuh (120 kW):

1. *Tables T6-1* and *T6-2* for appliance (s) within a structure or building having a tight construction (has windows and doors of

either close-fitting or sealed construction and the exterior walls are covered by a continuous, sealed vapour barrier and gypsum wallboard (drywall, plywood, or similar materials having sealed joints). The structure would meet the R-2000 construction requirements for an airtight envelope. If an appliance with a draft control device (i.e., draft diverter) and an appliance without a draft control device are installed within the same structure or enclosure, the required *free air* of the air supply opening shall be the greater of either:

   i) that required by *Table T6-1*, using the total input of only those appliances having draft control devices, or

   ii) that required by *Table T6-2*, using the total input of all appliances.

2. *Tables T6-3* and *T6-4* for appliances located within a structure or building having normal construction. If an appliance with a draft control device and an appliance without a draft control device are installed within the same structure or enclosure, the required free area of the air supply opening shall be the greater of either:

   i) that required by *Table T6-3*, using the total input of only those appliances having draft control devices, or

   ii) that required by *Table T6-4*, using the total input of all appliances.

3. As illustrated in *Figure 6-9*, when an appliance is located within an enclosure and permanent openings sized and located in accordance with (a) and (b) below are supplied to allow communication between the *enclosure* and the rest of the structure, the total volume of the structure may be used to determine air supply requirements, provided the structure is of normal construction. If permanent opening are not provide, then the volume of the *enclosure* shall be used to determine the air supply requirements.

(a) In all cases, an opening shall be provided which shall:

   i) have a free area of not less than 1 square inch per 1000 Btuh (2225 mm^2 per kW) of the total input of all appliances within the enclosure; and

   ii) be located neither more than 18 inches (450 mm) nor less than 6 inches (150 mm), above floor level.

(b) When one or more appliances are equipped with draft control devices, an additional opening shall be supplied having the same free area as the opening required in (a), and the opening shall be located as near the ceiling as practicable, but in no case lower than the relief opening of the lowest draft control device.

**Combustion Air Requirements for Appliances Having
Draft Control Devices When the Combined Input is up to and
including 400,000 Btuh (120 kW) and the Structure
is of Tight Construction***

Total Input of Appliances* Thosands of Btuh (KW)	Required Free Area of Air Supply Opening or Duct Sq. in (Sq. mm)	Acceptable Approx. Round Duct Equivalent** Diameter in Inches (mm)
25(8)	7(4500)	3(75)
50(15)	7(4500)	3(75)
75(23)	11(7000)	4(100)
100(30)	14(9000)	4(100)
125(37)	18(12000)	5(125)
150(45)	22(14000)	5(125)
175(53)	25(16000)	6(150)
200(60)	29(19000)	6(150)
225(68)	32(21000)	6(150)
250(75)	36(23000)	7(175)
275(83)	40(26000)	7(175)
300(90)	43(28000)	7(175)
325(98)	47(30000)	8(200)
350(105)	50(32000)	8(200)
375(113)	54(35000)	8(200)
400(120)	58(37000)	9(225)

* For total inputs falling between listed figures, use next largest listed input
** These figures are based on a maximum equivalent duct length of 20 ft.
   (6 m) . For equivalent duct lengths in excess of 20 ft. (6 m) up to and
   including a maximum of 50 ft. (15 m), increase round duct diameter by
   one size.
*** Constructed as a R-2000 type of structure

**Combustion Air Requirements for Appliances NOT Having
Draft Control Devices When the Combined Input is up to and
including 400,000 Btuh (120 kW) and the Structure
is of Tight Construction***

Total Input of Appliances* Thosands of Btuh (KW)	Required Free Area of Air Supply Opening or Duct Sq. in (Sq. mm)	Acceptable Approx. Round Duct Equivalent** Diameter in Inches (mm)
25(8)	4(2600)	2(50)
50(15)	4(2600)	2(50)
75(23)	5(3200)	3(75)
100(30)	7(4500)	3(75)
125(37)	9(5800)	4(100)
150(45)	11(7000)	4(100)
175(53)	13(8400)	4(100)
200(60)	14(9000)	5(125)
225(68)	16(10300)	5(125)
250(75)	18(12000)	5(125)
275(83)	20(13000)	5(125)
300(90)	22(14000)	6(150)
325(98)	23(15000)	6(150)
350(105)	25(16000)	6(150)
375(113)	27(17400)	6(150)
400(120)	29(19000)	6(150)

* For total inputs falling between listed figures, use next largest listed input
** These figures are based on a maximum equivalent duct length of 20 ft.
   (6 m) . For equivalent duct lengths in excess of 20 ft. (6 m) up to and
   including a maximum of 50 ft. (15 m), increase round duct diameter by
   one size.
*** Constructed as a R-2000 type of structure

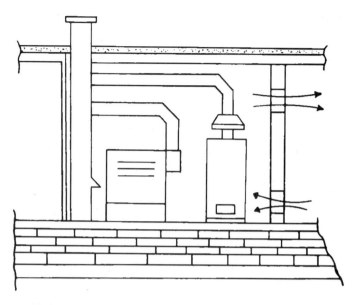

Figure 6-9: Inside structure or building air supply required to maintain adequate appliance(s) operation within an enclosure.

Table T6-3

Combustion Air Requirements For Appliances Having Draft Control Devices When the Combined Input is Up to and including 400,000 Btuh (120 kW) and the Structure is of Normal Construction

Total Input of Appliances* 1000 of Btuh (kW)	Volume of The Enclosure or Structure in Cubic Feet (Cubic Metres)														
	500 (14)	1000 (28)	2000 (57)	3000 (85)	4000 (113)	5000 (142)	6000 (170)	7000 (198)	8000 (227)	9000 (255)	10000 (283)	12500 (354)	15000 (425)	17500 (495)	20000 (566)
	Required Air Supply Opening Square Inches (1000 of mm2)														
25(8)	4(3)	4(3)	0	0	0	0	0	0	0	0	0	0	0	0	0
50(15)	7(5)	7(5)	7(5)	0	0	0	0	0	0	0	0	0	0	0	0
75(23)	11(7)	11(7)	11(7)	11(7)	11(7)	0	0	0	0	0	0	0	0	0	0
100(30)	14(9)	14(9)	14(9)	14(9)	14(9)	14(9)	0	0	0	0	0	0	0	0	0
125(37)	18(12)	18(12)	18(12)	18(12)	18(12)	18(12)	18(12)	18(12)	0	0	0	0	0	0	0
150(45)	22(14)	22(14)	22(14)	22(14)	22(14)	22(14)	22(14)	22(14)	22(14)	0	0	0	0	0	0
175(53)	25(16)	25(16)	25(16)	25(16)	25(16)	25(16)	25(16)	25(16)	25(16)	25(16)	25(16)	0	0	0	0
200(60)	29(19)	29(19)	29(19)	29(19)	29(19)	29(19)	29(19)	29(19)	29(19)	29(19)	29(19)	0	0	0	0
225(68)	32(21)	32(21)	32(21)	32(21)	32(21)	32(21)	32(21)	32(21)	32(21)	32(21)	32(21)	32(21)	0	0	0
250(75)	36(23)	36(23)	36(23)	36(23)	36(23)	36(23)	36(23)	36(23)	36(23)	36(23)	36(23)	36(23)	0	0	0
275(83)	40(26)	40(26)	40(26)	40(26)	40(26)	40(26)	40(26)	40(26)	40(26)	40(26)	40(26)	40(26)	40(26)	0	0
300(90)	43(28)	43(28)	43(28)	43(28)	43(28)	43(28)	43(28)	43(28)	43(28)	43(28)	43(28)	43(28)	43(28)	0	0
325(98)	47(30)	47(30)	47(30)	47(30)	47(30)	47(30)	47(30)	47(30)	47(30)	47(30)	47(30)	47(30)	47(30)	47(30)	0
350(105)	50(32)	50(32)	50(32)	50(32)	50(32)	50(32)	50(32)	50(32)	50(32)	50(32)	50(32)	50(32)	50(32)	50(32)	50(32)
375(113)	54(35)	54(35)	54(35)	54(35)	54(35)	54(35)	54(35)	54(35)	54(35)	54(35)	54(35)	54(35)	54(35)	54(35)	54(35)
400(120)	58(37)	58(37)	58(37)	58(37)	58(37)	58(37)	58(37)	58(37)	58(37)	58(37)	58(37)	58(37)	58(37)	58(37)	58(37)

* For total inputs falling between listed figures , use next largest input

Table T6-4

Combustion Air Requirements For Appliances NOT Having Draft Control Devices When the Combined Input is Up to and including 400,000 Btuh (120 kW) and the Structure is of Normal Construction

Total Input of Appliances* 1000 of Btuh (kW)	Volume of The Enclosure or Structure in Cubic Feet (Cubic Metres)														
	500 (14)	1000 (28)	2000 (57)	3000 (85)	4000 (113)	5000 (142)	6000 (170)	7000 (198)	8000 (227)	9000 (255)	10000 (283)	12500 (354)	15000 (425)	17500 (495)	20000 (566)
	Required Air Supply Opening Square Inches (1000 of mm2)														
25(8)	2(1)	0	0	0	0	0	0	0	0	0	0	0	0	0	0
50(15)	4(3)	4(3)	0	0	0	0	0	0	0	0	0	0	0	0	0
75(23)	5(3)	5(3)	5(3)	0	0	0	0	0	0	0	0	0	0	0	0
100(30)	7(5)	7(5)	7(5)	0	0	0	0	0	0	0	0	0	0	0	0
125(37)	9(6)	9(6)	9(6)	9(6)	0	0	0	0	0	0	0	0	0	0	0
150(45)	11(7)	11(7)	11(7)	11(7)	11(7)	0	0	0	0	0	0	0	0	0	0
175(53)	13(8)	13(8)	13(8)	13(8)	13(8)	13(8)	0	0	0	0	0	0	0	0	0
200(60)	14(9)	14(9)	14(9)	14(9)	14(9)	14(9)	0	0	0	0	0	0	0	0	0
225(68)	16(10)	16(10)	16(10)	16(10)	16(10)	16(10)	16(10)	0	0	0	0	0	0	0	0
250(75)	18(12)	18(12)	18(12)	18(12)	18(12)	18(12)	18(12)	18(12)	0	0	0	0	0	0	0
275(83)	20(13)	20(13)	20(13)	20(13)	20(13)	20(13)	20(13)	20(13)	20(13)	0	0	0	0	0	0
300(90)	22(14)	22(14)	22(14)	22(14)	22(14)	22(14)	22(14)	22(14)	22(14)	0	0	0	0	0	0
325(98)	23(15)	23(15)	23(15)	23(15)	23(15)	23(15)	23(15)	23(15)	23(15)	23(15)	0	0	0	0	0
350(105)	25(16)	25(16)	25(16)	25(16)	25(16)	25(16)	25(16)	25(16)	25(16)	25(16)	25(16)	0	0	0	0
375(113)	27(17)	27(17)	27(17)	27(17)	27(17)	27(17)	27(17)	27(17)	27(17)	27(17)	27(17)	0	0	0	0
400(120)	29(19)	29(19)	29(19)	29(19)	29(19)	29(19)	29(19)	29(19)	29(19)	29(19)	29(19)	0	0	0	0

* For total inputs falling between listed figures , use next largest input

Combustion Air Sizing Examples

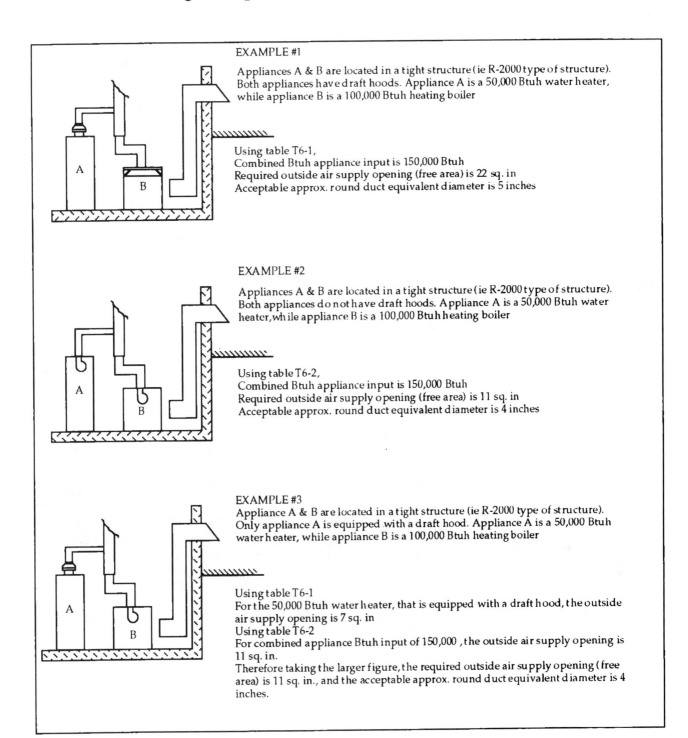

EXAMPLE #1

Appliances A & B are located in a tight structure (ie R-2000 type of structure). Both appliances have draft hoods. Appliance A is a 50,000 Btuh water heater, while appliance B is a 100,000 Btuh heating boiler

Using table T6-1,
Combined Btuh appliance input is 150,000 Btuh
Required outside air supply opening (free area) is 22 sq. in
Acceptable approx. round duct equivalent diameter is 5 inches

EXAMPLE #2

Appliances A & B are located in a tight structure (ie R-2000 type of structure). Both appliances do not have draft hoods. Appliance A is a 50,000 Btuh water heater, while appliance B is a 100,000 Btuh heating boiler

Using table T6-2,
Combined Btuh appliance input is 150,000 Btuh
Required outside air supply opening (free area) is 11 sq. in
Acceptable approx. round duct equivalent diameter is 4 inches

EXAMPLE #3

Appliance A & B are located in a tight structure (ie R-2000 type of structure). Only appliance A is equipped with a draft hood. Appliance A is a 50,000 Btuh water heater, while appliance B is a 100,000 Btuh heating boiler

Using table T6-1
For the 50,000 Btuh water heater, that is equipped with a draft hood, the outside air supply opening is 7 sq. in
Using table T6-2
For combined appliance Btuh input of 150,000 , the outside air supply opening is 11 sq. in.
Therefore taking the larger figure, the required outside air supply opening (free area) is 11 sq. in., and the acceptable approx. round duct equivalent diameter is 4 inches.

Combustion Air Sizing Examples

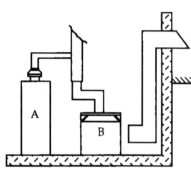

EXAMPLE #4

Appliances A & B are located in a normal (air tightness) structure having a volume of 8,000 cf
Both appliances have draft hoods. Appliance A is a 50,000 Btuh water heater, while appliance B is a 100,000 Btuh heating boiler

Using table T6-3,
Combined Btuh appliance input is 150,000 Btuh
Required outside air supply opening (free area) is 22 sq. in

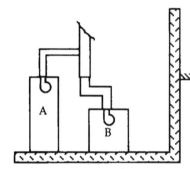

EXAMPLE #5

Appliances A & B are located in a normal (air tightness) structure having a volume of 8,000 cf
Both appliances do not have draft hoods. Appliance A is a 50,000 Btuh water heater, while appliance B is a 100,000 Btuh heating boiler

Using table T6-4,
Combined Btuh appliance input is 150,000 Btuh
Required outside air supply opening (free area) is 0 sq. in
Note: The air envelope of the structure is of sufficient size to provide all of the air requirements by natural infiltration.

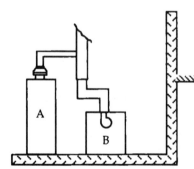

EXAMPLE #6

Appliance A & B are located in a normal (air tightness) structure having a volume of 8,000 cf.
Only appliance A is equipped with a draft hood. Appliance A is a 50,000 Btuh water heater, while appliance B is a 100,000 Btuh heating boiler

Using table T6-3
For the 50,000 Btuh water heater, that is equipped with a draft hood, the outside air supply opening is 0 sq. in
Using table T6-4
For combined appliance Btuh input of 150,000 , the outside air supply opening is 0 sq. in.
In both cases the required outside air supply opening is 0 sq. in.
Note: The air envelope of the structure is of sufficient size to provide all of the air requirements by natural infiltration.

Combustion Air Sizing Examples

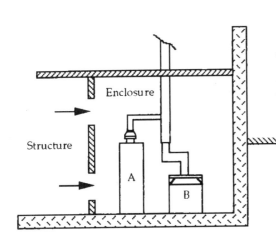

EXAMPLE #7

Appliances A & B are located in a normal (air tightness) structure having a volume of 15,000 cf.
Both appliances have draft hoods and are located in an enclosure that has openings communicating with the structure. Appliance A is a 50,000 Btuh water heater, while appliance B is a 100,000 Btuh heating boiler.

Using table T6-3
Since the enclosure has openings communicating with the structure, the volume of the structure can be used to determine the required outside air supply opening.

Combined Btuh appliance input is 150,000 Btuh
Required outside air supply opening (free area) is 0 sq. in
Note: The air envelope of the structure is of sufficient size to provide all of the air requirements by natural infiltration.

The size of the openings of the enclosure, based on 1 sq. in per 1000 Btuh of appliance input, is 150 sq. in
Since the appliances are equipped with draft hoods, there must be 2 opens each one sized at 150 sq. in.
The top opening not lower than the relief opening of the lowest draft hood.
The lower opening is located neither more than 18 inches, nor less than 6 inches above the level of the floor

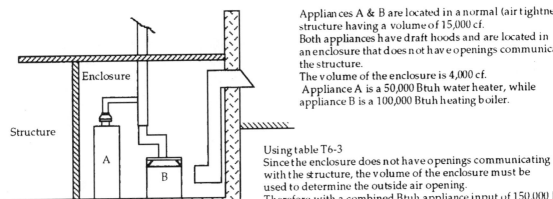

EXAMPLE #8

Appliances A & B are located in a normal (air tightness) structure having a volume of 15,000 cf.
Both appliances have draft hoods and are located in an enclosure that does not have openings communicating with the structure.
The volume of the enclosure is 4,000 cf.
Appliance A is a 50,000 Btuh water heater, while appliance B is a 100,000 Btuh heating boiler.

Using table T6-3
Since the enclosure does not have openings communicating with the structure, the volume of the enclosure must be used to determine the outside air opening.
Therefore with a combined Btuh appliance input of 150,000 Btuh, the required outside air supply opening (free area) is 22 sq. in.

Air Supply Openings and Ducts

The following are the requirements for air supply openings and ducts:

1. Air supply openings and ducts should terminate within one foot (300 mm) above, and within two feet (600 mm) horizontally from, the burner level of the appliance having the largest input.

2. A square or rectangular shaped duct shall only be used when the required free area of the air supply opening is 9 sq. inches (5800 mm²) or larger, and when used its smaller dimension shall not be less than 3 inches (75 mm).

3. An opening may be used in lieu of a duct to provide the outside air supply to an appliance(s).

4. An air supply inlet opening from the outdoors shall be equipped with a means to prevent the direct entry of rain and wind, and such means shall not *reduce* the required free area of the air supply opening.

5. An air supply inlet opening from the outdoors shall be located not less than 12 inches (300 mm) above the outside grade level.

6. The free area of an air supply opening shall be calculated by subtracting the blockage area of all fixed louvres, grilles or screens from the gross area of the opening.

Draft Controls

Draft Hoods
Appliances that utilize natural draft type of burners are designed to operate with draft hoods (or diverters), by which the chimney or vent draft is nullified. The primary function of the draft hood is to provide a neutral overfire draft condition in the combustion zone. This is accomplished by the introduction of dilution air into the relief opening of the draft diverter, breaking the venting action. However, the draft diverter's function is also to relieve a down-draft and prevent the down-draft from entering the appliance, and to vent the appliance through the draft diverter's relief opening if the appliance vent is blocked or restricted.

Types of Draft Hoods
There are four types of draft hoods or draft diverter designs to meet various applications:

Vertical Type: used mainly for hot water boilers and water heaters.

Horizontal Type: used mainly for older converted gravity warm air furnaces and boilers.

Horizontal to Vertical and Vertical to Horizontal Types: used mainly for design forced warm air furnaces.

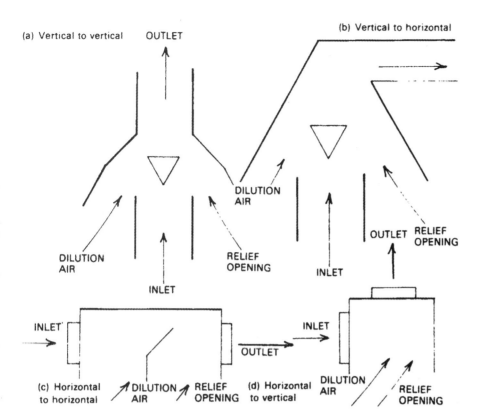

(a) Vertical to vertical

OUTLET

(b) Vertical to horizontal

DILUTION AIR

DILUTION AIR

RELIEF OPENING

INLET

INLET

OUTLET RELIEF OPENING

INLET

(c) Horizontal to horizontal

DILUTION AIR

RELIEF OPENING

OUTLET

(d) Horizontal to vertical

DILUTION AIR

RELIEF OPENING

Figure 6-10: Four types of draft diverters.

The applications for the different draft diverters are not totally exclusive. There are boilers that may use the horizontal to vertical type or the straight horizontal type. It is primarily the interior design of the unit that determines the type of draft diverter used. Most domestic and small commercial boilers are of a vertical flue design and as a result utilize the vertical type of draft diverter. *Figure 6-10* illustrates the four types of draft diverters.

Installation Requirements

The installation requirements for the draft diverter are the following:

1. Must be installed in the same room as the appliance. The draft diverter relief opening must experience the same atmospheric room conditions as the gas appliance.
2. Must be installed with reference to its horizontal or vertical plane.
3. Must be installed so that the relief opening is accessible for testing and is not blocked.
4. Draft diverter cannot be smaller than the flue collar size of the appliance.
5. Cannot be used with an appliance having a positive overfire draft or with an appliance having an induced draft.

a) Double acting barometric draft control for smaller rated gas fired furnaces, boiler or conversion burner installation.

b) Barometric draft control for commercial installations having gas or oil/gas firing

c) Single acting barometric draft control for residential oil firing equipment

Figure 6-11: Various types of barometric draft controls.

107

The Barometric Draft Control

Barometric draft controls are used on gas appliances that operate with a controlled *negative overfire draft* in the combustion chamber. These appliances are usually converted oil boilers or furnaces fired by a *fan assisted* type of conversion burner, as illustrated in *Figures 12-2* and *12-3*.

The double acting type barometric draft control is utilized for gas firing equipment. The double acting type will open inward to regulate the *up-draft*, while opening outward to relieve a *down-draft*. *Figure 6-11* illustrates the various types of barometric draft control.

For a fan assisted burner, all of the combustion air is mechanically supplied by a fan that is part of the burner. However, the air is not forced through the furnace or boiler and as a result a draft action is required to sustain the flow of the flue gases through the appliance and venting system. The draft must be sufficient to provide the required negative overfire draft in the combustion chamber, as well as overcoming the resistance of the heat exchanger at the firing rate of the appliance. To achieve this controlled draft condition, the barometric type of draft control is utilized.

Operation of Barometric Draft Control

The gate of the draft control is adjusted for the correct draft setting by a series of counter weights in the form of *washer weights* bolted to a holder mounted on the side of the draft control as illustrated in *Figure 6-12*. The gate of the draft control will open and allow just the right amount of diluted air into the appliance venting system to achieve the required overfire condition in the combustion chamber of the appliance. A pressure differential will exist across the gate of the barometric draft control. This pressure differential is the pressure difference between the interior (negative) up-draft condition of the vent and the exterior atmospheric pressure condition of the appliance room. If for any reason the up-draft were to increase, then the pressure differential across the gate is increased. The higher atmospheric pressure in the appliance room pushes against the gate allowing the gate to open inward increasing the amount of dilution air which in turn regulates the up-draft condition.

On the other hand, if the up-draft condition decreases, then the pressure differential across the gate is decreased, allowing the counter weight to move the gate back, closing off the amount of dilution air.

On a down-draft condition the gate moves outward to spill out the flue gases.

Figure 6-12 illustrates the operation of the barometric draft control in regulating an increasing up-draft condition, maintaining a modest up-draft condition and relieving a down-draft condition. *Figure 6-13* illustrates the operation of the barometric draft control for a fan assisted burner application.

a) Gate opening inward to regulate an increasing updraft.

b) Gate closing off to maintain a required modest updraft.

c) Gate opening outward to relieve down draft condition.

Figure 6-12: Double acting draft control.

The location of the draft control is important. For gas firing equipment, the preferred location is in a *Bull-Head Tee*. On a correctly installed bull-head tee the flue gases make a right angle turn behind the control in such a manner that the direction of the flue gases is not directed towards the gate of the draft control. *Figure 6-14* illustrates good and poor locations on gas firing equipment. The best locations on gas firing equipment are the best because the flue gases are not directed towards the gate of the draft control during normal up-draft conditions, but *are* so directed during a down-draft condition. The reversal of flow during a down-draft condition tends to entrain the flue gases through the draft control gate and maximum relief is possible.

Sizing the Barometric Draft Control

As a general rule, it is best to use a draft control of the same size as the flue pipe. That is, a 6 inch diameter control for a 6 inch diameter vent. For intermediate size vents and flues, it is preferable to use the next larger size of draft control to provide ample capacity. As there are a number of factors to be considered when selecting larger draft controls, manufacturer's recommendations should be followed.

Single Acting Barometric Draft Controls

Single acting barometric draft controls may be used for gas fired incinerators. Single acting barometric draft controls do not relieve down-draft conditions but will close off completely if experiencing any *back* pressure. The single acting barometric draft control used for incinerator operation should be set to maintain a low negative pressure adjacent to the firing door.

Automatic Vent Damper

The automatic vent damper is an energy conserving device located at the appliance draft diverter outlet *(see Figure 6-15)*.

It functions to reduce the appliance off cycle losses by preventing warm building air from migrating to the outside via the appliance venting system. During the off cycle, the damper is driven to the closed position isolating the appliance venting system from the building air.

As illustrated in *Figure 6-16*, the unit consists of:
i) damper actuator unit (i.e., damper motor)
ii) damper assembly
iii) built in end switches that:
  - de-energize the damper actuator at the open and closed positions
  - interlock the damper position with the burner ignition control system.

Figure 6-13: Operation of the barometric draft control of a gas power burner application.

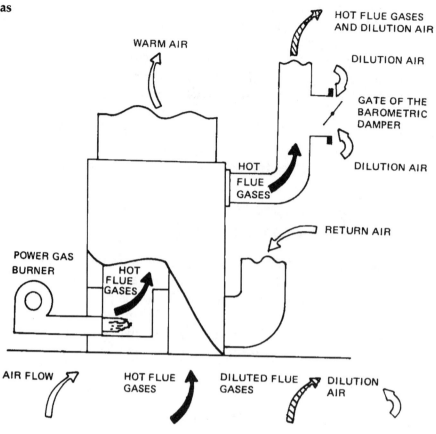

WARM AIR

HOT FLUE GASES AND DILUTION AIR

DILUTION AIR

GATE OF THE BAROMETRIC DAMPER

HOT FLUE GASES

DILUTION AIR

RETURN AIR

POWER GAS BURNER

HOT FLUE GASES

AIR FLOW HOT FLUE GASES DILUTED FLUE GASES DILUTION AIR

Figure 6-14: Locating the barometric draft control.

BEST LOCATIONS FOR GAS

BEST LOCATIONS FOR OIL OR SOLID FUELS

WRONG OR POOR LOCATIONS

WRONG

WRONG

WRONG

WRONG

WRONG

WRONG

POOR

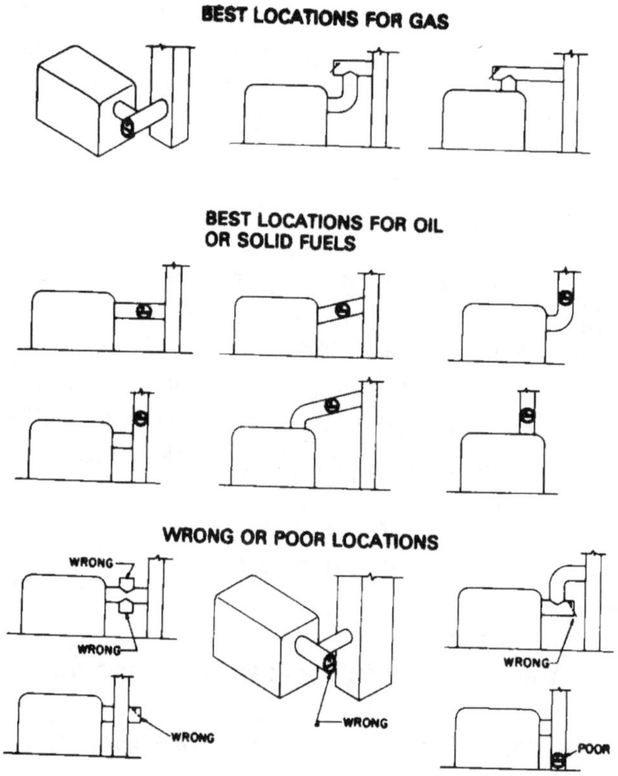

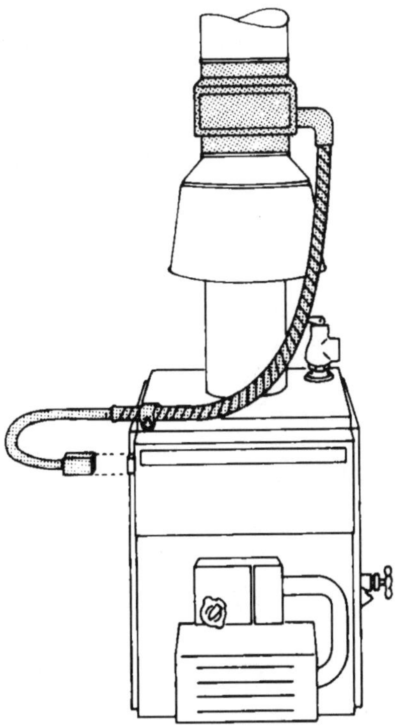

Figure 6-15: An automatic vent damper located at the appliance draft diverter outlet.

Figure 6-16: The automatic vent damper consists of — damper actuator (damper motor), damper assembly and built in end switches.

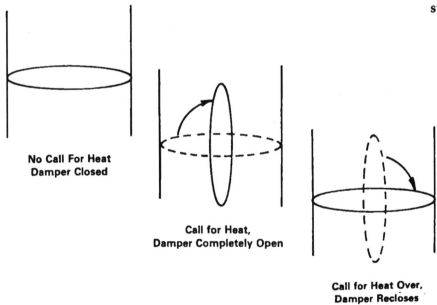

No Call For Heat Damper Closed

Call for Heat, Damper Completely Open

Call for Heat Over, Damper Recloses

Figure 6-17: Opening and closing sequence of an automatic vent damper.

Figure 6-18: Control sequence of a furnace that employs an automatic vent damper.

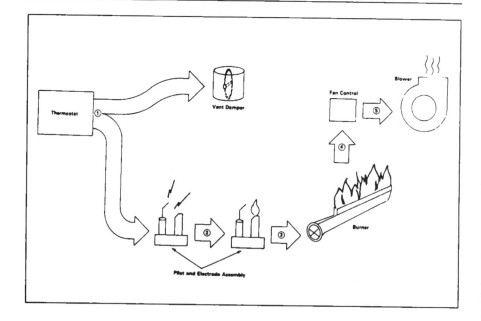

As illustrated in *Figures 6-17* and *6-18* when the thermostat calls for heat (1) the damper actuator is energized to drive the damper to the open position. When the damper is fully open, the damper's end switch is made stopping the damper activator and energizing the burner ignition control system (2) to establish pilot and main burner flames (3). Appliance is now in an operating mode (4) and (5). When the call for heat is over, the thermostat is open, the ignition system and main burner are de-energized and the damper actuator is again energized to drive the damper to the closed position.

Types of Gas Vents

The following are the types of vents used for gas equipment:

Type A   Masonry chimney, steel chimney, and factory built chimney *(see Figure 6-19)*

Type B   Double wall metal vent connector *(see Figure 6-19)*

Type BW   Oval double wall metal vent connector *(see Figure 6-20)*

Type C   Single wall metal vent connector

Type L   Similar to Type B, but made from greater heat and corrosion resistant materials. Used for venting oil and gas appliances where approved. However, not commonly used with straight gas equipment *(see Figure 6-19)*.

Type BH   Stainless steel, thermoplastic and PVC plastic vent used for special venting systems associated with high efficiency gas appliances *(see Chapters 14 & 15)* that employ negative or positive pressure venting of the products of combustion.

Figure 6-19: Types of gas venting.
1. **Type B venting**
2. **Type L venting**
3. **Type A venting**

Type A Vent

Type A flues or vents are used to vent the following gas equipment:
1. Conversion burners;
2. Incinerators;
3. Dual fuel burners (i.e., oil/gas burners).

Type A vents or chimneys must have the following:
1. A *clean-out* located near the base of the chimney, (*see Figure 6-22*).[3]
2. For masonry chimney, a tile liner as illustrated by *Figures 6-22* and *6-23* is recommended to protect the chimney in the event that condensation of the flue gases occurs. An unlined chimney can be fitted with a metal vent that can function as a liner. The inserted vent can be of rigid construction such as type B or L, or a flexible aluminum or stainless steel type as illustrated in *Figure 6-24*.

Figure 6-20: Types BW gas vent.

**Figure 6-21:
Venting components of
type B and C gas vents.**

---

[3] When a chimney liner is installed in a masonry chimney, the clean-out door at the base of the chimney is usually cemented shut.

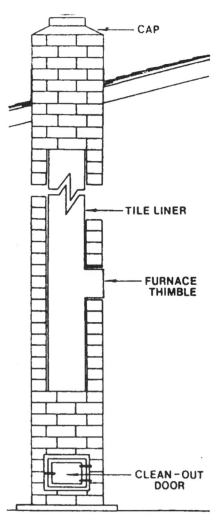

Figure 6-22: Location of a
chimney clean out.

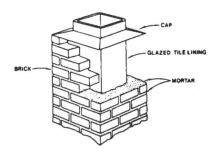

Figure 6-23: Tile liner of a
masonry chimney.

Figure 6-24: Flexible metal vent
liner.

Whether rigid or flexible construction, the metal vent liner must:
i)   Provide a continuous lining.
ii)   Extend above the top of the chimney not less than 6 inches (150 mm) and not more than 24 inches (600 mm);
iii) Sealed at the bottom and top at the point of entry and exit from the chimney;
iv)   Terminate with an appropriate vent cap;
v)   Contain not more than one field installed connection in the flexible portion of the liner, and where provided, the connection shall be made by means of a rigid connection.

Type B Vent

A Type B gas vent has the following applications associated with its insulation quality, created because of its double wall construction:
1.   Used to reduce the clearance between the gas vent and combustible material. *(See Table T6-5.)*
2.   Used as a chimney liner.
3.   Used for venting the appliance directly to the outside.
4.   Used to go through roofs, ceilings and floors.
5.   Used when the venting has a relatively long *lateral*, run in damp and cool areas.

Limitations of Type B Vent
Type B gas vents cannot be used where the flue gas exit temperature at the gas appliance flue collar is above 464°F (240°C). Because of this temperature limitation, Type B vents cannot be used between the appliance flue collar and the draft diverter inlet. They can only be used downstream of the draft diverter. As a general rule, Type B vents can only be used with gas appliances that have draft diverters and then only on the downstream side of the diverter.

When a single wall vent connector (Type C) connects an appliance to a Type B vent, the *Base Fitting* of the Type B vent shall be a Type B tee or elbow. The connection of the single wall vent connector to the Type B vent is usually accomplished by a *double wall* to a *single wall adapter*. Also, the minimum height of a Type B vent above the highest connected draft hood is 5 feet (1.5 m).

Type C Vent

Type C or single wall vent connectors must be constructed of a material having a corrosion resistance and heat durability equivalent to galvanized steel, when utilized as the vent connector between the appliance flue collar and the inlet to the appliance draft diverter. When a Type C or single wall vent connector is employed after the draft diverter it can be aluminum or galvanized steel.

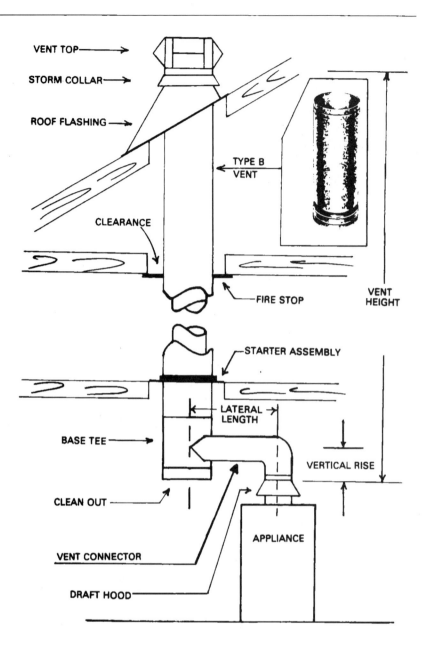

Figure 6-25: Application of type "B" gas vent being used to directly vent the appliance to the outside.

Appliance	Minimum Distance from Combustible Material — Inches (mm)	
	Type B Vent Connector	Other Than Type B Vent Connector
Boiler	1* (25)	6 (150)
Warm Air Furnace	1* (25)	6 (150)
Service Water Heater	1* (25)	6 (150)
Space Heater	1* (25)	6 (150)
Floor Furnace	3† (75)	9 (225)
Incinerator	Not Permitted	18 (450)
Conversion Burner (with draft hood)	6 (150)	9 (225)

* Except as otherwise certified.

† 3 inches (75 mm) for a distance of not less than 3 ft (900 mm) from the outlet of the draft hood. Beyond 3 ft (900 mm), the minimum clearance is 1 inch (25 mm).

Table T6-5: Vent Connector Clearance for Gas Appliances

Type C or single wall vents have the following restrictions:
1. Cannot be used as an outside vent (run outdoors);
2. Cannot run through roofs and ceilings;
3. If it runs through a partition it must employ a ventilated metal *thimble;*
4. Must eventually run to a Type B or Type A vent;
5. When running near combustible material must maintain the clearances as specified in *Table T6-5.*

Type BW Vent

A type BW gas vent is used to vent the *recessed* or *wall* type of space heater. When a Type BW vent is applied to vent the recessed type of heater, the vent should terminate not less than 12 feet (3.6 m) above the bottom of the heater and should have no lateral or horizontal sections, as illustrated in *Figure 6-26.*

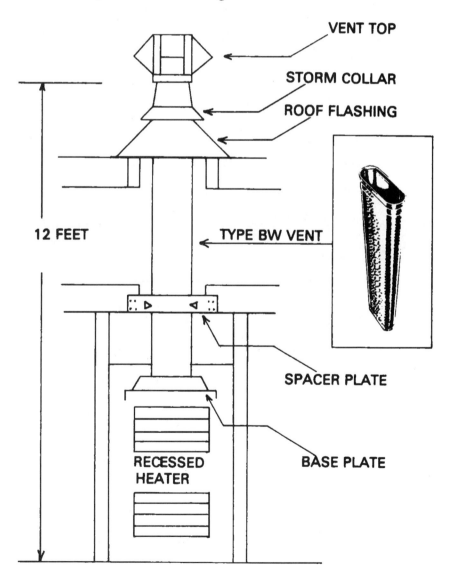

Figure 6-26: Application of type "BW" vent.

117

Assignment

1. State the purpose of venting a gas appliance.

2. State the products of combustion for natural gas and air.

3. What is meant by the terms:
   a) Perfect combustion
   b) Complete combustion
   c) Incomplete combustion

4. What gas must not be found in the products of combustion for natural gas? Why?

5. Briefly describe the venting action of a typical natural draft gas appliance.

6. List the two main venting problems associated with the venting of gas appliances.

7. Give two causes of each, as listed in question No. 6, and the correction needed to overcome the problem.

8. List the three requirements for air in the combustion process of a typical natural draft gas appliance.

9. State the function of a draft diverter or draft hood.

10. Give the four types of draft hoods utilized on natural draft appliances.

11. Give the installation requirements of a draft hood or diverter.

12. State the function of a barometric type of draft control.

13. Briefly describe the operation of the barometric draft control.

14. List and describe the five types of gas vents.

15. Give two applications of double wall metal vent connectors.

16. State the major restrictions for:
    a) Masonry chimney
    b) Type B vent
    c) Type C vent
    d) Type BW vent

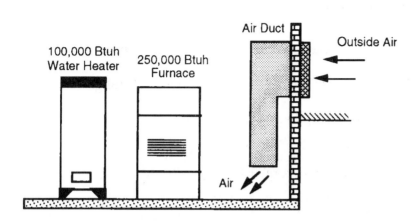

Figure 6-27: Assignment
Question #18

17. State the purpose of an automatic vent damper and give a brief description of its operation.

18. Determine the combustion air supply in square inches for the above installation when:

    a) both appliances are equipped with draft hoods and are located in a building of tight construction;

    b) both appliances are not equipped with draft hoods and are located in a building of tight construction;

    c) only the furnace is equipped with a draft hood and both appliances are located in a building of tight construction;

    d) both appliances are equipped with draft hoods and are located in a building of normal construction having a volume of 10,000 cubic feet;

    e) both appliances are not equipped with draft hoods and are located in a building of normal construction having a volume of 10,000 cubic feet;

    f) only the water heater is equipped with a draft hood and both appliances are located in a building of normal construction having a volume of 10,000 cubic feet.

19. Determine the combustion air supply for the installation on the following page when building air is supplied and both appliances are equipped with draft hoods.

Figure 6-28: Assignment
Question #21

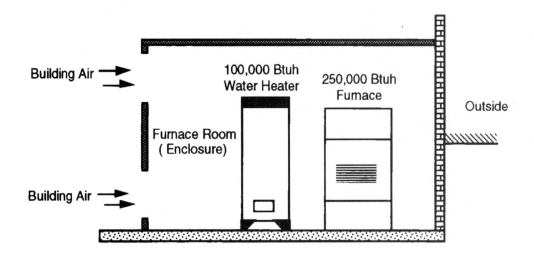

20. Give the location for each of the combustion air supply ducts in question #19.

21. Determine the combustion air supply to the building, illustrated in the above drawing, when the building is of normal construction. The volume of the structure is 12,500 cubic feet.

Venting—Part II— Venting Practice & Design

7

This section will deal with venting practice and design for conventional venting of individual and multiple appliance installations. However, before we proceed with venting practice and design, we must first look at how gas appliances are categorized as to their method of venting. *Figure 7-1* illustrates the various methods that can be used to vent gas appliances.

Venting Appliance Categories

The following are the venting categories that define a gas appliance in terms of its method of venting:

Category I
An appliance which operates with a non-positive vent pressure and with a flue or vent loss not less than 17 percent.[1] The appliance is vented conventionally by either a type B vent or a masonry chimney. The appliance can be either a natural draft appliance or a fan assisted appliance.

A *Natural Draft Appliance* is one in which a draft hood establishes a neutral over fire draft condition within the burner compartment. Natural draft or gravity venting is required to remove the flue gases to the outside through the appliance venting system.

A *Fan Assisted Appliance (see Figure 7-2)* is one in which an induced draft fan (ID fan) pulls the products of combustion across the appliance. However, the induced draft fan does not create a positive vent pressure. The appliance relies on the buoyant effects of the hot flue gases to vent them to the outside and like a natural draft appliance it is susceptible to spillage. The *zero pressure venting* allows the interconnection of another appliance, usually a water heater, to the venting system of the appliance. However, because the appliance is not equipped with a draft hood, the appliance operates with no dilution air. As a result, there is a higher concentration of water vapour in the flue gases. This increases the risk of condensation within the appliance venting system.

---

[1] A flue or vent loss of not less than 17% would generally necessitate a vent gas temperature at least 140°F (60°C) above its due point.

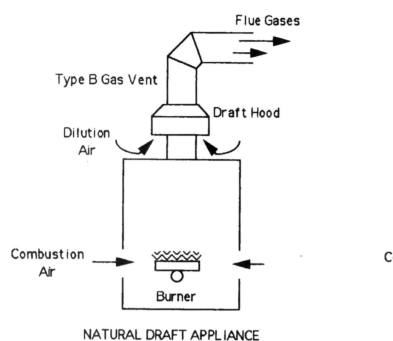

NATURAL DRAFT APPLIANCE

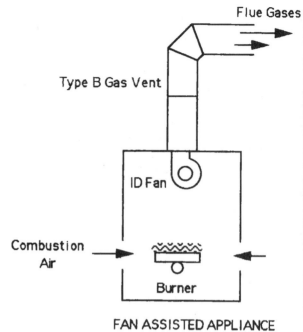

FAN ASSISTED APPLIANCE

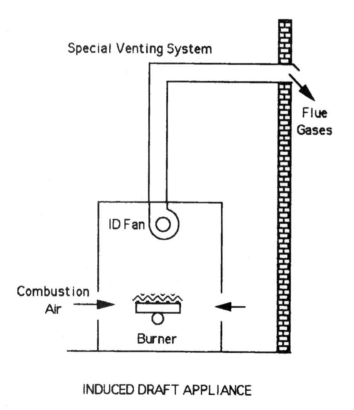

INDUCED DRAFT APPLIANCE

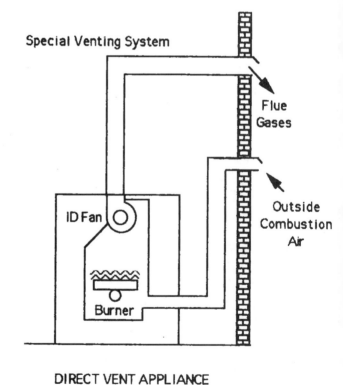

DIRECT VENT APPLIANCE

Figure 7-1: Methods of venting gas appliances.

Figure 7-2: Illustration of a fan
assisted furnace.

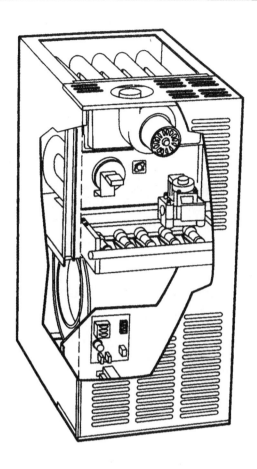

Natural draft and fan assisted appliances in tight buildings,
become susceptible to spillage when air exhaust equipment create a
substantial negative building pressure. Buildings that have a negative building pressure that is greater than 0.02"wc or 5 Pa should
not employ a natural draft or a fan assisted appliance.

Category II
An appliance which operates with a non-positive vent pressure and
with a flue or vent loss less than 17 percent. At this time, there are
no Category II appliances in operation.

Category III
An appliance which operates with a positive vent pressure and
with a flue or vent loss not less than 17 percent. The appliance is
usually an *Induced Draft Appliance*[2] in which an induced draft fan
not only pulls the products of combustion across the appliance but
also *power vents* them to the outside. The appliance employs a
Special Venting System (i.e., BH venting) that is recommended by the
appliance manufacturer such as thermoplastic vent pipe. The appliance can be vented horizontally through the wall *(see Figure 7-1)* or
vertically up a chimney that is dedicated to the appliance.

[2] The induced draft appliance can also be called an induced draft firing
appliance.

Positive vent pressures developed by the appliance prohibit the interconnection of any other appliance to the venting system of the unit. Also, as we will see in *Chapters 14 and 15* manufacturers' requirements of maximum and minimum vent runs, vent support, required slope and vent termination must be strictly followed.

Category IV

An appliance which operates with a positive vent pressure and with a flue or vent loss less than 17 percent. The appliance is usually a condensing type employing induced draft firing or pulse combustion *(see Figures 15-1 and 15-3)*. The appliance also will use special venting system (i.e., BH venting) recommended by the manufacturer such as PVC plastic pipe. The appliance is usually vented through the wall. The appliance can be a *Direct Vent Appliance* in which the appliance combustion chamber is sealed from the indoor environment. The appliance air supply is drawn directly from the outside using a PVC plastic intake air pipe *(see Figures 15-21 and 15-22)*.

Venting Practice

The venting of gas appliances must be done in a safe and effective manner. Local and national codes usually reflect venting practices that have been determined over a long period of time.

The following is an approximate summary of those requirements and standards that constitute good gas venting practice.

Manual Dampers

Manually operated dampers cannot be used in any flue or vent connector.

Automatic Vent Dampers

Automatic vent dampers are permitted in a residential building only where:
i)   the device is provided as an integral component of an approved appliance;
ii) appliance does not exceed 400,000 Btuh (120 kW);
iii) the appliance is vented to a Type B, L or factory built chimney or a masonry chimney having a vent liner.

Chimney & Vent Termination

As illustrated in *Figure 7-3*, masonry chimneys should extend at least 3 feet (900 mm) above the highest point where they pass through the roof of a building and by at least 2 feet (600 mm) higher than any part of the building within a horizontal distance of 10 feet (3 m).

Also, the gas vent (i.e., B, BW, L vent and factory built chimney) should extend at least 2 feet (600 mm) higher than any portion of

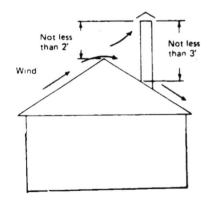

Figure 7-3

the building (e.g., ridge, wall or parapet) within 10 feet (3 m) of its terminal location.

For gas vents terminating on a sloped roof, the minimum distance for the vent terminal is in accordance with *Figure 7-4*.

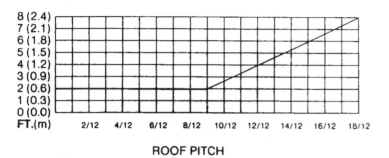

ROOF PITCH

Figure 7-4: Termination height for gas vents above sloped roof.

Keep the Number of Turns in the Venting System to a Minimum
As illustrated in *Figure 7-5*, the flue or vent connector should be installed to avoid short turns or other construction features which would create excessive resistance to the flow of flue gases. This means keeping the number of elbows down to a minimum since each elbow adds resistance to the overall vent action. Vent sizing tables for individual vents make an allowance for *two* 90 degree turns anywhere in the appliance venting system between the draft hood and vent top such as:

> One 90 degree elbow and one tee;
> Four 45 degree elbows;
> Two 90 degree elbows.

Each 90 degree turn in excess of the first two that are allowed will reduce the *vent connector* capacity by 10 percent for natural draft appliances and 15% for fan assisted appliances. Also, each 90 degree turn in the *common vent* reduces its capacity by 10 percent.

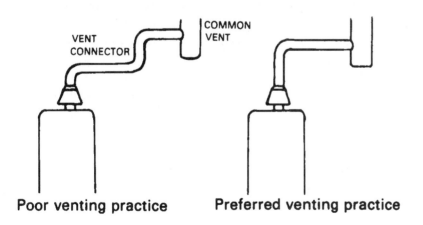

Poor venting practice   Preferred venting practice

Figure 7-5: Appliance venting system should keep the number of short turns to a minimum.

Pitch or Rise

For a single wall vent the flue or vent connector should maintain a pitch or rise from the appliance to the common vent or chimney. A rise of 1/4" to a foot of horizontal length should be maintained. Also, the horizontal or lateral run should be free from any dips or sags.

Venting into a Common Vent That Also Vents a Liquid Fuel

When venting a gas appliance into a chimney or common vent used for a liquid fuel appliance, the vent connector entrance into the chimney of the gas appliance must be above that of the other, regardless of input. However, a shop fabricated branch fitting, located as close as practical to the chimney, can be used to connect the vent connector of the gas appliance to the vent connector of the other fuel.

Venting Appliances of Unequal Input

When venting two gas appliances of unequal input into a chimney or common vent, the entrance of the vent connector of the appliance having the smaller input shall be located higher than the larger input appliance; or wherever possible, locate the common vent closer to or directly over the small appliance connector *(see Figure 7-8)*.

Venting Appliances of Equal Input

When venting two gas appliances of equal input into a chimney or common vent, the two vent connector locations into the chimney or common vent cannot be made opposite or adjacent to each other at the same level. However, as illustrated in *Figure 7-6*, they may be "Y"-ed into the chimney or common vent or located in a staggered position.

Mechanical Exhaust or Power Ventors

Mechanical exhaust or power ventors may be used to supplement a natural or gravity vent system that is experiencing problems. They are usually located near or at the vent outlet, preferably outdoors, thus maintaining a negative pressure throughout the appliance venting system. Any leakage that would develop would pass into the vent and not into the space through which the appliance vent passes.

A power ventor can increase the capacity of an appliance venting system up to four times the capacity indicated in the venting tables.

When using mechanical exhaust or power ventor with a gas appliance, provision should be made to prevent the flow of gas to the main burner in the event of failure of the power ventor. In this respect an *air switch* can be used to *interlock* the power ventor operation with that of the gas burner. *Note:* Mechanical exhaust or power ventors are restricted to commercial or industrial systems and *cannot* be used in a one or two family dwelling.

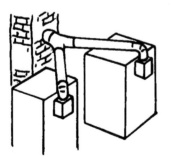

Figure 7-6: Two vent connectors handling equal capacity being "Y"-ed into a chimney.

Figure 7-7 illustrates two types of mechanical exhaust or power ventors.

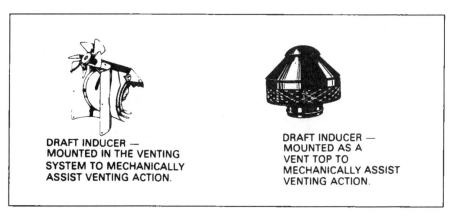

Figure 7-7: Mechanical exhaust or power ventors.

Entering the Common Vent

When two or more vent connectors enter a common vent or chimney, they should enter as high as possible, consistent with the required clearance for combustible material. *Figure 7-8* illustrates the preferred practice associated with the above situation.

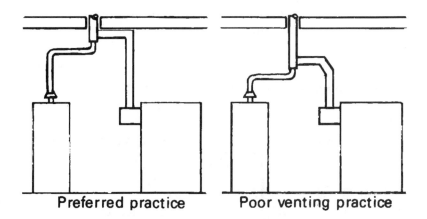

Preferred practice   Poor venting practice

Figure 7-8: Vent connector should be placed near ceiling.

The Length of Horizontal or Lateral Run

The horizontal or lateral run of the vent connector should be as short as possible and the appliance should be located as near the chimney or common vent as practical. The maximum length of the horizontal run for single wall vents should not exceed 75 percent of the chimney or common vent height and for Type B the maximum lateral run is 100 percent of the common vent height.

Normally, the higher the vent the greater the venting action. The horizontal or lateral portion of the vent connector adds only friction and resistance to the flow of the flue gases in the appliance venting system as illustrated in *Figure 7-9*. The normal rule of thumb for Type B venting is, maximum vent connector length of 1 1/2 feet for every inch of connector diameter; greater lengths require an increase in vent connector size, vertical rise or total vent height to obtain full venting capacity.

Figure 7-9: Good venting practice dictates that excessive lateral runs be kept to a minimum.

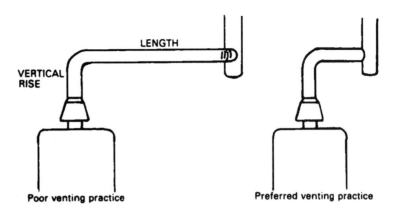

Increasing the Vertical Rise

Changing the vent connector to get an increase in the Vertical Rise just as it leaves the appliance adds to the overall venting action of the appliance venting system.

Clothes Dryers

Clothes dryers must be vented separately and not into the vent or chimney servicing the heating appliances. *(See Figure 7-10.)*

Figure 7-10: Clothes dryers must be vented separately to the outside.

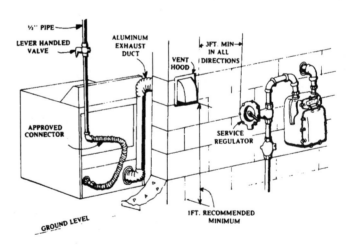

Chimney Connections

The following are points that lead to good chimney connections:

i)   the entrance of a vent connector into a chimney should be above the chimney clean out opening;

ii) the vent connector should not protrude into the chimney and thereby obstruct the chimney flue;

iii) a sleeve should be used to facilitate removal of the vent connector for cleaning;

iv) the space between a chimney liner should be sealed at the point of entry of a vent connector.

Venting Limitations for Fan Assisted Appliances

Because of the problem of condensation associated with the venting of these appliances, the following limitation are applied to fan assisted appliances:

i)   may be commonly vented into an existing masonry chimney if:
    a)   the chimney is venting at least one natural draft appliance,
    b)   the vent connectors and chimney must be sized by the appropriate vent sizing table;
ii) cannot singularly vent a fan assisted appliance into a tile-lined masonry chimney. The chimney must be facilitated with a metal chimney liner prior to venting a fan assisted appliance.

Vent Sizing and Design

The proper design of the appliance venting system, that will ensure the effective operation of the appliance, is determined by the following basic factors:

Draft

As illustrated in *Figure 6-1*, draft is due to the difference in weight or density (i.e., the level of buoyancy) between a column of hot flue gases and an equivalent column of cooler outside air (i.e., room air). Thus, the hotter the flue gases and the higher the vent, the greater will be the overall venting action or draft.

Vent Resistance

The flow of the flue gases generated by the draft is reduced by friction and by the need to provide initial acceleration to the flue gas stream at the start of the venting system. Small vent pipes, long lengths of lateral run, restrictions or changes in direction all contribute to resistance in the flow of the flue gases and as such impede good venting.

Heat Transfer

The velocity of the flue gases through the appliance venting system must be high enough to offset a large amount of heat transfer which would:

i)   Decrease the amount of draft developed in the venting system;
ii) Lead to the possible development of condensation. This is especially true for fan assisted appliances that operate without dilution air.

Building Pressure

Buildings may develop high levels of negative pressure as a result of tight construction and the required application of mechanical ventilation. The appliance flue gases must develop sufficient buoyancy producing the required venting action which will overcome the resulting downdraft caused by the negative building pressure.

Natural draft and fan assisted appliances are *spillage susceptible appliances*. Their applications are restricted to buildings having a maximum negative building pressure of 0.02"wc (5 Pa).

Figures 7-11 and 7-12 illustrate the basic vent configurations for type B vent and tile lined masonry chimney.

Vent Sizing for Individual Appliances

In determining the correct vent size (D) for an individual appliance installation, the following must be known:

1. The total vent height (H)—the height of the vent from the draft hood outlet, or flue collar outlet in the case of an fan assisted appliance, to the vent cap;

2. The Btuh capacity rating of the appliance—the vent tables are expressed in thousands Btuh of vent capacity;

3. The length of the vent connector in feet (L)—the lateral or horizontal run as differentiated from the vertical rise.

Note: Always design the appliance venting system for the *Sea-Level* input rating of the appliance, regardless of the actual *De-rated* operating input required by the local altitude.

The following is the procedure for using *Tables T7-1, T7-2 T7-3 and T7-4* in determining the required vent size of an individual appliance.[1]

1. Determine the total vent height (H) and the total lateral length (L) needed for the vent.

2. In Tables T7-1, T7-2, T7-3 and T7-4, read down the total vent height column (H) to the proper number.

3. In the lateral (L) space to the right of the correct (H), pick the proper lateral length (using zero for the straight vertical vents).

4. Read across the proper (L) row to the column that shows a vent capacity equal to or just greater than the appliance capacity in Btuh. *Note:*
   i) Fan assisted appliances have a minimum and maximum vent capacity. The minimum vent capacity represents the lowest vent capacity that will not promote condensation.
   ii) Natural draft appliances have both a maximum vent capacity for appliances located in buildings having normal construction and a DP (depressurization) vent capacity for appliances located in tight buildings

[1] The tables showing Type B gas vent with double-wall vent connectors are used when sizing a single wall chimney vent liner.

Figure 7-11: Vent configuration for type B vent.

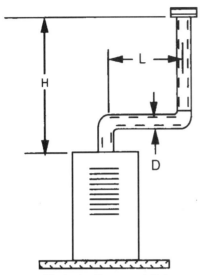

Single Appliance Installation
Type B Vent with Double-wall Vent Connector

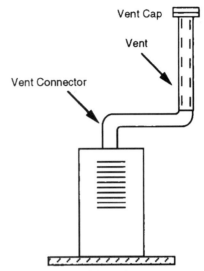

Single Appliance Installation
Type B Vent with Single wall Vent Connector

H = Vent Height
D = Vent Connector/Vent Diameter
L= Lateral Length of Vent Connector
R = Vent Connector Vertical Rise

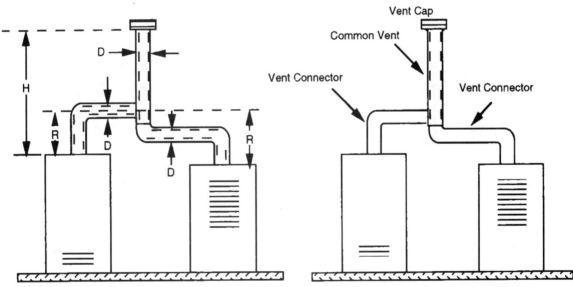

Multiple Appliance Installation
Type B Common Vent with Double Wall Vent Connector

Multiple Appliance Installation
Type B Common Vent with Single Wall Vent Connector

Figure 7-12: Vent configurations for a tile lined masonry chimney.

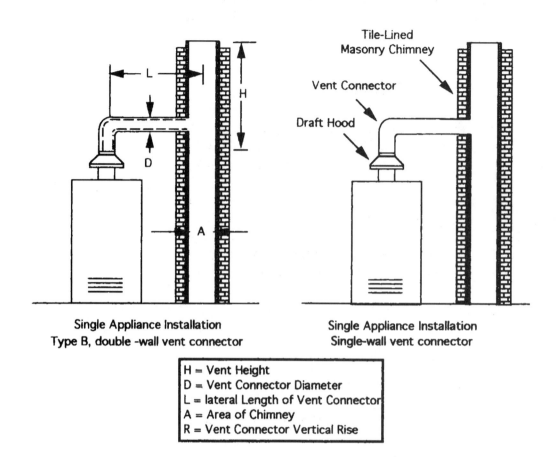

Single Appliance Installation
Type B, double -wall vent connector

Single Appliance Installation
Single-wall vent connector

H = Vent Height
D = Vent Connector Diameter
L = lateral Length of Vent Connector
A = Area of Chimney
R = Vent Connector Vertical Rise

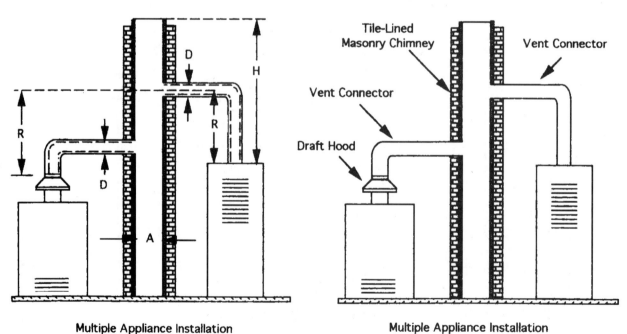

Multiple Appliance Installation
Type B, double -wall vent connector

Multiple Appliance Installation
Single-wall vent connector

5. If the vent size shown at the top of the column is equal or larger than the appliance draft diverter, use the vent size shown. However, if the vent size is smaller than the draft hood, follow the instructions below in *Draft Hood to Vent Reductions*.

Draft Hood to Vent Reduction

A draft hood to vent reduction can take place for venting systems having a total vent height of 10 feet (3 m) or more. For systems less than 10 feet (3 m) the vent should be at least as large as the draft hood diverter.

For venting systems of 12 inches (304.8 mm) in diameter or less, the draft hood to vent reduction is one pipe size. For example, a 6 to 5 inch or 12 to 10 inch reduction would be one pipe size reduction. Larger venting systems can have a draft hood to vent reduction of two pipe sizes, for example a 24 inch to 20 inch reduction.

Examples 1, 2 and *3* illustrate the sizing of single appliance installations.

Vent Sizing for Multiple Appliances

A venting system that vents two or more appliances on the same floor into a common vent is a combined or multiple appliance venting system *(see Figures 7-11 & 7-12)*.

In determining the correct vent size for a multiple appliance installation, the following must be known:

1. The total vent height (H)—the vertical distance from the highest draft hood outlet, or flue collar outlet in the case of fan assisted appliances, to the vent top or cap;

2. Vertical rise—the vertical distance of the appliance's draft hood or flue collar to the junction of the highest appliance entrance into the common vent;

3. The common vent—that portion of the vent system above the lowest interconnection.

In sizing for a combined or multiple appliance installation, two components of the system are sized individually:

1. The individual appliance vent connector that rises and makes the connection to the common vent;

2. The common vent.

Table T7-1: Type B Vent Sizing

Capacity in 1000 Btuh of Type B Gas Vent With Double-Wall Vent Connectors Serving a Single Appliance

Vent and Vent Connector Diameter (D) - Inches

Height (H) ft.	Lateral (L) ft.	3" Fan Assist Min	3" Fan Assist Max	3" Nat. Draft Max	3" Nat. Draft DP	4" Fan Assist Min	4" Fan Assist Max	4" Nat. Draft Max	4" Nat. Draft DP	5" Fan Assist Min	5" Fan Assist Max	5" Nat. Draft Max	5" Nat. Draft DP	6" Fan Assist Min	6" Fan Assist Max	6" Nat. Draft Max	6" Nat. Draft DP	7" Fan Assist Min	7" Fan Assist Max	7" Nat. Draft Max	7" Nat. Draft DP
6	0	0	78	46	29	0	152	86	53	0	251	141	87	0	375	205	127	0	524	285	177
	2	13	51	36	22	18	97	67	41	27	157	105	64	32	232	157	96	44	321	217	132
	4	21	49	34	20	30	94	64	38	39	153	103	61	50	227	153	90	66	316	211	124
	6	25	46	32	19	36	91	61	36	47	149	100	59	59	223	149	88	78	310	205	121
8	0	0	84	50	37	0	165	94	69	0	276	155	113	0	415	235	172	0	583	320	234
	2	12	57	40	29	16	109	75	55	25	178	120	88	28	263	180	131	42	365	247	180
	5	23	53	38	27	32	103	71	50	42	171	115	82	53	255	173	123	70	356	237	168
	8	28	49	35	25	39	98	66	47	51	164	109	77	64	247	165	117	84	347	227	161
10	0	0	88	53	42	0	175	100	79	0	295	166	131	0	447	255	201	0	631	345	273
	2	12	61	42	34	17	118	81	65	23	194	129	103	26	289	195	156	40	402	273	218
	5	23	57	40	32	32	113	77	62	41	187	124	99	52	280	188	150	68	392	263	210
	10	30	51	36	28	41	104	70	55	54	176	115	90	67	267	175	137	88	376	245	191
15	0	0	94	58	50	0	191	112	96	0	327	187	161	0	502	285	245	0	716	390	335
	2	11	69	48	41	15	136	93	80	20	226	150	129	22	339	225	194	38	475	316	272
	5	22	65	45	38	30	130	87	74	39	219	142	121	49	330	217	184	64	463	300	255
	10	29	59	41	35	40	121	82	70	51	206	135	115	64	315	208	177	84	445	288	245
	15	35	53	37	31	48	112	76	65	61	195	128	109	76	301	198	168	98	429	275	234
20	0	0	97	61	55	0	202	119	107	0	349	202	182	0	540	307	276	0	776	430	387
	2	10	75	51	46	14	149	100	90	18	250	166	149	20	377	249	224	33	531	346	311
	5	21	71	48	43	29	143	96	85	38	242	160	142	47	367	241	214	62	519	337	300
	10	28	64	44	39	38	133	89	79	50	229	150	134	62	351	228	203	81	499	321	286
	15	34	58	40	36	46	124	84	75	59	217	142	126	73	337	217	193	94	481	308	274
	20	48	52	35	31	55	116	78	69	69	206	134	119	84	322	206	183	107	464	295	263

Note:

DP-max. vent capacity for an appliance equipped with a draft hood
   that is located in a tight structure (sustaining depressurization of up to 5Pa or 0.02 "wc)

Nat. Draft- natural draft appliance (appliance equipped with a draft hood

Fan Assist- fan assisted appliance (appliance equipped with an ID fan)

Min- minimum Btuh vent capacity

Max- maximum Btuh vent capacity

Capacity (in 1000 Btuh) of Type B Gas Vent With Single-Wall Vent Connectors Serving a Single Appliance

Vent and Vent Connector Diameter (D) - Inches

Height (H) ft.	Lateral (L) ft.	3" Fan Assist Min	3" Fan Assist Max	3" Nat. Draft Max	3" Nat. Draft DP	4" Fan Assist Min	4" Fan Assist Max	4" Nat. Draft Max	4" Nat. Draft DP	5" Fan Assist Min	5" Fan Assist Max	5" Nat. Draft Max	5" Nat. Draft DP	6" Fan Assist Min	6" Fan Assist Max	6" Nat. Draft Max	6" Nat. Draft DP	7" Fan Assist Min	7" Fan Assist Max	7" Nat. Draft Max	7" Nat. Draft DP
6	0	38	77	45	28	59	151	85	53	85	249	140	87	126	373	204	126	165	522	284	176
	2	39	51	36	22	60	96	66	40	85	156	104	63	123	231	156	95	159	320	213	130
	4	NR	NR	33	19	74	92	63	37	102	152	102	60	146	225	152	90	187	313	208	123
	6	NR	NR	31	18	83	89	60	35	114	147	99	58	163	220	148	87	207	307	203	120
8	0	37	83	50	37	58	164	93	68	83	273	154	112	123	412	234	171	161	580	319	233
	2	39	56	39	28	59	108	75	55	83	176	119	87	121	261	179	131	155	363	246	180
	5	NR	NR	37	26	77	102	69	49	107	168	114	81	151	252	171	121	193	352	235	167
	8	NR	NR	33	23	90	95	64	45	122	161	107	76	175	243	163	116	223	342	225	160
10	0	37	87	53	42	57	174	99	78	82	293	165	130	120	444	254	201	158	628	344	272
	2	39	61	41	33	59	117	80	64	82	193	128	102	119	287	194	155	153	400	272	281
	5	52	56	39	31	76	111	76	61	105	185	122	98	148	277	186	149	190	388	261	209
	10	NR	NR	34	27	97	100	68	53	132	171	112	87	188	261	171	133	237	369	241	188
15	0	36	93	57	49	56	190	111	95	80	325	186	160	116	499	283	243	153	713	388	334
	2	38	69	47	40	57	136	93	80	80	225	149	128	115	337	224	193	148	473	314	270
	5	51	63	44	37	75	128	86	73	102	216	140	119	144	326	217	184	182	459	298	253
	10	NR	NR	39	33	95	116	79	67	128	201	131	111	182	308	203	173	228	438	284	241
	15	NR	NR	NR	NR	NR	NR	72	61	158	186	124	105	220	290	192	163	272	418	269	229
20	0	35	96	60	54	54	200	118	106	78	346	201	181	114	537	306	275	149	772	428	385
	2	37	74	50	45	56	148	99	89	78	248	165	149	113	375	248	223	144	528	344	310
	5	50	68	47	42	73	140	94	84	100	239	158	141	141	363	239	213	178	514	334	297
	10	NR	NR	41	36	93	129	86	77	125	223	146	130	177	344	224	199	222	491	316	281
	15	NR	NR	NR	NR	NR	NR	80	71	155	208	136	121	216	325	210	187	264	469	301	268
	20	NR	NR	NR	NR	NR	NR	NR	NR	186	192	126	112	254	306	196	174	309	448	285	254

Note:
DP - max. vent capacity for an appliance equipped with a draft hood that is located in a tight structure (sustaining depressurization of up to 5Pa or 0.02 "wc)

Nat. Draft - natural draft appliance (appliance equipped with a draft hood)

Fan Assist - fan assisted appliance (appliance equipped with an ID fan)

Min - minimum Btuh vent capacity

Max - maximum Btuh vent capacity

NR - not recommended since condensation and/or pressurization of the venting system is a possibility

Table T7-2: Type B Vent Sizing

135

Table T7-3: Type A Vent Sizing

Capacity (In 1000 Btuh) of Tile-Lined Masonry Chimney With Type B Double-Wall Vent Connectors Serving a Single Appliance

Vent Connector Diameter (D)- Inches

Height (H) ft.	Lateral (L) ft.	3" Fan Assist Min	3" Fan Assist Max	3" Nat. Draft Max	3" Nat. Draft DP	4" Fan Assist Min	4" Fan Assist Max	4" Nat. Draft Max	4" Nat. Draft DP	5" Fan Assist Min	5" Fan Assist Max	5" Nat. Draft Max	5" Nat. Draft DP	6" Fan Assist Min	6" Fan Assist Max	6" Nat. Draft Max	6" Nat. Draft DP	7" Fan Assist Min	7" Fan Assist Max	7" Nat. Draft Max	7" Nat. Draft DP
15	2	N/A	N/A	35*	30*	N/A	N/A	67	58	N/A	N/A	114	98	N/A	N/A	179	154	N/A	N/A	250	215
	5	N/A	N/A	33*	28*	N/A	N/A	62	53	N/A	N/A	107	92	N/A	N/A	164	141	N/A	N/A	231	199
	10	N/A	N/A	28*	24*	N/A	N/A	55*	47*	N/A	N/A	97	82	N/A	N/A	153	130	N/A	N/A	216	184
	15	N/A	N/A	NR	NR	N/A	N/A	48*	41*	N/A	N/A	89*	76*	N/A	N/A	141	120	N/A	N/A	201	171
20	2	N/A	N/A	38*	34*	N/A	N/A	74	67	N/A	N/A	124	112	N/A	N/A	201	181	N/A	N/A	274	247
	5	N/A	N/A	36*	32*	N/A	N/A	68*	61*	N/A	N/A	116	104	N/A	N/A	184	166	N/A	N/A	254	229
	10	N/A	N/A	NR	NR	N/A	N/A	60*	53*	N/A	N/A	107*	95*	N/A	N/A	172	153	N/A	N/A	237	211
	15	N/A	N/A	NR	NR	N/A	N/A	NR	NR	N/A	N/A	97*	86*	N/A	N/A	159	142	N/A	N/A	220	196
	20	N/A	N/A	NR	NR	N/A	N/A	NR	NR	N/A	N/A	83*	74*	N/A	N/A	148*	132*	N/A	N/A	206	183
30	2	N/A	N/A	41*	38*	N/A	N/A	82*	67*	N/A	N/A	137	127	N/A	N/A	216	201	N/A	N/A	303	282
	5	N/A	N/A	NR	NR	N/A	N/A	76*	71*	N/A	N/A	128*	119*	N/A	N/A	198	184	N/A	N/A	281	261
	10	N/A	N/A	NR	NR	N/A	N/A	67*	62*	N/A	N/A	115*	107*	N/A	N/A	184*	171*	N/A	N/A	263	245
	15	N/A	N/A	NR	NR	N/A	N/A	NR	NR	N/A	N/A	107*	100*	N/A	N/A	171*	159*	N/A	N/A	243*	226
	20	N/A	N/A	NR	NR	N/A	N/A	NR	NR	N/A	N/A	91*	85*	N/A	N/A	159*	148*	N/A	N/A	227*	211
	30	N/A	N/A	NR	NR	N/A	N/A	NR	NR	N/A	N/A	N/R	N/R	N/A	N/A	N/R	N/R	N/A	N/A	188*	175
Min. Internal Chimney Area Square Inches		12				19				28				38				50			
Max. Internal Chimney Area Square Inches		49				88				137				198				269			

* Possibility of continuous condensation

Note:

DP-max. vent capacity for an appliance equipped with a draft hood that is located in a tight structure (sustaining depressurization of up to 5Pa or 0.02 "wc)

Nat. Draft- natural draft appliance (appliance equipped with a draft hood)

Fan Assist- fan assisted appliance (appliance equipped with an ID fan)

Min- minimum Btuh vent capacity

Max- maximum Btuh vent capacity

N/A- Not applicable

NR- not recommended since condensation and/or pressurization of the venting system is a possibility

Capacity (in 1000 Btuh) of Tile-Lined Masonry Chimney With Single-Wall Vent Connectors Serving a Single Appliance

Height (H) ft.	Lateral (L) ft.	3" Fan Assist Min	3" Fan Assist Max	3" Nat. Draft Max	3" Nat. Draft DP	4" Fan Assist Min	4" Fan Assist Max	4" Nat. Draft Max	4" Nat. Draft DP	5" Fan Assist Min	5" Fan Assist Max	5" Nat. Draft Max	5" Nat. Draft DP	6" Fan Assist Min	6" Fan Assist Max	6" Nat. Draft Max	6" Nat. Draft DP	7" Fan Assist Min	7" Fan Assist Max	7" Nat. Draft Max	7" Nat. Draft DP
15	2	N/A	N/A	35*	30*	N/A	N/A	67	58	N/A	N/A	113	97	N/A	N/A	178	153	N/A	N/A	249	214
	5	N/A	N/A	32*	28*	N/A	N/A	61	52	N/A	N/A	106	91	N/A	N/A	163	140	N/A	N/A	230	198
	10	N/A	N/A	27*	23*	N/A	N/A	54*	46*	N/A	N/A	96	82	N/A	N/A	151	128	N/A	N/A	214	182
	15	N/A	N/A	NR	NR	N/A	N/A	46*	39*	N/A	N/A	87*	74*	N/A	N/A	138	117	N/A	N/A	198	168
20	2	N/A	N/A	38*	34*	N/A	N/A	73	66	N/A	N/A	123	111	N/A	N/A	200	180	N/A	N/A	273	246
	5	N/A	N/A	35*	32*	N/A	N/A	67*	60*	N/A	N/A	115	104	N/A	N/A	183	165	N/A	N/A	252	227
	10	N/A	N/A	NR	NR	N/A	N/A	59*	53*	N/A	N/A	105*	93*	N/A	N/A	170	151	N/A	N/A	235	209
	15	N/A	N/A	NR	NR	N/A	N/A	NR	NR	N/A	N/A	95*	85*	N/A	N/A	156	139	N/A	N/A	217	193
	20	N/A	N/A	NR	NR	N/A	N/A	NR	NR	N/A	N/A	80*	71*	N/A	N/A	144*	128*	N/A	N/A	202	180
30	2	N/A	N/A	41*	38*	N/A	N/A	81*	75*	N/A	N/A	136	126	N/A	N/A	215	200	N/A	N/A	302	281
	5	N/A	N/A	NR	NR	N/A	N/A	75*	70*	N/A	N/A	127*	118*	N/A	N/A	196	182	N/A	N/A	279	259
	10	N/A	N/A	NR	NR	N/A	N/A	66*	61*	N/A	N/A	113*	105*	N/A	N/A	182*	169*	N/A	N/A	260	242
	15	N/A	N/A	NR	NR	N/A	N/A	NR	NR	N/A	N/A	105*	98*	N/A	N/A	168*	156*	N/A	N/A	240*	223*
	20	N/A	N/A	NR	NR	N/A	N/A	NR	NR	N/A	N/A	88*	82*	N/A	N/A	155*	144*	N/A	N/A	223*	207*
	30	N/A	N/A	NR	NR	N/A	N/A	NR	NR	N/A	N/A	N/R	N/R	N/A	N/A	N/R	N/R	N/A	N/A	182*	169*
Min. Internal Chimney Area Square Inches		12				19				28				38				50			
Max. Internal Chimney Area Square Inches		49				88				137				198				269			

* Possibility of continuous condensation

Note:

DP-max. vent capacity for an appliance equipped with a draft hood
    that is located in a tight structure (sustaining depressurization of up to 5Pa or 0.02 "wc)

Nat. Draft- natural draft appliance (appliance equipped with a draft hood)

Fan Assist- fan assisted appliance (appliance equipped with an ID fan)

Min- minimum Btuh vent capacity

Max- maximum Btuh vent capacity

N/A- Not applicable

NR- not recommended since condensation and/or pressurization of the venting system is a possibility

Table T7-4: Type A Vent Sizing

137

Examples: #1, #2, and #3.

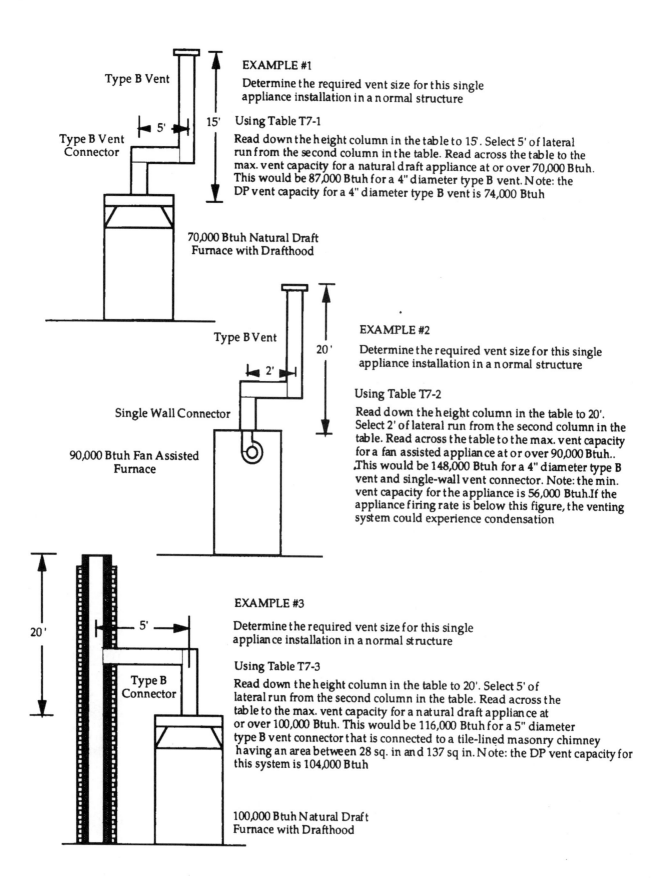

EXAMPLE #1

Determine the required vent size for this single appliance installation in a normal structure

Using Table T7-1

Read down the height column in the table to 15'. Select 5' of lateral run from the second column in the table. Read across the table to the max. vent capacity for a natural draft appliance at or over 70,000 Btuh. This would be 87,000 Btuh for a 4" diameter type B vent. Note: the DP vent capacity for a 4" diameter type B vent is 74,000 Btuh

Type B Vent

Type B Vent Connector

15'

5'

70,000 Btuh Natural Draft Furnace with Drafthood

EXAMPLE #2

Determine the required vent size for this single appliance installation in a normal structure

Using Table T7-2

Read down the height column in the table to 20'. Select 2' of lateral run from the second column in the table. Read across the table to the max. vent capacity for a fan assisted appliance at or over 90,000 Btuh.. This would be 148,000 Btuh for a 4" diameter type B vent and single-wall vent connector. Note: the min. vent capacity for the appliance is 56,000 Btuh. If the appliance firing rate is below this figure, the venting system could experience condensation

Type B Vent

20'

2'

Single Wall Connector

90,000 Btuh Fan Assisted Furnace

EXAMPLE #3

Determine the required vent size for this single appliance installation in a normal structure

Using Table T7-3

Read down the height column in the table to 20'. Select 5' of lateral run from the second column in the table. Read across the table to the max. vent capacity for a natural draft appliance at or over 100,000 Btuh. This would be 116,000 Btuh for a 5" diameter type B vent connector that is connected to a tile-lined masonry chimney having an area between 28 sq. in and 137 sq in. Note: the DP vent capacity for this system is 104,000 Btuh

20'

5'

Type B Connector

100,000 Btuh Natural Draft Furnace with Drafthood

The following is the procedure in determining the required vent size of a combined or multiple appliance installation:

A. *Determine the size of each vent connector.*
   1. Determine the total vent height of the system;
   2. Determine the connector rise for each appliance;
   3. Using *Tables T7-5, T7-6, T7-7* and *T7-8* find the vent connector size for each appliance. Enter the table at the total vent height. Read across to the vent connector rise for the first appliance and continue across the proper vent connector rise row to the required vent Btuh capacity for the appliance. Read the vent connector size at the top of the column.
   4. Repeat step No. 3 for each appliance.

B. *Determining the size of the common vent.*
   1. Determine the combined Btuh capacity of all appliances for the multiple vent system.
   2. Enter the common vent table of *Tables T7-5, T7-6 T7-7* and *T7-8* at the total vent height used in part A.
   3. Continue across until the first value equals or exceeds the combined Btuh input rating of the appliances;
   4. Read the size of the common vent needed at the top of the column. It should be noted that the common vent must be as large as the largest connector, regardless of the result of the sizing from the tables. If two or more vent connectors are the same size, the common vent should be at least one size larger.

Examples 4 and 5 illustrate the sizing of multiple appliance installations. (See page 145.)

Table T7-5: Type B Vent Sizing

Capacity (in 1000 Btuh) of Type B Gas Vent With Double-Wall Vent Connectors Serving Two or More Appliances

Vent Connector Capacity

Height (H) ft.	V Con. Rise (R) ft.	3" Fan Assis Min	3" Fan Assis Max	3" Nat. Draft Max	3" Nat. Draft DP	4" Fan Assis Min	4" Fan Assis Max	4" Nat. Draft Max	4" Nat. Draft DP	5" Fan Assis Min	5" Fan Assis Max	5" Nat. Draft Max	5" Nat. Draft DP	6" Fan Assis Min	6" Fan Assis Max	6" Nat. Draft Max	6" Nat. Draft DP	7" Fan Assis Min	7" Fan Assis Max	7" Nat. Draft Max	7" Nat. Draft DP
10	1	22	43	28	22	34	78	50	39	49	123	78	61	65	189	113	88	89	257	154	120
	2	23	47	33	26	36	86	59	46	51	136	93	73	67	206	134	105	91	282	182	142
	3	24	50	37	29	37	92	67	52	52	146	104	81	69	220	150	117	94	303	205	160
15	1	21	50	30	26	33	89	53	45	47	142	83	71	64	220	120	102	88	298	163	139
	2	22	53	35	30	35	96	63	54	49	153	99	84	66	235	142	121	91	320	193	164
	3	24	55	40	34	36	102	71	60	51	163	111	94	68	248	160	136	93	339	218	185
20	1	21	54	31	28	33	99	56	50	46	157	87	78	62	246	125	113	86	334	171	154
	2	22	57	37	33	34	105	66	59	48	167	104	94	64	259	149	134	89	354	202	182
	3	23	60	42	38	35	110	74	67	50	176	116	104	66	271	168	151	91	371	228	205

Common Vent Capacity

Vent Height H ft.	4" Fan+Fan	4" Fan+Nat	4" Nat+Nat	4" DP(F+N)	4" DP(N+N)	5" Fan+Fan	5" Fan+Nat	5" Nat+Nat	5" DP(F+N)	5" DP(N+N)	6" Fan+Fan	6" Fan+Nat	6" Nat+Nat	6" DP(F+N)	6" DP(N+N)	7" Fan+Fan	7" Fan+Nat	7" Nat+Nat	7" DP(F+N)	7" DP(N+N)
10	110	97	76	79	62	169	141	124	110	97	243	194	178	151	139	367	299	233	242	189
15	125	112	95	91	77	195	164	144	139	122	283	228	206	194	175	427	352	299	280	238
20	136	123	111	102	92	215	183	160	165	144	314	255	229	230	206	475	394	355	310	279

Note:

DP-max. vent capacity for an appliance equipped with a draft hood that is located in a tight structure (sustaining depressurization of up to 5Pa or 0.02 "wc)

Nat. Draft- natural draft appliance (appliance equipped with a draft hood)

Fan Assist- fan assisted appliance (appliance equipped with an ID fan)

Min- minimum Btuh vent capacity

Max- maximum Btuh vent capacity

Fan+Fan- vent capacity for two or more fan assisted appliances

Fan+Nat- vent capacity for one or more fan assisted appliances & one or more natural draft appliances

Nat+Nat- vent capacity for two or more natural draft appliances

DP(F+N)-vent capacity for combined fan assisted and natural draft appliances when located in a tight structure (sustaining depressurization of up to 5 Pa)

DP(N+N)-vent capacity for two or more natural draft appliances located in a tight structure (sustaining depressurization of up to 5 Pa)

Capacity (in 1000 Btuh) of Type B Gas Vent With Single-Wall Vent Connectors Serving Two or More Appliances

Vent Connector Capacity

Height (H) ft.	V Con. Rise (R) ft.	3" Fan Assis Min	3" Fan Assis Max	3" Nat. Draft Max	3" Nat. Draft DP	4" Fan Assis Min	4" Fan Assis Max	4" Nat. Draft Max	4" Nat. Draft DP	5" Fan Assis Min	5" Fan Assis Max	5" Nat. Draft Max	5" Nat. Draft DP	6" Fan Assis Min	6" Fan Assis Max	6" Nat. Draft Max	6" Nat. Draft DP	7" Fan Assis Min	7" Fan Assis Max	7" Nat. Draft Max	7" Nat. Draft DP
6	1	NR	NR	26	16	NR	NR	46	28	NR	NR	71	43	NR	NR	102	62	207	223	140	85
	2	NR	NR	31	19	NR	NR	55	34	NR	85	85	52	168	182	123	75	215	251	167	102
	3	NR	NR	34	21	NR	NR	62	38	121	131	95	58	174	198	138	84	222	273	188	115
15	1	NR	NR	29	25	79	87	52	44	116	138	81	69	177	214	116	99	238	291	158	134
	2	NR	NR	34	29	83	94	62	53	121	150	97	82	185	230	138	117	246	314	189	161
	3	NR	NR	39	33	87	100	70	60	127	160	109	93	193	243	157	133	255	333	215	183
30	1	47	60	31	29	77	110	57	53	113	175	89	83	169	278	129	120	226	380	175	163
	2	50	62	37	34	81	115	67	62	117	185	106	99	177	290	152	141	236	397	208	193
	3	54	64	42	39	85	119	76	71	122	193	120	112	185	300	172	160	244	412	235	219

Common Vent Capacity

Vent Height H ft.	4" Fan +Fan	4" Fan +Nat	4" Nat +Nat	4" DP (N+N)	5" Fan +Fan	5" Fan +Nat	5" Nat +Nat	5" DP (N+N)	6" Fan +Fan	6" Fan +Nat	6" Nat +Nat	6" DP (N+N)	7" Fan +Fan	7" Fan +Nat	7" Nat +Nat	7" DP (N+N)
6	89	78	64	39	136	113	100	69	200	158	144	96	304	244	196	120
15	121	108	88	75	189	159	140	135	275	221	200	188	416	343	274	233
30	145	132	113	105	236	202	179	188	350	286	257	239	533	446	349	325

Note:

DP-max. vent capacity for an appliance equipped with a draft hood that is located in a tight structure (sustaining depressurization of up to 5Pa or 0.02 "wc)

Nat. Draft- natural draft appliance (appliance equipped with a draft hood)

Fan Assist- fan assisted appliance (appliance equipped with an ID fan)

Min- minimum Btuh vent capacity

Max- maximum Btuh vent capacity

Fan+Fan- vent capacity for two or more fan assisted appliances

Fan+Nat- vent capacity for one or more fan assisted appliances & one or more natural draft appliances

Nat+Nat- vent capacity for two or more natural draft appliances

DP(F+N)-vent capacity for combined fan assisted and natural draft appliances when located in a tight structure (sustaining depressurization of up to 5Pa or 0.02 "wc)

DP(N+N)-vent capacity for two or more natural draft appliances located in a tight structure (sustaining depressurization of up to 5 Pa)

NR- not recommended since condensation and/or pressurization of the venting system is a possibility

Table T7-6: Type B Vent Sizing

Table T7-7: Type A Vent Sizing

Capacity (in 1000 Btuh) of Masonry Chimney With Double-Wall Vent Connectors Serving Two or More Appliances

Vent Connector Capacity

Height (H) ft.	V Con. Rise (R) ft.	3" Fan Assist Min	3" Fan Assist Max	3" Nat. Draft Max.	3" Nat. Draft DP	4" Fan Assist Min	4" Fan Assist Max	4" Nat. Draft Max.	4" Nat. Draft DP	5" Fan Assist Min	5" Fan Assist Max	5" Nat. Draft Max.	5" Nat. Draft DP	6" Fan Assist Min	6" Fan Assist Max	6" Nat. Draft Max.	6" Nat. Draft DP
6	1	24	NR	21	13	39	62	40	24	52	106	67	41	65	194	101	62
	2	26	43	28	17	41	79	52	32	53	133	85	52	67	230	124	76
	3	27	49	34	21	42	92	61	37	55	155	97	59	69	262	143	87
15	1	24	48	23	20	38	93	44	37	54	154	74	63	72	277	144	97
	2	25	55	31	26	39	105	55	47	56	174	89	76	74	299	134	114
	3	26	59	35	30	41	115	64	54	57	189	102	87	76	319	153	130
30	1	24	54	25	23	37	111	48	45	52	192	82	76	69	357	127	118
	2	25	60	32	30	38	122	58	54	54	208	95	88	72	376	145	135
	3	26	64	36	33	40	131	66	61	56	221	107	100	74	392	163	152

Common Vent Capacity

Minimum Internal Chimney Area in Square Inches

Vent Height H ft.	12 Fan +Fan	12 Fan +Nat	12 DP (F+N)	12 Nat +Nat	12 DP (N+N)	19 Fan +Fan	19 Fan +Nat	19 DP (F+N)	19 Nat +Nat	19 DP (N+N)	28 Fan +Fan	28 Fan +Nat	28 DP (F+N)	28 Nat +Nat	28 DP (N+N)	38 Fan +Fan	38 Fan +Nat	38 DP (F+N)	38 Nat +Nat	38 DP (N+N)
6	NR	74	45	25	15	NR	119	73	46	28	NR	178	109	71	43	NR	257	157	103	63
15	NR	90	77	36	31	NR	152	129	67	57	NR	233	198	106	90	NR	334	284	152	129
30	NR	NR	NR	NR	NR	NR	NR	NR	NR	NR	NR	270	251	137	127	NR	404	376	198	184

Note:

DP-max. vent capacity for an appliance equipped with a draft hood that is located in a tight structure (sustaining depressurization of up to 5Pa or 0.02 "wc)

Nat. Draft- natural draft appliance (appliance equipped with a draft hood)

Fan Assist- fan assisted appliance (appliance equipped with an ID fan)

Min- minimum Btuh vent capacity

Max- maximum Btuh vent capacity

Fan+Fan- vent capacity for two or more fan assisted appliances

Fan+Nat- vent capacity for one or more fan assisted appliances & one or more natural draft appliances

Nat+Nat- vent capacity for two or more natural draft appliances

DP(F+N)-vent capacity for combined fan assisted and natural draft appliances when located in a tight structure (sustaining depressurization of

DP(N+N)-vent capacity for two or more natural draft appliances located in a tight structure (sustaining depressurization of up to 5 Pa)

NR- not recommended since condensation and/or pressurization of the venting system is a possibility

Capacity (in 1000 Btuh) of Tile-Lined Masonry Chimney With Single-Wall Vent Connectors Serving Two or More Appliance:

Vent Connector Capacity

Height (H) ft.	V Con. Rise (R) ft.	3" Fan Assist Min	3" Fan Assist Max	3" Nat. Draft Max	3" Nat. Draft DP	4" Fan Assist Min	4" Fan Assist Max	4" Nat. Draft Max	4" Nat. Draft DP	5" Fan Assist Min	5" Fan Assist Max	5" Nat. Draft Max	5" Nat. Draft DP	6" Fan Assist Min	6" Fan Assist Max	6" Nat. Draft Max	6" Nat. Draft DP
6	1	NR	NR	21	14	NR	NR	39	25	NR	NR	66	43	179	191	100	65
	2	NR	NR	28	18	NR	NR	52	34	NR	NR	84	55	186	227	123	80
	3	NR	NR	34	22	NR	NR	61	40	134	153	97	63	193	258	142	92
15	1	NR	NR	23	20	NR	NR	43	37	129	151	73	62	199	271	112	95
	2	NR	NR	30	26	92	103	54	46	135	170	88	75	207	295	132	112
	3	NR	NR	34	29	96	112	63	54	141	185	101	86	215	315	151	128
30	1	NR	NR	24	23	86	108	47	45	126	187	80	76	193	347	124	118
	2	NR	NR	31	29	91	119	57	54	132	203	93	88	201	366	142	135
	3	NR	NR	35	33	95	127	65	62	138	216	105	100	209	381	160	152

Common (Chimney) Capacity

Common Vent Equivalent Chimney Diameter (D)- Inches

Vent Height H ft	4" Fan(+Fan)	4" Fan(+Nat)	4" DP(F+N)	4" Nat(+Nat)	4" DP(N+N)	5" Fan(+Fan)	5" Fan(+Nat)	5" DP(F+N)	5" Nat(+Nat)	5" DP(N+N)	6" Fan(+Fan)	6" Fan(+Nat)	6" DP(F+N)	6" Nat(+Nat)	6" DP(N+N)	7" Fan(+Fan)	7" Fan(+Nat)	7" DP(F+N)	7" Nat(+Nat)	7" DP(N+N)
6	NR	73	44	25	15	NR	118	71	45	27	NR	176	106	71	43	NR	255	153	102	61
15	NR	88	75	36	31	NR	149	127	66	56	NR	230	196	105	89	NR	335	285	150	128
30	NR	NR	NR	NR	NR	NR	NR	NR	NR	NR	NR	266	247	135	126	NR	398	370	195	181

Note:

DP-max. vent capacity for an appliance equipped with a draft hood
   that is located in a tight structure (sustaining depressurization of up to 5Pa or 0.02 "wc)

Nat. Draft- natural draft appliance (appliance equipped with a draft hood)

Fan Assist- fan assisted appliance (appliance equipped with an ID fan)

Min- minimum Btuh vent capacity

Max- maximum Btuh vent capacity

Fan+Fan- vent capacity for two or more fan assisted appliances

Fan+Nat- vent capacity for one or more fan assisted appliances & one or more natural draft appliances

Nat+Nat- vent capacity for two or more natural draft appliances

DP(F+N)-vent capacity for combined fan assisted and natural draft appliances when located in a tight structure (sustaining depressurization of

DP(N+N)-vent capacity for two or more natural draft appliances located in a tight structure (sustaining depressurization of up to 5 Pa)

NR- not recommended since condensation and/or pressurization of the venting system is a possibility

Table T7-8: Type A Vent Sizing

Table T7-9: Masonry Chimney Liner Dimensions with Circular Equivalents

Masonry Chimney Liner Dimensions with Circular Equivalents

Nominal Liner Size Inches	Inside Dimensions of Liner in Inches	Inside Diameter or Equivalent Diameter	Equivalent Area Square Inches
4 X 8	2 1/2 X 6 1/2	4	12.2
		5	19.6
		6	28.3
		7	38.3
8 X 8	6 3/4 X 6 1/2	7.4	42.7
		8	50.3
8 X 12	6 1/2 X 10 1/2	9	63.6
		10	70.5
12 X 12	9 3/4 X 9 3/4	10.4	83.3
		11	95
12 X 16	9 1/2 X 13 1/2	11.8	107.5
		12	113
		14	153.9
16 X 16	13 1/4 X 13 1/4	14.5	162.9
		15	176.7
16 X 20	13 X 17	16.2	206.1
		18	254.4
20 X 20	16 3/4 X 16 3/4	18.2	260.2
		20	314.1
20 X 24	16 1/2 X 20 1/2	20.1	314.2
		22	380.1
24 X 24	20 1/4 X 20 1/4	22.1	380.1
		24	452.3
24 X 28	20 1/4 X 24 1/4	24.1	456.2
28 X 28	24 1/4 X 24 1/4	26.4	543.3
		27	572.5

Note: When liner sizes differ dimensionally from those shown in the above table, equival diameters may be determined from published tables for square and rectangular ducts of equivalent carrying capacity.

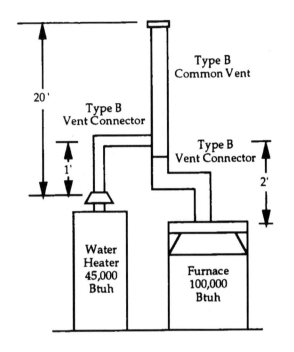

EXAMPLE # 4

Determine the required vent size for this multiple appliance installation in a normal structure

Using Table T7-5

Sizing Vent Connectors

Read down the height column in the vent connector capacity table to 20 ft. Select 1' vertical rise for the water heater. Read across the table to the max. vent capacity for the natural draft water heater at or over 45,000 Btuh. This would be 56,000 Btuh for a 4" diameter type B vent connector. Next; select the 2' vertical rise for the natural draft furnace and reading across the table find its max. vent capacity at or over 100,000 Btuh. This would be 104,000 Btuh for a 5" diameter type B vent connector

Sizing Common Vent

Select 20 ft. for vent height. Read across the table to the vent capacity for a Nat + Nat vent arrangement at or over 145,000 Btuh. This would be 160,000 Btuh for a 5' diameter type B common vent

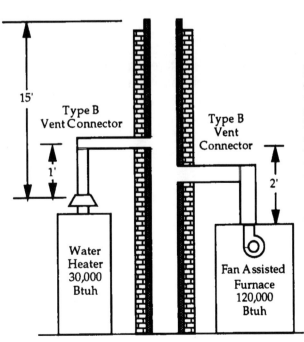

EXAMPLE # 5

Determine the required vent size for this multiple appliance installation in a normal structure

Using Table T7-7

Sizing Vent Connectors

Read down the height column in the vent connector capacity table to 15 ft. Select 1' vertical rise for the water heater. Read across the table to the max. vent capacity for the natural draft water heater at or over 30,000 Btuh. This would be 44,000 Btuh for a 4" diameter type B vent connector. Next; select the 2' vertical rise for the fan assisted furnace and reading across the table find its max. vent capacity at or over 120,000 Btuh. This would be 174,000 Btuh for a 5" diameter type B vent connector. Note: the min. vent capacity for the assisted furnace is 56,000 Btuh. Below this point condensation is a possibility

Sizing Common Vent

Select 15 ft. for vent height. Read across the table to the vent capacity for a Fan + Nat vent arrangement at or over 150,000 Btuh. This would be 152,000 Btuh for a chimney having a minimum internal area of 19 sq. in.

Venting Components

Figures 7-13 and *7-14* illustrate the different vent components that can be used in a vent system. The following is a brief comment on some of the components.

Round Vent Connector Pipe: Sections of vent connector pipe are usually locked together (screw or twist to lock).

Vent Tops (or Caps): These are designed to prevent blockage of the gas vent (e.g., bird's nest) as well as to prevent rain from entering the vent. Also, the design of the vent top or cap reduces the possibility of down-draft due to wind conditions.

Roof Flashings: These are fitted around the gas vent at the roof to prevent rain, etc., from entering around the vent.

Increaser (or Reducer): These are components used to change vent sizes usually from smaller to larger or vice versa.

Storm Collar: This is an additional flashing added to the main flashing to keep out snow or rain.

Support Assembly (Starter): This will position the vent properly within the venting system allowing for adequate clearance between the vent and the surrounding combustible material.

Fire Stop Spacer: This must be installed at each floor or ceiling level.

Base Tee: This is the fitting that facilitates the connection of the appliance vent connector to the common vent.

Figure 7-13: Vent fittings and components.

ROUND VENT CONNECTOR PIPE

TEE

DRAFT HOOD CONNECTOR

90° ADJUSTABLE ELBOW

45° ADJUSTABLE ELBOW

INCREASER

TEE CAP

SUPPORT ASSEMBLY (STARTING)

FIRE STOP SPACER

VENT TOP (CAP)

ROOF FLASHING

STORM COLLAR

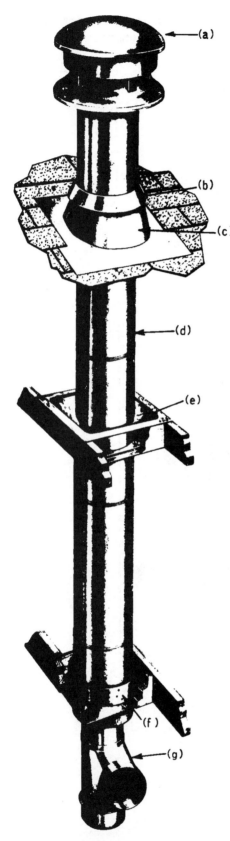

A VENT TOP (CAP)

B STORM COLLAR

C ROOF FLASHING

D ROUND VENT CONNECTOR PIPE

E FIRE STOP SPACER

F SUPPORT / STARTING / ASSEMBLY

G BASE TEE

Figure 7-14: Components of a venting system assembled as a complete vent.

Assignment

1. Define the following appliances:

   a) Category I

   b) Category II

   c) Category III

   d) Category IV

2. Briefly describe the method of venting for each appliance in Question #1.

3. State the correct venting practice for the following:

   a) Manually operated dampers

   b) Termination of a:

   i) Masonry chimney
   ii) 8 inch diameter Type B vent located on a flat roof
   iii) 4 inch diameter Type B vent located on a sloped roof having a pitch of 12/12

   c) When venting a gas water heater into a chimney used for venting an oil fired furnace

   d) Venting gas appliances into a common vent:

   i) In which the appliances are of equal input
   ii) In which the appliances are of unequal input

   e) Application of mechanical exhaust

   f) Automatic vent dampers

   g) Chimney connection

4. Of the three systems illustrated in Figure 7-15, which one would be the preferred venting practice? Why? What is wrong with the other two?

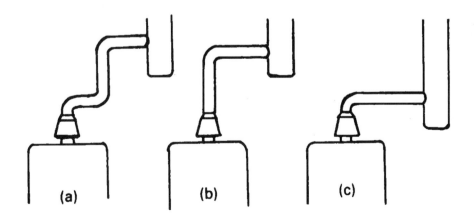

(a) (b) (c)

Figure 7-15: Assignment — Question #4

5. Size the venting system illustrated in Figure 7-16.
   Note: The following is the required data to size each of the installations shown in Figure 7-16.

   a) type B gas vent with double wall vent connectors
      - natural draft appliance Btuh input is 120,000 Btuh
      - vent height is 20'
      - lateral run of vent connector is 10'

   b) tile-lined masonry chimney with single-wall vent connectors
      - natural draft appliance Btuh input is 60,000 Btuh
      - vent height is 20'
      - lateral run of vent connector is 2'

   c) type B gas vent with double wall vent connectors
      - both appliances are natural draft appliances located in a building having normal construction
      - vent height is 15'
      - appliance A input is 40,000   Btuh, its vertical rise is 1'
      - appliance B input is 90,000 Btuh, its vertical rise is 3'

   d) masonry chimney with double-wall vent connectors both appliances are natural draft appliances located in a building having normal construction
      - vent height is 30'
      - appliance A input is 60,000 Btuh, its vertical rise is 1'
      - appliance B input is 120,000 Btuh, its vertical rise is 2'

6. Size the following venting systems.

   a) type B gas vent with double wall vent connectors
      - fan assisted appliance having a Btuh input of 120,000 Btuh
      - vent height is 20'
      - lateral run of vent connector is 10'

   b) type B gas vent with double wall vent connectors
      - both located in a building having normal construction
      - vent height is 15'
      - appliance A input is 40,0000 Btuh, its vertical rise is 1'
      - appliance B input is 90,000 Btuh, its vertical rise is 3'
      - appliance A is a natural draft appliance
      - appliance B is a fan assisted appliance

Figure 7-16: Assignment — Question #5.

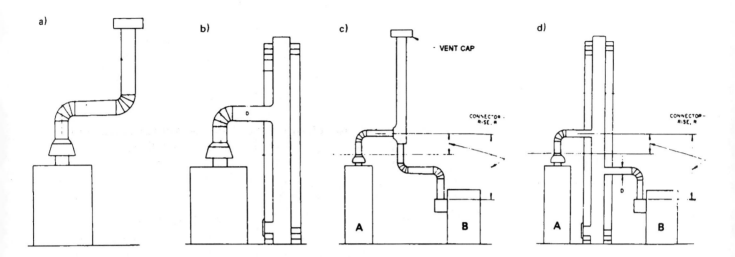

a)   b)   c)   d)

VENT CAP

CONNECTOR-
RISE, R

CONNECTOR-
RISE, R

A   B

A   B

D

8   The Atmospheric Burner

The atmospheric burner can be defined as a burner or combustion system which utilizes the energy in a gas stream to induce air at atmospheric pressure to be mixed with gas. This *partial mixture* of air and gas prior to the combustion process creates a stable and clean blue flame that is called a *bunsen* or *blue flame*.

The Operation of the Atmospheric Burner

Figure 8-1 is an illustration showing the operating components of the atmospheric burner. Using *Figure 8-1*, we can describe the operation of the atmospheric burner as follows:

1. Gas, under a manifold pressure (i.e., 3.5"wc or .87 kPa standard manifold pressure) flows up to the gas orifice of the burner.

2. As the gas flows through the orifice in the form of a gas stream or jet, it picks up velocity at the expense of its manifold pressure.

3. A suction area is created at the throat of the burner due to the gas stream picking up velocity. This suction area at the throat of the burner induces outside air, at atmospheric conditions, through the primary air shutter of the mixer head.

4. This induced air, called *primary air*, is mixed with the gas stream issuing from the gas orifice at the throat in the mixer head of the burner. The gas and air continue to be mixed down the mixing tube of the burner.

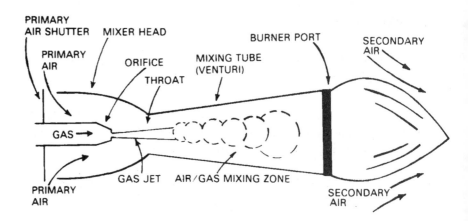

Figure 8-1: Operating components of the atmospheric burner.

5. The mixing tube of the burner is of a *venturi* design in which the cross-sectional area of the tube becomes progressively larger as the gas and air mixture approaches the burner port(s). As a result, the velocity of the mixture is reduced and the pressure of the mixture is increased. This increase in mixture pressure is called *static regain* and is required to give the mixture enough head pressure to burn at the burner port(s).

6. Combustion takes place at the burner port(s) as the partially premixed mixture of gas and air is ignited at the burner port(s). *Secondary air* via the secondary air opening surrounds the flame and completes the combustion process.

Depending upon the burner design, approximately 30–50% of the total air required for combustion is primary air. This necessitates a supply of secondary air to envelop the combustion process in order to complete it.

The primary air shutter will be set to give the correct amount of primary air to be mixed with the gas at the required Btuh or kW rating of the burner. Once this setting on the air shutter has been established, giving the desired *flame characteristics* for the Btuh rating of the burner, then any reduction of burner input will not affect the air/gas ratio and the flame characteristics. This is a result of the direct relationship between the amount of primary air and the amount of suction created at the burner throat. If the gas pressure decreases (giving less gas to the burner), the velocity of the gas stream through the gas orifice is less, creating a lower suction at the throat area which induces a smaller amount of primary air. Therefore, once set, the air/gas ratio is maintained throughout the *turndown range* of the burner.

Figure 8-2 illustrates the primary air shutter of the mixer head of the burner. *Figure 8-3* is a photograph of a typical forced warm air furnace in which the primary air shutters have been adjusted to give the correct flame characteristics. *Note:* The air shutters are of the modified butterfly type.

Terminology

The following terms are used in the description of the operation of the atmospheric burner.

Partial Premixing: This is a combustion system in which some of the air required for the combustion process is partially premixed with the fuel prior to the combustion process.

Bunsen Flame: This is a blue flame as a result of some premixing of air and fuel which takes place prior to the combustion process.

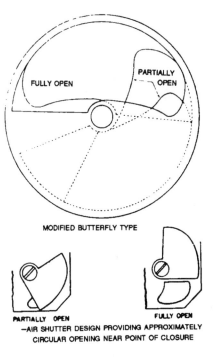

Figure 8-2: **The primary air shutter.**

Figure 8-3: Primary air shutters adjusted on a typical forced warm air furnace to give the correct flame characteristics.

Primary Air: This is the air that is premixed with the fuel prior to the combustion process. Approximately 30–50% of the total air required is primary air. It is the primary air that establishes the flame characteristics.

Secondary Air: This is the air that is mixed with the fuel at the point of combustion and which surrounds the flame to ensure the complete combustion of the fuel. Approximately 50–70% of the total air required is secondary air.

Flame Characteristics: The flame characteristics are the color, shape and intensity of the flame. A *lean* or *oxidizing* flame, sometimes referred to as a hard flame, is one that has too much air and insufficient fuel. It is a small, very sharp intense blue flame. A *rich* or *carbonizing* flame, sometimes referred to as a *reducing* or *luminous* flame, is one in which there is too much fuel and not enough air. It is a soft, rather large floating yellowish flame.

The *perfect* flame or *neutral* flame is one which has sufficient intensity to give flame stability. Its color is blue, however, it is not a brilliant blue or as intense as the lean or hard flame.[1]

The primary air shutter setting controls the amount of primary air which determines the flame characteristics achieved by the burner. Once the flame characteristics have been set, they remain constant throughout the *turndown range* of the burner (the maximum and minimum firing rate of the burner).

---

[1] There may be a slight orange or red tint in a normal flame usually in the form of streaks. This is caused by dust particles in the air and cannot be eliminated. It does not denote any sign of insufficient air supply.

Limitations of the Atmospheric Burner: The atmospheric burner has a range of operation through which flame stability is achieved. Flame stability is the ability of the flame to stay or be retained on the burner port(s).

Flame lifting and *flashback* are operating limits that are imposed on the burner. *Figure 8-4* illustrates the opposing velocities of the air/gas mixture and flame front in which flame stability occurs when they are equal. Flashback takes place when the flame front velocity exceeds that of the mixture velocity and flame lifting occurs when the opposite takes place.

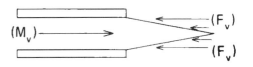

Figure 8-4: Flame stability occurring when the air/gas mixture velocity (M_V) equals the flame front velocity (F_V).

The limitations placed on an atmospheric burner due to flame stability can be defined as the turndown ratio of the burner. Turndown ratio is:

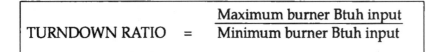

$$\text{TURNDOWN RATIO} \quad = \quad \frac{\text{Maximum burner Btuh input}}{\text{Minimum burner Btuh input}}$$

If the maximum Btuh input is exceeded, then flame lifting will occur, and if the gas burner Btuh or kW input is reduced below its minimum, then the flame is *quenched* on the burner port(s), or depending upon the conditions, flame flashback will be experienced.

Turndown ratio is important since the controlability of the gas heating unit is increased, given a burner with a substantial turndown ratio. *Figure 8-5* illustrates the performance characteristics of an atmospheric gas burner with respect to flame stability, flame lifting, yellow tipping and flashback.

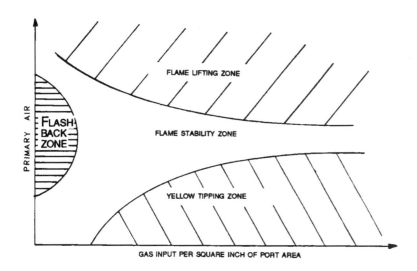

(Burner Port Loading)

Figure 8-5: Burner performance characteristics.

Flame Lifting: The atmospheric burner flame, having reasonable air supply, should be stable and quiet. However, if too much primary air is used or the burner port loading is too high, the burner flame will have a tendency to lift and blow off the burner port(s) as illustrated in *Figure 8-6*.

Figure 8-6: Flame lifting.

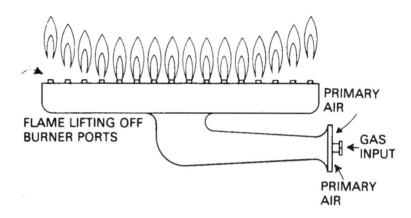

PRIMARY AIR

FLAME LIFTING OFF BURNER PORTS

GAS INPUT

PRIMARY AIR

Under the condition of flame lifting, the flame can be noisy. Also, the flame cone may break apart so that complete combustion is not achieved. Carbon monoxide and aldehydes can be formed by a lifting or blowing flame and the overall efficiency of the appliance is reduced.

The burning velocity of a gas is highest with about 100% primary air mixture. However, with a slower burning fuel gas, such as natural gas, a gain in burning velocity, associated with a higher primary air supply, is offset by a higher flow or air/gas mixture velocity through the burner ports due to the increase of primary air supply. The lifting flame will usually settle down on the burner port(s) if the primary air is reduced.

Higher burner port loading, usually caused by *over-rating* of the burner, will also develop high flow or air/gas mixture velocities through the burner port(s). This too will result in flame lifting.

Flashback: Under some conditions, the air/gas mixture or flow velocity is less than the burning velocity at the burner port(s). When this happens, the flame tends to strike back through the burner port(s) to ignite the mixture inside the burner port(s) and mixing tube, creating what is called flashback.

However, a properly designed and adjusted burner will not give flashback during normal burner operations. Yet, under certain conditions flashback can be created. With reference to *Figure 8-5*, a burner set with a high amount of primary air and low burner port loading can be subject to a flashback condition. The increase in primary air will result in a higher burning speed, and a decrease in burner port loading will create a lower flow or air/gas mixture velocity. The net result is a condition in which the burning velocity is greater than the air/gas mixture velocity, creating a flashback condition.

Flashback as *extinction pop* may happen when the gas burner is turned off. Even though the gas jet is cut off and does not induce air, primary air may still flow into the burner. The mixture in the burner changes from the normal operating air/gas mixture to one of all air. The flow rate through the burner port(s) is decreased to zero. In this condition it is possible for the burning speed or velocity to be greater than the flow or air/gas mixture velocity and flashback may occur as a tiny explosion or pop. Extinction pop does not present a hazard, however it can be annoying.

Yellow Tipping: *Figure 8-7* illustrates the relationship between flame characteristics and primary air. When proper amounts of primary air are provided to a burner, a normal (hard) blue flame with definable inner and outer flame cones is a result. As the primary air is reduced, the inner cone of the flame is lengthened. Eventually the inner cone disappears as the primary air is further reduced and *yellow tips* appear in the flame. If no primary air is supplied the flame will become all yellow.

The yellow tips are caused by glowing carbon particles in the flame, hence the term *luminous* flame. Also, if the flame is impinged on a cool surface chilling the combustion reaction, sooting and carbon monoxide will be formed.

Burner Design and Port Construction

The design of an atmospheric burner, as well as other types of burner systems, must have the following required characteristics:

1. Complete combustion of the gas.

2. Rapid ignition and carry over of the flame across the entire burner. *Delayed ignition* as caused by improper or poor flame travel to the main burner, or by poor flame distribution over the burner ports should not be experienced.

3. Reasonable quiet operation during ignition, burning and extinction. There should be no noise associated with the ignition of the main flame—that is, a light explosion, or puff caused by delayed ignition. Also, there should be no flame noise (i.e., *flame roar*) during the burning period caused by excessive aeration of the burner flame.

4. No excessive lifting of the flame from the burner port(s).

5. Uniform heat spread over the entire area to be heated. Note the application of the *flame target* and *flame spreader* in *Figures 8-8 and 8-9.*

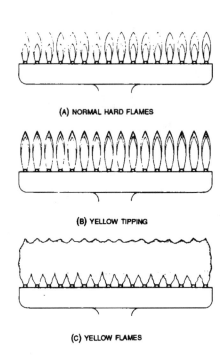

(A) NORMAL HARD FLAMES

(B) YELLOW TIPPING

(C) YELLOW FLAMES

Figure 8-7: The relationship between primary air supply and flame characteristics

6. A reasonable turndown ratio without flashback or flame lifting.

7. Well constructed to provide a long service life. In the past most burners were made from cast iron. Today, most burners are made from heat resistant sheet metal or stamped steel.

The atmospheric burner design and construction is characterized by the burner port design. The following are the types of atmospheric burners used in the field today:

Mono Port

For mono or single port burners the burner outlet is simply an extension of the burner's mixing tube. As the flame leaves the burner outlet, it is directed towards a metal plate or baffle that spreads the burner flame to achieve a uniform heat spread over the appliance heating surface.

Mono or single port atmospheric burners are mainly used as *conversion burners* in which a solid or liquid fuel appliance is converted to natural gas. There are basically two types of mono port burners:

a) inshot — see Figure 8-8
b) upshot — see Figure 8-9

Figure 8-8: Mono port atmospheric inshot conversion burner. Note the flame target and runner pilot that facilitates pilot lighting once burner is installed in a converted furnace or boiler.

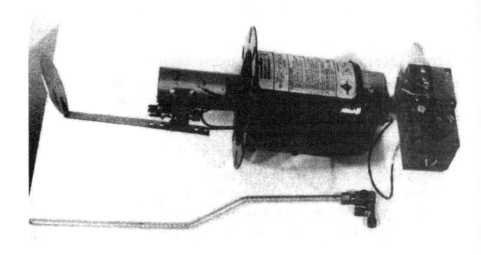

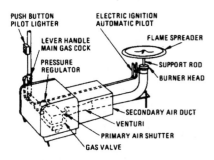

Figure 8-9: Upshot mono port atmospheric conversion burner. Note the push button (Piezo crystal) pilot lighter that when pushed in will generate a spark to light the pilot.

Multiple Port

Multiple burners are equipped with a *burner head* which is the top part of the burner containing the burner ports *(see Figure 8-6)*. The burner port construction located on the burner head determines the type of burner design. The following are the various types of multiple port burners:

a) Drilled Port: made of cast iron with a series of small drilled holes *(see Figure 8-10)*. Note that the ports can be raised as illustrated in *Figure 8-11*, in which case the burner is called a *raised drilled port burner*.

b) Slotted Port: burner head is equipped with elongated slots either running across the burner head (i.e., slotted port cast iron) or along the full length of the burner head (i.e., slotted port sheet metal) — *see Figure 8-10*.

c) Ribbon Port: has a continuous opening down each side of the burner head creating the appearance of a ribbon. The ribbon is usually corrugated stainless steel.

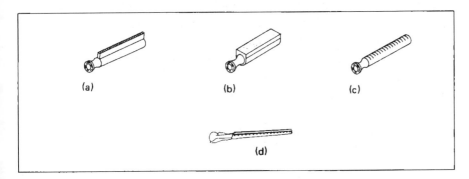
(a)   (b)   (c)

(d)

Figure 8-10: Multiple port burners:
a) ribbon port;
b) drilled port;
c) slotted port cast iron;
d) slotted port sheet metal.

The Atmospheric Burner Assembly

The gas appliance is equipped with a burner assembly when it is fired by more than one burner. Each individual burner is supplied by a common manifold. The manifold and the burners being fed from it is called a *burner assembly* or *burner tray*.

As illustrated by *Figure 8-11*, the atmospheric burner assembly consists of the following:

1. The gas control valve.

2. Gas pilot tubing.

3. Pressure tap plug allowing the measurement of manifold pressure.

4. Pilot tube fittings.

5. Locking screws for primary air shutter.

6. Burner (assembly) manifold.

7. Orifice spud.

8. a) Individual burners (in this instance raised drilled port burners).
   b) Primary air shutters.

9. Pilot burner equipped with a flame sensing device (i.e., thermocouple or thermopile).

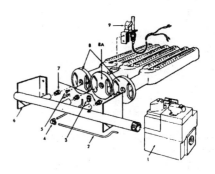

Figure 8-11: Typical atmospheric burner assembly

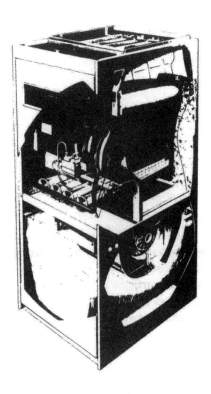

Figure 8-12: Typical atmospheric burner assembly used on a typical forced air furnace.

As a unit, the burner assembly is mounted in the combustion chamber of the appliance *(see Figure 8-12)* and can be easily removed as a complete assembly for appliance cleaning and inspection *(see Figure 8-13)*.

Burner assemblies that utilize slotted port burners are usually equipped with *cross over igniters* that are attached to each burner *(see Figure 8-14)*. This allows one pilot to ignite several burners by having the cross over igniters bridging the ignition flame from burner to burner. However, it is extremely important that the cross over igniters are in alignment and that their slotted ports are free from dirt or scaling. This will ensure against delay ignition upon burner start up which will be caused by the sudden ignition of pockets of raw gas that have accumulated in the combustion chamber of the appliance.

The Burner Orifice

The gas burner orifice serves two functions:

1. Meters the gas flow rate through the burner giving a set Btuh or kW input rate to the gas appliance. The orifice must be the correct size. If the orifice is too large, the burner cannot handle the required input resulting in improper combustion. If the orifice is too small, then the appliance will operate at a reduced Btuh or kW input rate.

2. Directs the gas flow down the centre line of the burner mixing tube ensuring maximum gas jet velocity and inspiration of primary air. A misaligned orifice will create poor flame characteristics due to inadequate primary air supply.

Types of Orifices:

There are three main types of gas orifices:
> Fixed
> Adjustable
> Cap (or universal)

Fixed Orifice
Fixed orifices are the most common of the three types of orifices. As illustrated in *Figure 8-16(a)* they are simply a drilled opening in a brass orifice spud. The brass orifice spud is supplied with a male thread allowing it to be screwed into the manifold of the burner assembly. *See Figure 8-11.*

The fixed orifice is characterized by a set angle of approach which varies with the interior design of the orifice as illustrated in *Figure 8-16(a)*. Also, the interior V-shape of the orifice spud provides a means for centering insuring that the orifice will be drilled straight and in the exact centre of the spud.

Figure 8-13: Atmospheric burner assembly removed from a hot water boiler (note the runner pilot to facilitate pilot lighting).

When cleaning this or any other type of orifice, a soft instrument such as a broom straw, wire brush bristle, etc., should be used in order not to damage the shape or size of the orifice.

Adjustable Orifice

Adjustable orifices, as illustrated in *Figure 8-16(b)*, are used on gas ranges and industrial burners. *(See Figure 8-15.)* The needle inside the orifice spud is adjustable to increase or decrease the effective opening of the orifice. The gas flow rate can be altered from zero, having the needle tight against the orifice wall, or to the full rate with the needle backed away from the orifice wall.

Cap or Universal Orifice

Cap or universal orifices are used mainly on dual fuel appliances (i.e., natural gas/propane gas) in which only a slight adjustment is needed to burn either fuel.

As illustrated in *Figure 8-16(c)*, the needle has an orifice drilled through it and is sized for propane operation. For propane operation the orifice hood is screwed in until the needle point blocks off the orifice in the hood. For natural gas operation the orifice hood is screwed away from the needle. This allows the gas to flow through both the fixed orifice in the needle and around the opening between the shoulder and the edge of the orifice in the hood. With this arrangement, the propane has a fixed rate whereas the natural gas rate is adjustable. To adjust for varying propane flow rates, the orifice through the needle has to be changed.

Orifice Sizing

The gas orifice size determines the flow rate or rated input of the burner in cfh (m³/h) or Btuh (kW) (e.g., cfh X 1000 = Btuh rated input). The orifice size can be determined by either a formula or by orifice capacity tables.

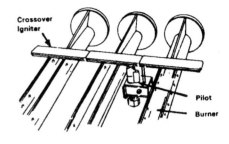

Figure 8-14: Atmospheric burner assembly consisting of slotted port burners equipped with cross over igniters.

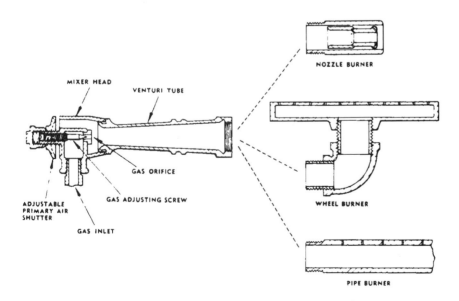

Figure 8-15: Typical industrial atmospheric burner.

Figure 8-16a: Gas Orifices
(a) Fixed orifices illustrating the various angles of approach inside the fixed orifice spud.

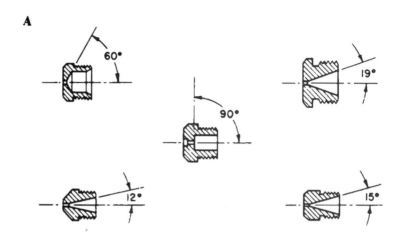

Figure 8-16b:
(b) Adjustable orifices.

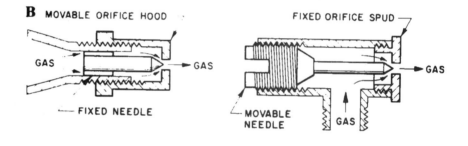

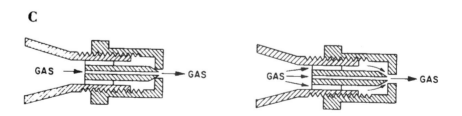

Figure 8-16c:
(c) Universal or cap orifices.

162

Orifice Sizing Formula

The following is an orifice sizing formula that determines the required size for an orifice for low pressure gas application (for gas pressure below 1/2 psig or 3.5 kPa).

$$Q = 1660 \; K.A. \sqrt{\frac{P}{S.g.}}$$

Where :
Q = the gas flow rate in cfh
K = Co-efficient of discharge, a function of orifice design, (i.e., angle of approach) usually a constant at 0.90 for domestic gas burners
P = Pressure drop across the orifice in "wc (i.e., the manifold pressure of the burner)
S.g. = the specific gravity of the gas (0.6)
A = Area of the orifice in square inches

The above formula illustrates the relationship between the gas flow through the orifice and the pressure drop across the orifice, the area of the orifice and the specific gravity of the gas. Taking each separately we have:

1. The flow of the gas through the orifice varies depending on the available gas pressure. If the gas pressure is increased, the flow through the orifice is increased. Specifically, the flow of the gas through the orifice varies directly to the square root of the pressure drop across the orifice.

$$Q \propto \sqrt{P}$$

Doubling the available manifold pressure would not double the flow rate through the orifice. If the flow rate is to be doubled, then the pressure drop across the orifice must be four times the original drop to achieve a doubling of the gas flow rate. (Note: $\sqrt{4} = 2$.)

2. The flow of the gas through the orifice varies depending on the size of the orifice. If the orifice size was increased, the flow through the orifice is increased. Specifically, the flow of the gas through the orifice varied directly to the area of the orifice.

$$Q \propto A$$

By doubling the orifice size, the flow rate through the orifice would be doubled.

3. The flow of the gas through the orifice varies depending on the specific gravity of the gas. For heavier fuel gases having a higher specific gravity, such as propane, less gas would flow through the orifice. Specifically, the flow of the gas through the orifice varies inversely to the square root of the specific gravity of the gas.

$$Q \propto \sqrt{\frac{1}{S.g.}}$$

This factor is important in fuel conversion such as propane to natural gas conversion.

Orifice Capacity Table

In actual application gas orifices are sized by using orifice capacity tables which are based on the orifice size formula. *Table T8-1* is such a table for natural gas having a specific gravity of 0.60 with the orifice having a 0.90 co-efficient discharge.

Gas orifices are designated according to D.M.S. *drill numbers* in which the actual area of the orifice corresponds to the area created by the D.M.S. drill. D.M.S. stands for *Drill Manufacturer's Standard* which is equivalent to standard twist drills or steel gauge numbers. *Figure 8-17* is an illustration of a set of D.M.S. drills known in the trade as *thumb drills*.

The orifice capacity *Table T8-1* ranges from a No. 80 drill size to No. 1 drill size. Beyond No. 1 drill size, letters are used to denote larger diameter drill sizes.

Table T8-1: Orifice Sizing Table for Natural Gas Having 0.60 Specific Gravity

Orifice Size (Decimal or DMS)	Gas Pressure at Orifice - Inches Water Column								
	3	3.5	4	5	6	7	8	9	10
.008	.17	.18	.19	.23	.24	.26	.28	.29	.30
.009	.21	.23	.25	.28	.30	.33	.35	.37	.39
.010	.27	.29	.30	.35	.37	.41	.43	.46	.48
.011	.33	.35	.37	.42	.45	.48	.52	.55	.59
.012	.38	.41	.44	.50	.54	.57	.62	.65	.70
80	.48	.52	.55	.63	.69	.73	.79	.83	.88
79	.55	.59	.64	.72	.80	.84	.90	.97	1.01
78	.70	.76	.78	.88	.97	1.04	1.10	1.17	1.24
77	.88	.95	.99	1.11	1.23	1.31	1.38	1.47	1.55
76	1.05	1.13	1.21	1.37	1.52	1.61	1.72	1.83	1.92
75	1.16	1.25	1.34	1.52	1.64	1.79	1.91	2.04	2.14
74	1.33	1.44	1.55	1.74	1.91	2.05	2.18	2.32	2.44
73	1.51	1.63	1.76	1.99	2.17	2.32	2.48	2.64	2.78
72	1.64	1.77	1.90	2.15	2.40	2.52	2.69	2.86	3.00
71	1.82	1.97	2.06	2.33	2.54	2.73	2.91	3.11	3.26
70	2.06	2.22	2.39	2.70	2.97	3.16	3.38	3.59	3.78
69	2.25	2.43	2.61	2.96	3.23	3.47	3.68	3.94	4.14
68	2.52	2.72	2.93	3.26	3.58	3.88	4.14	4.41	4.64
67	2.69	2.91	3.12	3.52	3.87	4.13	4.41	4.69	4.94
66	2.86	3.09	3.32	3.75	4.11	4.39	4.68	4.98	5.24
65	3.14	3.39	3.72	4.28	4.62	4.84	5.16	5.50	5.78
64	3.41	3.68	4.14	4.48	4.91	5.23	5.59	5.95	6.26
63	3.63	3.92	4.19	4.75	5.19	5.55	5.92	6.30	6.63
62	3.78	4.08	4.39	4.96	5.42	5.81	6.20	6.59	6.94
61	4.02	4.34	4.66	5.27	5.77	6.15	6.57	7.00	7.37
60	4.21	4.55	4.89	5.52	5.95	6.47	6.91	7.35	7.74
59	4.41	4.76	5.11	5.78	6.35	6.78	7.25	7.71	8.11
58	4.66	5.03	5.39	6.10	6.68	7.13	7.62	8.11	8.53
57	4.84	5.23	5.63	6.36	6.96	7.44	7.94	8.46	8.90
56	5.68	6.13	6.58	7.35	8.03	8.73	9.32	9.92	10.44
55	7.11	7.68	8.22	9.30	10.18	10.85	11.59	12.34	12.98
54	7.95	8.59	9.23	10.45	11.39	12.25	13.08	13.93	14.65
53	9.30	10.04	10.80	12.20	13.32	14.29	15.27	16.25	17.05
52	10.61	11.46	12.31	13.86	15.26	16.34	17.44	18.57	19.53
51	11.82	12.77	13.69	15.47	16.97	18.16	19.40	20.64	21.71
50	12.89	13.92	14.94	16.86	18.48	19.77	21.12	22.48	23.65

Orifice Size (Decimal or DMS)	3	3.5	4	5	6	7	8	9	10
49	14.07	15.20	16.28	18.37	20.20	21.60	23.06	24.56	25.83
48	15.15	16.36	17.62	19.88	21.81	23.31	24.90	26.51	27.89
47	16.22	17.52	18.80	21.27	23.21	24.93	26.62	28.34	29.81
46	17.19	18.57	19.98	22.57	24.72	26.43	28.23	30.05	31.61
45	17.73	19.15	20.52	23.10	25.36	27.18	29.03	30.90	32.51
44	19.45	21.01	22.57	25.57	27.93	29.87	31.89	33.96	35.72
43	20.73	22.39	24.18	27.29	29.87	32.02	34.19	36.41	38.30
42	23.10	24.95	26.50	29.50	32.50	35.24	37.63	40.07	42.14
41	24.06	25.98	28.15	31.69	34.81	37.17	39.70	42.27	44.46
40	25.03	27.03	29.23	33.09	36.20	38.79	41.42	44.10	46.38
39	26.11	28.20	30.20	34.05	37.38	39.97	42.68	45.44	47.80
38	27.08	29.25	31.38	35.46	38.89	41.58	44.40	47.27	49.73
37	28.36	30.63	32.99	37.07	40.83	43.62	46.59	49.60	52.17

Orifice Size (Decimal or DMS)	3	3.5	4	5	6	7	8	9	10
36	29.76	32.14	34.59	39.11	42.76	45.77	48.88	52.04	54.74
35	32.36	34.95	36.86	41.68	45.66	48.78	52.10	55.46	58.34
34	32.45	35.05	37.50	42.44	46.52	49.75	53.12	56.55	59.49
33	33.41	36.08	38.79	43.83	48.03	51.46	54.96	58.62	61.55
32	35.46	38.30	40.94	46.52	50.82	54.26	57.95	61.70	64.89
31	37.82	40.85	43.83	49.64	54.36	58.01	61.96	65.97	69.39
30	43.40	46.87	50.39	57.05	62.09	66.72	71.22	75.86	79.80
29	48.45	52.33	56.19	63.61	69.62	74.45	79.52	84.66	89.04
28	51.78	55.92	59.50	67.00	73.50	79.50	84.92	90.39	95.09
27	54.47	58.83	63.17	71.55	78.32	83.59	89.27	95.04	99.97
26	56.73	61.27	65.86	74.57	81.65	87.24	93.17	99.19	104.57
25	58.87	63.58	68.22	77.14	84.67	90.36	96.50	102.74	108.07
24	60.81	65.67	70.58	79.83	87.56	93.47	99.83	106.28	111.79
23	62.10	67.07	72.20	81.65	89.39	94.55	100.98	107.49	113.07
22	64.89	70.08	75.21	85.10	93.35	99.60	106.39	113.24	119.12
21	66.51	71.83	77.14	87.35	95.63	102.29	109.24	116.29	122.33
20	68.22	73.68	79.08	89.49	97.99	104.75	111.87	119.10	125.28
19	72.20	77.98	83.69	94.76	103.89	110.67	118.55	125.82	132.36
18	75.53	81.57	87.56	97.50	108.52	116.03	123.92	131.93	138.78
17	78.54	84.82	91.10	103.14	112.81	120.33	128.52	136.82	143.91
16	82.19	88.77	95.40	107.98	118.18	126.78	135.39	144.15	151.63
15	85.20	92.02	98.84	111.74	122.48	131.07	139.98	149.03	156.77
14	87.10	94.40	100.78	114.21	124.44	133.22	142.28	151.47	159.33
13	89.92	97.11	104.32	118.18	128.93	138.60	148.00	157.58	165.76
12	93.90	101.41	108.52	123.56	135.37	143.97	153.75	163.69	172.13
11	95.94	103.62	111.31	126.02	137.52	147.20	157.20	167.36	176.03
10	98.30	106.16	114.21	129.25	141.82	151.50	161.81	172.26	181.13
9	100.99	109.07	117.11	132.58	145.05	154.71	165.23	175.91	185.03
8	103.89	112.20	120.65	136.44	149.33	160.08	170.96	182.00	191.44
7	105.93	114.40	123.01	139.23	152.56	163.31	174.38	185.68	195.30
6	109.15	117.88	126.78	142.88	156.83	167.51	178.88	190.46	200.36
5	111.08	119.97	128.93	145.79	160.08	170.82	182.48	194.22	204.30
4	114.75	123.93	133.22	150.41	164.36	176.18	188.16	200.25	210.71
3	119.25	128.79	137.52	156.26	170.78	182.64	195.08	207.66	218.44
2	128.48	138.76	148.61	168.64	184.79	197.66	211.05	224.74	235.58
1	136.35	147.26	158.25	179.33	194.63	209.48	223.65	238.16	250.54
A	145.34	155.48	165.62	189.28	206.18	219.70	236.60	250.12	263.63
B	150.36	160.85	171.33	195.81	213.29	227.25	244.76	258.74	272.73
C	155.45	166.30	177.14	202.44	220.52	234.98	253.06	267.51	281.97
D	160.63	171.84	183.04	209.19	227.87	242.81	261.46	276.44	291.38
E	165.89	177.47	189.05	216.05	235.34	250.77	270.06	285.49	300.93
F	175.43	187.61	199.78	227.75	248.70	265.02	285.40	301.70	318.02
G	180.81	193.43	206.04	235.49	256.50	273.33	294.35	311.18	327.99
H	187.81	200.91	214.01	244.59	266.42	283.89	305.74	323.20	340.67
I	196.38	210.08	223.77	255.75	278.58	296.85	319.68	337.95	356.20
J	203.66	217.87	232.08	265.24	288.92	307.87	331.55	350.49	396.44
K	209.59	224.22	238.84	272.95	297.33	316.82	341.19	360.69	380.18
L	223.23	240.49	257.75	290.71	316.68	337.44	363.40	384.17	404.92
M	231.00	247.12	263.23	300.83	327.69	349.18	376.03	397.52	419.01
N	242.09	258.98	275.06	315.27	343.42	365.94	394.09	416.61	439.13
O	265.05	283.54	302.03	345.18	376.00	400.66	431.47	456.13	480.79
P	276.92	296.24	315.56	360.64	392.84	418.60	450.80	476.56	502.32
Q	292.57	312.98	333.39	381.03	415.05	442.26	476.28	503.49	530.71
R	305.03	326.33	347.62	397.26	432.73	461.10	496.59	524.95	553.32
S	321.45	344.01	366.57	418.62	456.01	485.91	523.28	553.19	583.09
T	340.19	363.92	387.65	443.04	482.59	514.24	553.79	585.44	617.09
U	359.46	383.54	409.61	468.14	509.93	543.36	585.17	618.60	652.04
V	377.26	403.58	429.90	491.31	535.17	570.27	614.14	649.23	684.33
W	395.48	423.07	450.66	515.05	561.04	597.83	643.82	680.60	717.39
X	418.34	447.53	476.72	544.82	593.47	632.39	681.03	719.94	758.86
Y	433.23	463.45	493.67	564.20	614.58	654.87	705.25	745.56	785.86
Z	452.75	484.33	515.91	589.64	642.26	684.38	737.02	779.11	821.26

The table gives flow rates in cfh for each orifice size at various gas pressures ranging from three inches of water column to ten inches of water column.

To select the correct orifice the following procedure is followed:

1. Determine the required flow rate through the burner orifice. This is usually obtained from the appliance rating plate in which:

$$\text{Flow Rate Through Burner Orifice in cfh} = \frac{\text{Btuh Appliance Rated Input}}{1000 \text{ Btu/cf}}$$

2. Determine the required burner manifold pressure; again, this is usually obtained from the appliance rating plate.

Figure 8-17: Thumb drills.

3. Under the right pressure column, trace down the column until you arrive at or just below the required cfh flow rate.[2]

4. At the required flow rate, move directly to the left and read out the required orifice size.

Example
What is the required orifice size for a burner in which the rated input is 100,000 Btuh and is operated at a manifold pressure of 3.5" wc. The solution is the following:

1. Rated input of the burner is 100,000 Btuh.

2. Therefore, the flow rate through the burner orifice is:

$$\frac{100,000 \text{ Btuh}}{1000 \text{ Btu/cf}} = 100 \text{ cfh}$$

3. Under the 3.5"wc pressure column, figure 97.11 cfh would be the closest figure to 100 cfh.

4. Moving directly to the left, the orifice size is No. 13.

SPECIFIC GRAVITY	CORRECTION FACTOR	SPECIFIC GRAVITY	CORRECTION FACTOR
0.45	1.155	0.95	0.795
0.50	1.095	1.00	0.775
0.55	1.045	1.05	0.756
0.60	1.000	1.10	0.739
0.65	0.961	1.15	0.722
0.70	0.926	1.20	0.707
0.75	0.894	1.25	0.693
0.80	0.866	1.30	0.679
0.85	0.840	1.35	0.667
0.90	0.817	1.40	0.655
		1.52	0.630

Table T8-2: Flow Rate Correction Factors for Fuel Gases Having a Specific Gravity Other Than 0.60

[2] Most gas utilities would rather have the appliance marginally under-rated than marginally overrated (i.e., to within 90–100% of the full rated capacity of the appliance).

Compensation for Specific Gravity Change

A fuel gas having a specific gravity less than 0.60 will have a greater flow rate through the gas orifice, just as a fuel gas having a specific gravity greater than 0.60 will have a lower flow rate through the gas orifice. To compensate or correct for the change in specific gravity, the flow rate is multiplied by a correction factor, the product of which is the true flow rate through the orifice for that particular fuel gas. *Table T8-2* is a table listing the flow rate correction factors for fuel gases having a specific gravity other than 0.60.

The flow rate correction factors listed in *Table T8-2* provide the means by which *Table T8-1* can be used to determine the required orifice size for other fuel gases. To select the required orifice size for fuel gas other than natural gas (0.60 specific gravity) the following procedure can be used:

1. Obtain the desired flow rate correction factor for the particular fuel gas from Table T8-2.

2. *Divide* the desired gas flow rate by this factor to give the *equivalent* flow rate of natural gas (0.60 specific gravity).

3. Using the natural gas equivalent flow rate found in step (2), use *Table T8-1* to select the required orifice size.

Example
Determine the required orifice size for a propane burner rated at 200,000 Btuh and operating with a manifold pressure of 10"wc.

1. Rated input of the burner is 200,000 Btuh.

2. Propane cfh flow rate through the orifice is:
   $$\frac{200{,}000 \text{ Btuh}}{2500 \text{ Btu/cf}} = 80 \text{ cfh}$$

3. Flow rate correction factor for propane from *Table T8-2* is:

0.630

4. The natural gas equivalent through the orifice is:

$\frac{80 \text{ cfh}}{0.630} = 127$ cfh

5. The required orifice size at 10"wc from *Table T8-1* is:

#20 [3]

---

[3] Propane appliances usually operate with a manifold pressure of 10–11" wc (2.49–2.74 kPa); therefore, for a given appliance input rating the propane orifice will always be smaller.

Compensation for Altitude on Burner Input Setting

The heat input rating for appliances used at higher altitudes must be reduced or *de-rated* since air at higher altitudes contains less oxygen.

Most equipment manufacturers specify their equipment input rating for elevations up to 2000 feet (600 m). Therefore, for equipment at elevations above 2000 feet (600 m), the burner input rating should be reduced by 4% for each 1000 feet (300 m) above sea level.

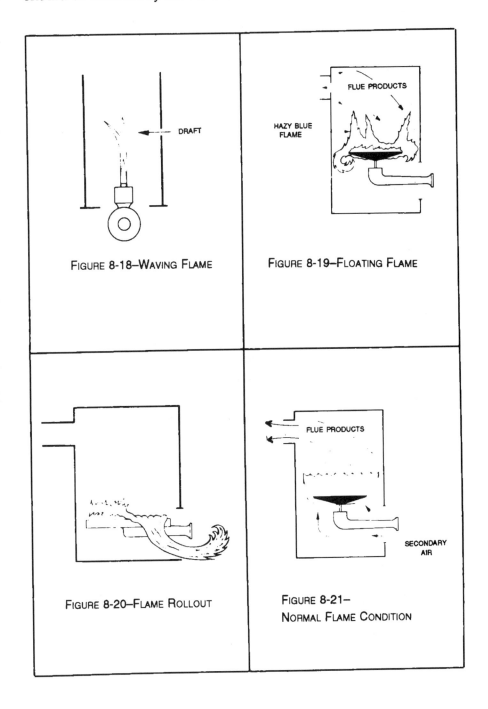

FIGURE 8-18–WAVING FLAME

FIGURE 8-19–FLOATING FLAME

FIGURE 8-20–FLAME ROLLOUT

FIGURE 8-21–
NORMAL FLAME CONDITION

Burner Problems

The following is a brief digest of possible burner problems that can be experienced in the field. Results and corrections are given for each possible burner problem.

Condition	Results	Correction	Illustrations
FLAME LIFTING	i) Noisy ii) Incomplete Combustion iii) Reduced appliance efficiency	i) Reduce primary air ii) Reduce appliance input	Figure 8-6
FLASH BACK	i) Burning inside mixing tube ii) Incomplete combustion iii) Sooting of burner	i) Reduce primary air ii) Increase burner input	
EXTINCTION POP	i) Noisy ii) Pilot outage	i) Reduce primary air ii) Increase gas pressure using a smaller gas orifice size	
YELLOW TIPPING	i) Sooting ii) Incomplete combustion	i) Increase primary air ii) Clean primary air opening	Figure 8-7
FLUCTUATING FLAME Where the length of burner flame may fluctuate or shorten over a period of time	i) Possible incomplete combustion if flame impinges on a cool surface	i) Make sure gas pressure is steady at burner orifice ii) Clean burner orifice for possible blockage	
WAVING FLAME Draft across burner may cause flame to be unstable	i) Possible incomplete combustion if flame impinges on a cool surface ii) Pilot outage	i) Correct draft condition ii) Possible cracked heat exchanger-replace	Figure 8-18
FLOATING FLAME A lazy flame with undefined cones, reaching for air. Tends to roll in combustion chamber	i) Severe incomplete combustion ii) Possible pilot outage	i) Reduce over-firing of burner ii) Remove possible vent and flue blockage iii) Remove soot or dust to increase secondary air supply	Figure 8-19
FLAME ROLL OUT Flame rolling out of combustion chamber when burner starts up	i) Possible fire hazard ii) Scorch appliance finish iii) Burn wiring and possible control damage iv) Possible burner flash back	i) Reduce over-firing ii) Remove possible vent and flue blockage iii) Increase secondary air supply iv) Employ a 2-step control valve to establish natural draft in appliance before full gas input	Figure 8-20
DELAYED IGNITION	i) Noisy ignition ii) Flame roll out (see results of flame roll out) iii) Possible pilot outage	i) Correct-cross over igniter alignment ii) Clean cross-over igniters iii) Correct pilot position	
NORMAL FLAME	i) Complete combustion ii) Stable flame iii) High appliance efficiency	i) Correct primary and secondary air supply ii) Correct firing rate iii) Adequate venting and clear flue passages	Figure 8-21

Assignment

1. Draw and label a simple diagram illustrating the operation of the atmospheric gas burner.

2. Briefly describe the operation of the atmospheric burner and specifically state how the air/gas ratio is maintained throughout the turndown range of the burner.

3. Define the following terms:

   a) Partial premixing
   b) Primary air
   c) Secondary air
   d) Flame characteristics

   e) Turndown ratio
   f) Flame stability
   g) Bunsen flame
   h) Burner assembly

4. Match the following adjectives to the appropriate flames:

   LEAN   HARD   PERFECT
   CARBONIZING   LUMINOUS   OXIDIZING
   NEUTRAL   RICH   REDUCING

   a) A flame having too much primary air supply
   b) A flame having too little primary air supply
   c) A flame having the correct primary air supply

5. Briefly describe the condition and give the results and corrections for the following:

   a) Flame lifting
   b) Flash-back
   c) Extinction pop
   d) Yellow tipping

   e) Fluctuating flame
   f) Waving flame
   g) Floating flame
   h) Flame roll out
   i) Delayed ignition

6. Identify the burners illustrated in *Figure 8-22*, and identify other types of atmospheric burner port construction.

7. List three types of gas burner orifices and state a possible application of each.

8. What are the factors that determine the gas flow rate through a gas burner orifice?

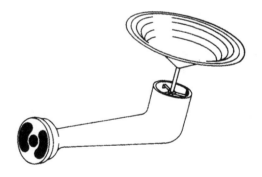

Figure 8-22: Assignment
Question #6

9. Using the orifice capacity table, determine the correct orifice size for the following:

a) A single burner rated at 60,000 Btuh and operated at a manifold pressure of 3.5 inches of water column.

b) A three burner gas furnace having an overall appliance input rating of 120,000 Btuh and operated at a manifold pressure of 3.5 inches of water column.

c) Same appliance as described in part "B", however, the furnace is supplied with propane gas having a specific gravity of 1.52 and a manifold pressure of 10" wc.

Principles of Gas Controls — Part 1

9

This chapter consist of four major sections: principles and application of flame safeguard systems, ignition equipment, gas valves and control circuits.

Principles of Flame Safeguard

The gas burner system is an automatic system. The thermostat calls for heat and energizes a gas control valve. A standing pilot will automatically light the main flame which is cycled on and off by the thermostat.

Since a *standing* or *constant* pilot is part of the automatic burner system, protection must be incorporated within this system to prevent the burner being energized if the pilot flame has gone out. It must have some type of *flame safeguard protection*. On residential gas equipment the flame safeguard feature is usually a *thermocouple* that is constantly being energized by a standing pilot flame.

The thermocouple is a thermal electric device in which power developed by the thermocouple will hold in a coil of a valve located in the main gas line. If the pilot flame goes out, the thermocouple is de-energized and the coil of the valve will drop out, shutting off the main gas supply to the burner.

Definition of a Thermocouple and Powerpile

A thermocouple is a thermal electric device consisting of two dissimilar metals joined together at two junctions. If one of the junctions is heated, there will be created between the junctions a DC *(direct current)* voltage. The amount of DC voltage produced is determined by the temperature difference between the two junctions.

The simple iron-constantan thermocouple illustrated in *Figure 9-1* generates a very low output voltage in the *millivolt* range. The temperature at the hot junction is approximately 1200–1400°F (649–760°C) and at the cold junction approximately 760–800°F (404–427°C).

If thermocouples are wired in series, then the device is called a *thermopile* or *power pile*. See Figure 9-2.

Figure 9-1: A simple iron-constan-tan thermocouple.

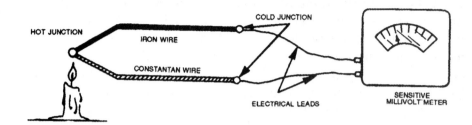

Figure 9-2: The thermopile or powerpile.

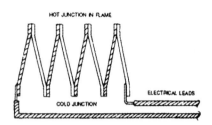

Figure 9-3 and 9-4: Photographs of a typical thermocouple and thermopile.

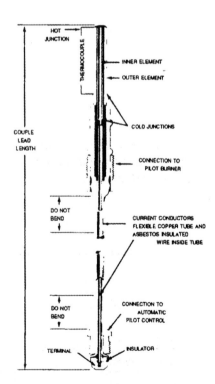

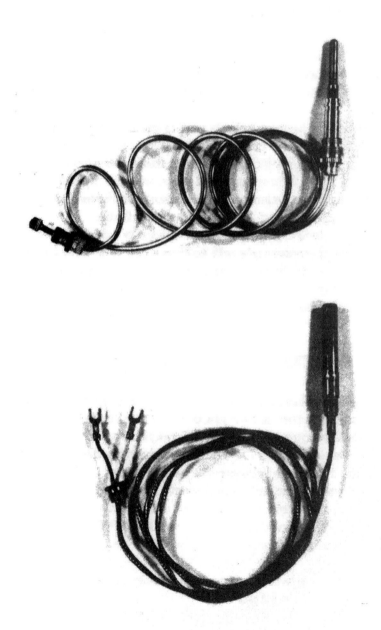

Figure 9-5: A cut-away view of a single thermocouple.

The voltage output from a thermopile is the sum of the voltages produced by the individual thermocouples that are wired in series with each other, thereby forming the thermopile. The thermopile has a unique application for gas equipment since the pilot flame can be used as a source of power. The thermopile, energized by the pilot flame, develops sufficient power to operate a gas valve, thermostat and safety unit control. This is a *self-energizing* or *generating control system* since it generates its own power supply. *(See Figure 9-51)*.

Figure 9-5 is an illustration showing a cut-away view of a single thermocouple. *Figures 9-6 and 9-7* illustrate pilot burners in which a thermocouple and thermopile or powerpile are mounted. The physical size will allow you to recognize a single thermocouple from a thermopile or powerpile since the thermopile is larger. When a pilot burner and thermopile or powerpile come together as a package it is often a *pilot generator.*

Figure 9-6: Pilot burner with mounted thermocouple.

Figure 9-7: Pilot burner with mounted thermopile or power-pile, often called a pilot generator.

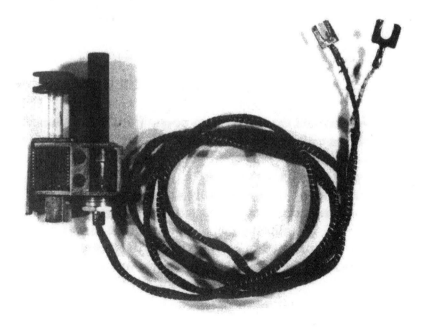

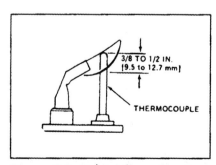

Figure 9-8: Proper flame location on thermocouple tip.

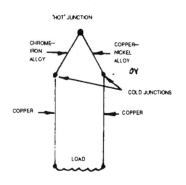

Figure 9-9: The thermocouple and power unit coil.

Figure 9-10: The power unit coil.

Figure 9-11: The simple flame safeguard system consisting of a pilot, thermocouple and power unit coil in the gas valve

For both the thermocouple and the thermopile, the pilot flame should encompass approximately 3/8"–1/2" (9.5–12.7 mm) of the thermocouple or thermopile tip as shown in *Figure 9-8*. This will ensure adequate voltage output from the thermocouple or thermopile. A small mirror can prove helpful in checking the position of the pilot flame within the particular appliance. *See Figure 8-3, 8-8 and 8-9*.

The application of the thermocouple, as a means of providing flame safeguard protection, is through an electromagnetic coil or *power unit coil* that is energized by the thermocouple. *Figure 9-9* is a simple illustration of a thermocouple and power unit coil that is located within a valve in the gas line.

Figure 9-10 is an illustration of the actual power unit coil and *Figure 9-11* illustrates the simple flame safeguard system consisting of a pilot, thermocouple and power unit coil in the gas valve.

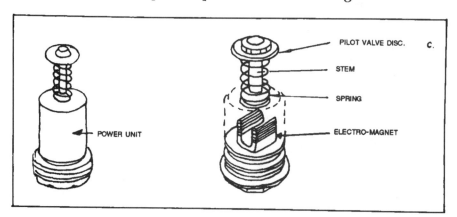

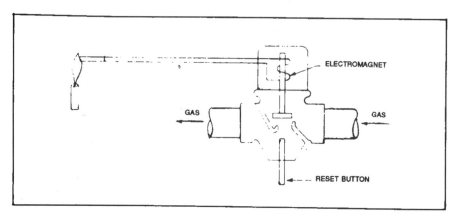

The power unit coil that receives its power from the thermocouple is sometimes called a *pilotstat coil*, and the valve or device that shuts the main gas supply off upon pilot flame failure (i.e., outage) is called a *pilotstat* or *safety shut off valve*.

The pilotstat valve can be a separate valve as illustrated in *Figure 9-11* or a component of a *combination control valve* as illustrated in *Figure 9-12*. The pilotstat coil or power unit is simply screwed into the valve as illustrated in *Figure 9-13* and the thermocouple is in turn screwed into the pilotstat coil or power unit as shown in *Figure 9-14*.

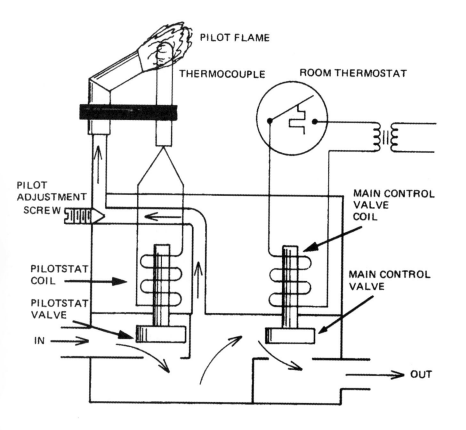

PILOT FLAME

THERMOCOUPLE

ROOM THERMOSTAT

PILOT ADJUSTMENT SCREW

MAIN CONTROL VALVE COIL

PILOTSTAT COIL

PILOTSTAT VALVE

MAIN CONTROL VALVE

IN

OUT

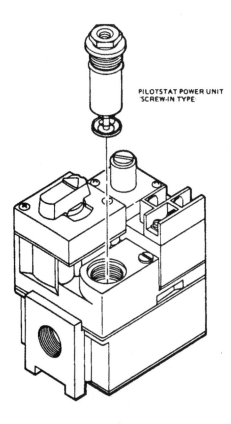

Figure 9-12: The pilotstat as a component of a combination control valve.

PILOTSTAT POWER UNIT 'SCREW-IN TYPE'

Figure 9-13: The pilotstat coil or power unit is screwed into the control valve.

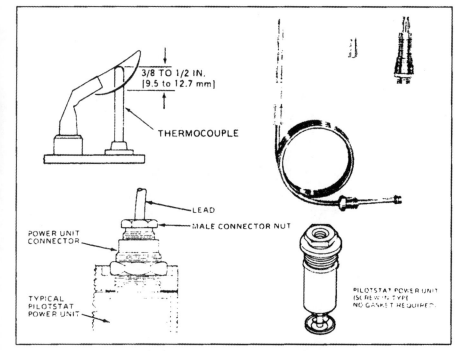

3/8 TO 1/2 IN.
[9.5 to 12.7 mm]

THERMOCOUPLE

LEAD

MALE CONNECTOR NUT

POWER UNIT CONNECTOR

TYPICAL PILOTSTAT POWER UNIT

PILOTSTAT POWER UNIT
(SCREW-IN TYPE
NO GASKET REQUIRED)

Figure 9-14: The thermocouple is screwed into the pilotstat coil or power unit.

The voltage produced by a thermocouple is DC (direct current) and the range of a single thermocouple is approximately 20–30 millivolts. For thermopiles the voltage output is approximately 750 millivolts. *Note:* 1000 millivolts (M.V.) equals one volt; also, systems that function on millivolts are known as *extra low voltage systems* or *millivolt systems.*

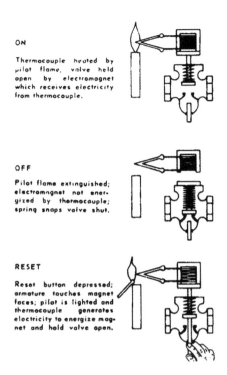

ON

Thermocouple heated by pilot flame, valve held open by electromagnet which receives electricity from thermocouple.

OFF

Pilot flame extinguished; electromagnet not energized by thermocouple; spring snaps valve shut.

RESET

Reset button depressed; armature touches magnet faces; pilot is lighted and thermocouple generates electricity to energize magnet and hold valve open.

Figure 9-15: Resetting the pilot-stat valve.

Since the voltage generated is very low, the coil of the power unit can only hold in the valve stem once it is energized. It is not like a solenoid that acts as a sucking coil that will draw the valve stem up into the centre of the coil and thereby open the valve. For the pilot-stat valve to function, the valve must be *reset* (i.e., manually opening the valve and allowing the coil to hold the valve open once energized). *See Figure 9-15.*

Testing the Flame Safeguard System

The simple flame safeguard system can be tested using a millivolt meter as illustrated in *Figure 9-16.* When using the millivolt meter, make sure that:

1. You have the correct polarity when attaching the meter leads. Wrong polarity will give a backward needle deflection; in which case simply reverse the meter leads (remember this is DC).

2. You have the correct scale when testing for a thermocouple or powerpile. The thermopile test will require the higher scale on the meter. Using the lower scale could destroy the meter.

3. Allow sufficient time for meter to indicate the full voltage output from the thermocouple or thermopile.

Open Circuit Test

An open circuit test determines the full voltage output from a thermocouple. *Figure 9-17* is a schematic, illustrating an open circuit test and *Figure 9-18* shows that actual millivolt meter application in determining the voltage output from the thermocouple. The range from a single thermocouple should be approximately 20–30 millivolts.

Figure 9-16: The millivolt meter.

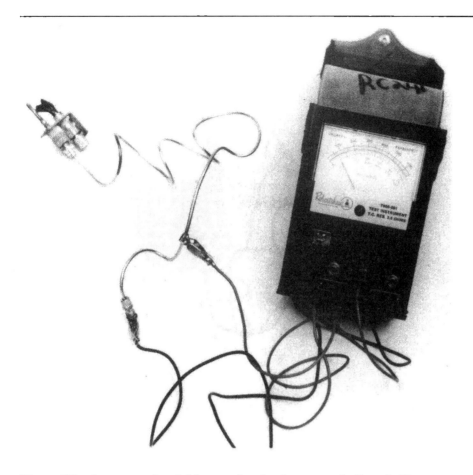

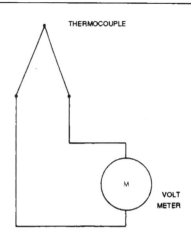

Figure 9-17: Schematic drawing of the open circuit test.

Figure 9-18: Actual millivolt meter application for open circuit test.

The millivolt meter should be set for the lower scale (i.e., 0–50 M.V.). One meter lead is attached to the thermocouple's lead, the other to the thermocouple's terminal adapter as shown in *Figure 9-22*.

Closed Circuit Test

The closed circuit test determines the voltage drop across the power unit coil (i.e, pilotstat coil) and indicates if the coil is adequately energized to hold the valve in the open position. *Figure 9-19* is a schematic illustrating a closed circuit test and *Figure 9-20* shows the actual meter application in determining the voltage drop across the coil. For a single thermocouple the voltage drop across the coil should be approximately 10–15 millivolts, one half of the open circuit test.[1]

---

[1] In a closed circuit test, the thermocouple is under a load condition since power is being supplied to the pilotstat coil or power unit. A reading substantially below the normal expected value would indicate that the thermocouple has a high internal resistance and should be replaced. A reading substantially above the normal expected value would indicate that the pilotstat coil or power unit has a high operating resistance and should be checked.

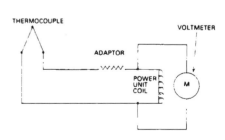

Figure 9-19: Schematic drawing of the closed circuit test.

Figure 9-20: Actual millivolt meter application for closed circuit test.

Figure 9-21: Millivolt meter adapter used for closed circuit test.

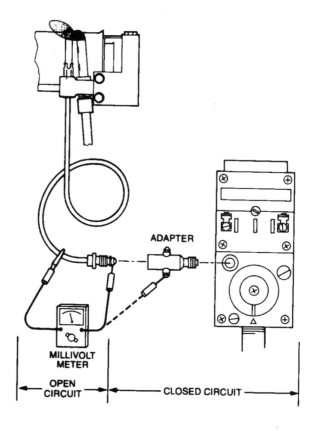

Figure 9-22: Millivolt meter arrangement for open and closed circuit testing.

As in the open circuit test, the meter is set at the lower scale (e.g., 0–50 M.V.). The millivolt meter adapter, illustrated in *Figure 9-21*, is assembled, together with the thermocouple, in the valve bushing and tightened finger tight plus 1/4 turn. One meter lead is attached to the thermocouple lead; the other to the screwed post that is mounted on the side of the meter adapter as illustrated in *Figure 9-22*.

Drop Out Test
The drop out test determines the minimum voltage drop across the coil that will just hold it in. It is conducted the same way as a closed circuit test having the same millivolt meter application. However, in this test the pilot flame is turned off and the thermocouple is allowed to slowly de-energize the pilotstat coil or power unit, allowing it to drop out. For a normal coil and single thermocouple, this is approximately 2–4 millivolts.

Flame Failure Response Test
The flame failure response test is simply timing the period for the power unit or pilotstat coil to drop out placing the system in a *safety shut down condition*. The normal *flame failure response time* is approximately one minute. The maximum flame failure response time required by most national and local codes is one and a half minutes.

Terminal Block Connection
As illustrated in *Figures 9-23 and 9-24*, some thermocouples are equipped with a small *terminal block* located between the thermocouple's tip and its power coil terminal. The terminal block provides a terminal attachment for leads to a high limit switch. Thus a high limit switch is put in series with the power unit coil to cause the pilotstat or safety shut off valve to drop out if the water or air temperature becomes excessive.

To test the high limit switch, connect the millivolt meter adapter and thermocouple's power unit coil terminal as you would in a closed circuit test. Now place the leads of the millivolt meter across the terminal block's high limit connections as illustrated in *Figure 9-25*. A full open circuit reading means that the high limit switch is open and a reading of 4 millivolts or less indicates that the high limit switch is closed.

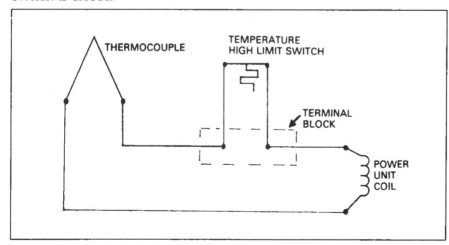

Figure 9-23: Schematic drawing of a terminal block wiring arrangement.

Figure 9-24: Terminal block.

Open and Closed Circuit Test for Powerpiles

The open and closed circuit test for powerpile systems are illustrated in *Figures 9-26 and 9-27.* For both the open and closed circuit test, it is important to remember that the high scale must be used (i.e., 0–1000 M.V.) on the millivolt meter. This is simply to protect the meter from damage that could occur if the lower scale is used.

In the open circuit test, the leads of the millivolt meter are attached to the leads of the powerpile as illustrated in *Figure 9-26.* With the leads so attached, the output voltage generated by the powerpile will be indicated by the millivolt meter.

For the closed circuit test, the powerpile leads are connected to the powerpile valve. The thermostat leads are disconnected from the valve. With the powerpile connected to the gas valve and the thermostat circuit disconnected, the millivolt meter leads can now be attached to the valve's powerpile terminals as illustrated in *Figure 9-27.* The closed circuit voltage across the pilotstat coil can now be indicated by the millivolt meter.

For powerpile systems there are actually two closed circuit tests. There is the closed circuit test to obtain the voltage drop across the pilotstat coil as described above; and, a closed circuit test to obtain the voltage drop across the thermostat, high limit and the main valve coil when the system is completely energized (i.e., the thermostat is closed calling for heat). For the latter, the closed circuit voltage (i.e., output voltage of the powerpile) is substantially lower since the powerpile is under maximum load conditions. *Figure 9-63* gives the expected millivolt readings of a typical millivolt control system.

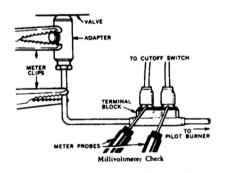

Figure 9-25: Testing the high limit (cut off switch) at the terminal block.

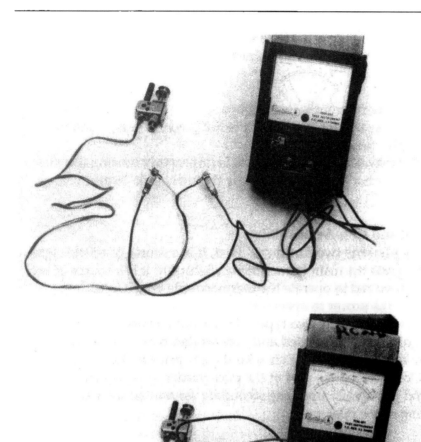

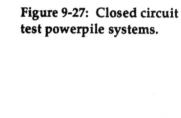

Figure 9-26: Open circuit test powerpile systems.

Figure 9-27: Closed circuit test powerpile systems.

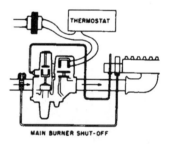

MAIN BURNER SHUT-OFF

Figure 9-28: Non 100% pilot protection.

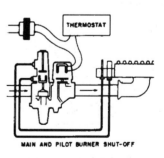

MAIN AND PILOT BURNER SHUT-OFF

Figure 9-29: 100% pilot protection.

Gas Pilots

Automatic Gas Pilots

The standing or constant pilot on a gas burner is defined as an automatic pilot; automatic in that if the pilot goes out it will automatically de-energize the main gas supply to the burner. There are two types of automatic pilot systems employed on residential gas equipment: the *non 100% pilot protection type* and the *100% pilot protection type*. The non 100% pilot protection type of the automatic pilot system, as illustrated in *Figure 9-28* is one in which only the main flame (or burner flame) is protected against pilot outage. The 100% pilot protection type of automatic pilot, illustrated in *Figure 9-29* protects both the pilot and main flame against pilot outage. If for one reason the pilot flame goes out, then the thermocouple will cool down de-energizing the pilotstat coil, closing the pilotstat and shutting off the gas supply to both the pilot and main burner.

It should be noted that false safety conditions can occur in both systems giving nuisance shut down. If this occurs check for the following:

1. Loose thermocouple connections.
2. Pilot flame is not burning at the hot junction of the thermocouple. *See Figure 9-8.*
3. Pilot may be under gassed and is improperly heating thermocouple's hot junction giving low thermocouple output voltage.

Aerated and Non-Aerated Pilots

The gas pilot has two functions. First, it is a source of reliable ignition to ignite the main burner flame. Secondly, it is a source of heat energy required to operate the thermocouple which in turn provides the power to operate the flame safeguard system.

There are basically two types of pilot burners used on residential gas equipment, the aerated and non-aerated types. Aerated pilots utilize some premixing of air with the gas prior to the burning of the pilot flame on the port of the pilot burner. Non-aerated pilots depend exclusively upon the secondary air around the flame for the burning of the pilot gas.

Aerated Pilot

Aerated pilots develop a rather sharp, intense blue flame as a result of the premixing of air and gas. These pilots have relatively stable flame characteristics and are not affected, to the same extent, as the non-aerated type by draft and main flame variations. Also, aerated pilots tend to give better thermocouple response.

However, aerated pilots are subject to problems of dust and lint that may block or clog the small primary air inlet. This is especially so for burners located near the floor such as water heaters; also, because of the hotter pilot flame, due to the primary air mixing, aerated pilots tend to give shorter thermocouple life.

Non-Aerated Pilot

Non-aerated pilots are designed to give a softer blue flame since they have no primary air features. These pilots do not experience the same problems of dust and lint as the aerated type. Also, they tend to promote longer thermocouple life since they give less *torching* (the harder, sharper and hotter pilot flame associated with aerated pilots).

However, changes in pilot supply pressure can affect these pilots more than the aerated type. If the supply pressure is too high, then the pilot will experience *flame roar* giving a noisy pilot operation and lower thermocouple life. If the supply pressure is too low, then there is insufficient heat giving low thermocouple output voltage. Also, these pilots are affected by draft and main flame variations.

Incinerating Pilot

The incinerating pilot is a variation of the aerated type of pilot. In this type of pilot, the primary air is drawn through a tube or air duct which passes around the pilot flame *incinerating* any lint or dust that could be in the primary air, thus overcoming the disadvantage associated with the regular type of aerated pilot.

Target Pilot

In this type of pilot burner design the gas stream is discharged through a pilot orifice thereby entraining air in the opening. The resulting air/gas mixture will burn against a target type of hood that is located a short distance from the pilot orifice. The target hood functions to direct the pilot flame, helping to determine the flame pattern as well as protecting the flame from drafts.

Figure 9-30 illustrates the operation of the aerated, non-aerated, incinerating and target types of pilots.

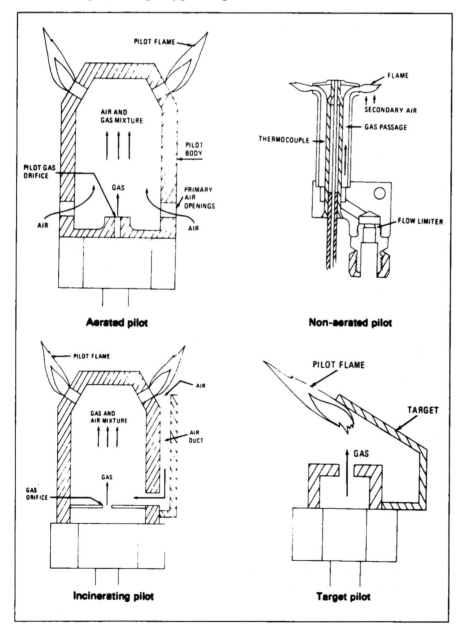

Figure 9-30: Types of pilot operations.

Figure 9-31 is a photograph of an aerated pilot employing a protective dust and lint screen, target pilot, an aerated pilot with the screen removed and an incinerator pilot.

Figure 9-31: Types of pilots.

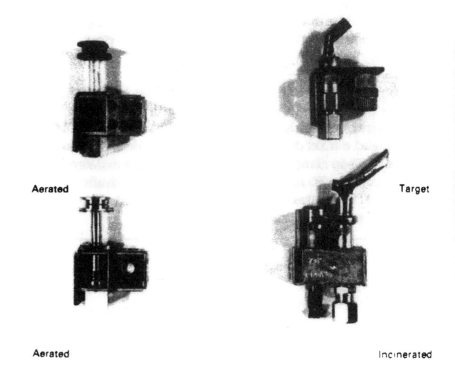

Aerated

Target

Aerated

Incinerated

Figure 9-32: Assembled parts of an aerated pilot burner.

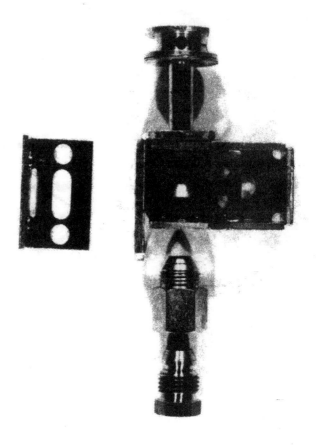

Figure 9-32 is a photograph showing the assembled parts of an aerated pilot burner. Notice the pilot bracket mounting, pilot orifice spud and the *break away* ferule 1/4" tube compression nut. Also, notice the bell type of design primary air inlet.

Types of Ignition Equipment

Figure 9-33 illustrates the various types of pilot burners, thermocouples and thermopiles. As mentioned previously, the pilot burner together with the thermopile or powerpile as a package is often referred to as a powerpile or pilot generator.

Figure 9-34 is an exploded view of a target type pilot burner with thermocouple and pilot line tubing. Also, illustrated in the same figure is the *insert* pilot orifice and the 1/4" compression fitting that connects the pilot burner to the 1/4" O.D. (standard) pilot line tubing.

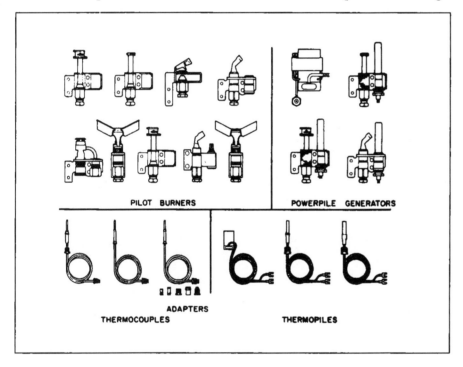

Figure 9-33: Types of ignition equipment.

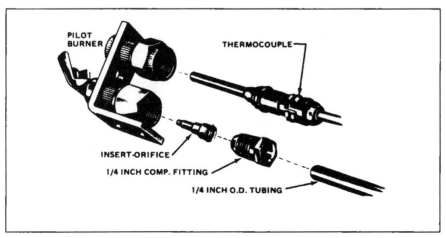

Figure 9-34: Exploded view of a target type of pilot.

Figure 9-35 illustrates the flame patterns of various types of pilots in which there is one or two ignition flames for main burner ignition and one flame to keep the thermocouple in an energized state.

Figure 9-35: Various types of pilot burner flame patterns.

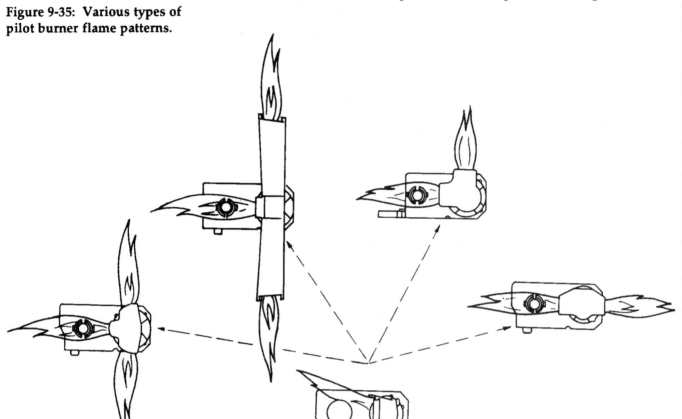

Pilot Location

Figure 9-36(a) illustrates the effect of a draft on a pilot flame being pulled away from the thermocouple. Even with normal venting action, the inrush of secondary air across the pilot burner may sometimes be strong enough to pull the flame away from the thermocouple so that the pilotstat may drop out.

As illustrated in *Figure 9-36(b)*, proper shielding of the pilot flame may alleviate the problem. The pilot burner shield should be of just the sufficient size and location to eliminate this unsatisfactory condition and should never be fitted so closely around the pilot burner so as to starve it of secondary air.

Figure 9-37 illustrates the effect of poor pilot mounting to the main burner. When mounting the pilot burner, it should be rigidly affixed to the main burner at the proper distance and level to effect a smooth and quick light off of the main burner flame.

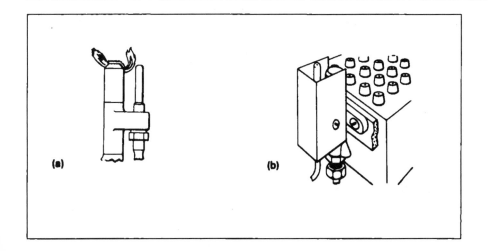

Figure 9-36: Effects of draft on pilot flame(a) and correction with proper shielding (b).

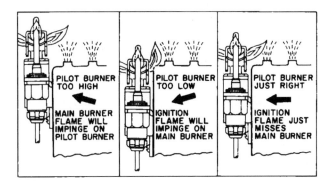

PILOT BURNER TOO HIGH

MAIN BURNER FLAME WILL IMPINGE ON PILOT BURNER

PILOT BURNER TOO LOW

IGNITION FLAME WILL IMPINGE ON MAIN BURNER

PILOT BURNER JUST RIGHT

IGNITION FLAME JUST MISSES MAIN BURNER

Figure 9-37: Pilot location.

The following are rules to be followed for the location of the pilot burner:

1. Pilot burner must be positioned for easy access, observation and lighting.

2. Pilot burner must be rigidly mounted so that the ignition flame remains properly positioned with respect to the main burner flame.

3. Pilot flame must not be exposed to falling scale which could impair ignition of main burner.

4. Pilot flame must not impinge on adjacent parts; main burner flame must not contact or impinge on pilot burner.

5. The pilot flame must have ample air supply free of the products of combustion.

6. The pilot should not receive the full force of igniting or extinguishing puffs from the main burner.

7. The pilot should not be exposed to draft conditions that will extinguish the pilot flame or pull it away from the thermocouple or thermopile.

Pilot Turndown Test (Minimum Pilot Test)

Gas pilots of minimum size should effect ignition of the gas from the main burner within four seconds from the time that the gas is admitted to the main burner. The gas pilot of minimum size, or what is called the *minimum pilot*, is the smallest possible pilot that will just hold the pilotstat or power unit coil in.

To ensure that a minimum pilot will provide effective main flame ignition within four seconds, a pilot turndown test should be conducted. The pilot turndown test consists of the following steps:

1. With pilot and main burner lit, shut off main burner by lowering the thermostat temperature setting or by turning gas cock to the pilot position on a gas control valve.

2. Turn pilot flame down in steps to allow thermocouple to cool until pilotstat or safety shut-off power unit just drops *causing safety shut down*.

3. Back pilot gas adjustment up very slightly. Relight pilot burner (power unit coil should just hold in).

4. Turn main burner on by adjusting thermostat temperature setting above room temperature. Main burner should light within *four seconds* without flame roll out. If not, recheck pilot location and repeat test.

5. Readjust pilot gas to obtain normal pilot flame, enveloping 3/8 to 1/2 inch (9.5–12.7 mm) of thermocouple tip. *(See Figure 9-8.)*

Pilot Burner Service Analysis

Figure 9-38 is a chart giving pilot burner service analysis.

The Pilotstat

The pilotstat is the device that will initiate a *safety shut off* or *safety shut down* of the gas supply in the event of a pilot outage. The pilotstat can take three separate forms or applications:

1. As a separate valve (called the *safety shut off valve).

2. As an electromagnetic switch or relay (called the *safety switch*).

3. As a component of a *combination control valve*.

Pilotstat as a Separate Valve
The pilotstat as a separate valve in the gas line is usually found on older types of burner systems. As in the other two applications, the pilotstat can provide for either 100% or non 100% pilot protection. *Figures 9-39(a) and 9-39(b)* illustrate the pilotstat as a separate valve.

	TYPES	CAUSES	REMEDY
YELLOW / LIGHT BLUE	LAZY YELLOW FLAME	1. Dirty lint screen or primary air opening. 2. Orifice too big.	1. Clean pilot burner as required, removing lint screen. 2. Replace orifice inlet fitting.
	WAVING BLUE FLAME	1. Excessive draft at pilot location. 2. Recirculating products of combustion.	1. Relocate pilot, or 2. Install protecting baffle.
	SMALL BLUE FLAME	1. Low gas pressure. 2. Clogged pilot-burner orifice. 3. Clogged pilot-line filter. 4. Improper orifice (too small).	1. Increase pressure to normal. 2. Clean pilot burner orifice. 3. Clean filter. 4. Install correct orifice.
	NOISY LIFTING BLOWING FLAME	1. High gas pressure.	1. Reduce pressure.
	HARD SHARP FLAME	1. Characteristic of manufactured, butane-air, and propane-air. 2. Orifice too small.	1. Install correct orifice inlet fitting.
	NORMAL FLAME Mostly blue, steady. Envelops ¼″ to ½″ of thermocouple tip.	1. Proper installation.	1. None needed.

Figure 9-38: Pilot burner service analysis.

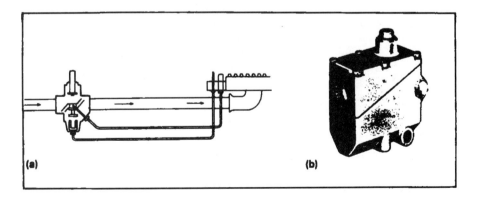

(a)   (b)

Figure 9-39: Pilotstat as a separate valve.

The Pilotstat as an Electromagnetic Switch or Relay

The pilotstat can be utilized as an electromagnetic switch or relay in which the only valve in the gas line is the *automatic control valve*. However, power to the control valve is subject to interruption by the pilotstat switch should the pilot go out and de-energize the pilotstat coil. *Figures 9-40(a), 9-40(b) and 9-40(c)* illustrate this type of pilotstat arrangement. (*Note:* This is a non 100% pilot protection system whereas *Figure 9-41* illustrates a *wall mounted* pilotstat switch that provides for 100% pilot protection.)

Figure 9-40:) Pilotstat as an electromagnetic switch or relay.

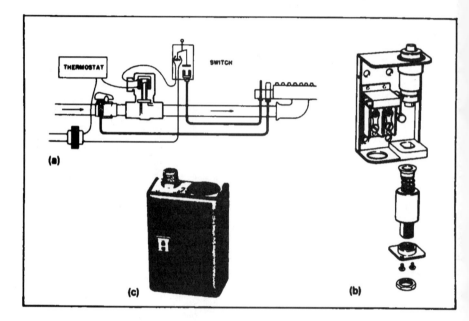

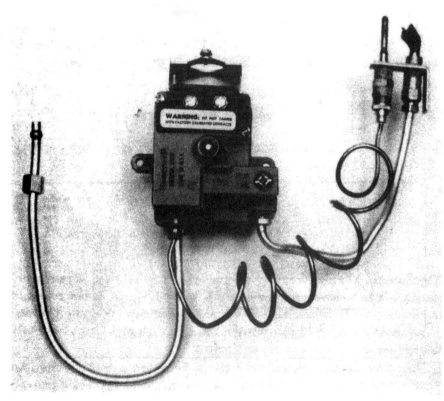

Figure 9-41: Wall mounted pilotstat switch with 100% pilot protection.

Pilotstat as a Part of a Combination Control Valve

The pilotstat can be applied as a part of a *combination control valve* in which the pilotstat and the main control valve coil are together in one valve body.[2] This form of pilotstat arrangement is the form most often found on today's gas equipment. *Figures 9-42(a) and 9-42(b)* illustrate this type of arrangement.

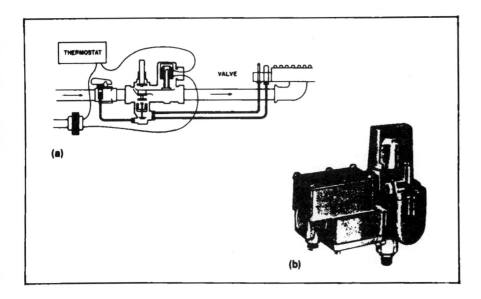

Figure 9-42: Pilotstat as part of a combination control valve.

Control Valves

The gas control valve, sometimes referred to as the *automatic control valve*, functions to open or energize when the thermostat calls for heat and to close or de-energize when the demand for heat has been satisfied. The control valve can operate as a solenoid or diaphragm type of valve.

Figure 9-43 illustrates the wiring circuit of a control valve in series with the thermostat. It should be noted that the thermostat's heating anticipator is set by the amperage drawn by the coil of the gas valve. Also, since the heating anticipator is in series with the valve coil, the coil should *never* be shorted out of the circuit since it would burn out the anticipator.

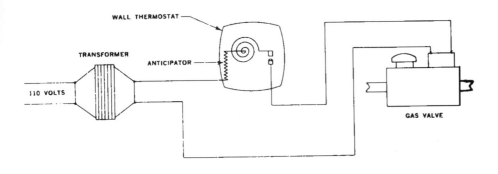

Figure 9-43: The wiring circuit of a control valve in series with the thermostat.

[2] In this arrangement the pilotstat is "in line" with the main gas control valve *(Figure 9-12)*.

The Solenoid Valve

Normally, solenoid valves are not used on residential gas equipment. However, they are used extensively on commercial and industrial equipment as pilot valves and automatic shut off valves. *Figures 9-44(a) and 9-44(b)* illustrate the operation and type of solenoid valves that can be used on gas equipment.

The action of the solenoid valve can be described as the following: An electric current passing through the *solenoid coil (see Figure 9-45)* causes a magnetic field to be built up which attracts a steel armature or plunger, thus opening the valve. When the current is shut off, spring loading returns the plunger to its normal position, closing the valve and hence shutting off the gas supply.

Figure 9-44: The solenoid valve.

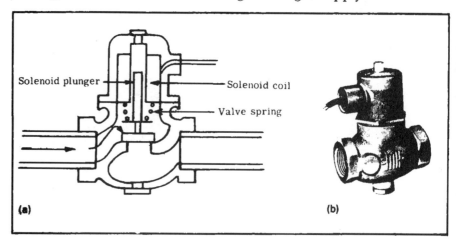

(a) Solenoid plunger — Solenoid coil — Valve spring (b)

Figure 9-45: The solenoid coil.

Diaphragm Valves

Diaphragm gas valves, as illustrated in *Figure 9-46*, are powered by gas pressure as the primary force for opening and closing the valve. These valves can be operated electrically by opening and closing a small *bleed line* through the actions of a small *electrical operator*.

The diaphragm valve opens and closes in response to the opening and closing of the bleed line. Both *internal* and *external* bleed line types of diaphragm valves are available. External bleed valves require porting of the bleed gas to a location near a constant burning pilot as illustrated in *Figure 9-47*. On internal bleed models, bleed gas is ported back into the control valve outlet or manifold.

As illustrated in *Figure 9-48* external bleed valves operate on this bleed line principle. When the vent port is closed and the pressure port is opened, both sides of the diaphragm are exposed to inlet gas pressure and gravity, and the valve's spring action will move the diaphragm to its closed position.

Opening the vent and closing the pressure port, by applying power to the electric operator, lowers the gas pressure above the diaphragm. This reduction in pressure above the diaphragm allows the greater pressure beneath the diaphragm to open the valve. These valves have a momentary pulse bleed at the start of the valve opening allowing for a *slow opening function*. The valve, opening slowly, will condition the combustion chamber for firing, reducing the effect of flame roll out.

Figure 9-46: The diaphragm valve.

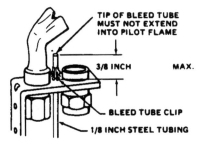

TIP OF BLEED TUBE
MUST NOT EXTEND
INTO PILOT FLAME

3/8 INCH   MAX.

BLEED TUBE CLIP

1/8 INCH STEEL TUBING

Figure 9-47: Connecting bleed gas tubing for external bleed type of valves.

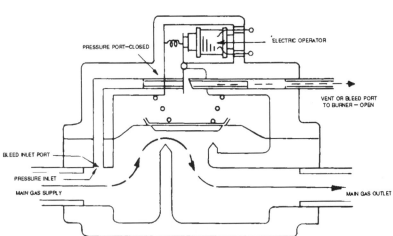
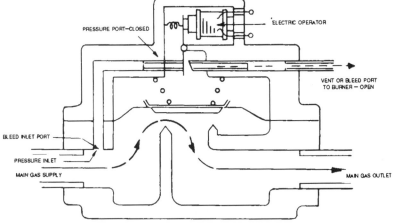

PRESSURE PORT—CLOSED

ELECTRIC OPERATOR

VENT OR BLEED PORT
TO BURNER — OPEN

BLEED INLET PORT

PRESSURE INLET

MAIN GAS SUPPLY

MAIN GAS OUTLET

Figure 9-48: External bleed type of diaphragm valve.

For internal bleed diaphragm valves, the outlet bleed gas is ported into the outlet of the control valve when the valve is opened. This eliminates the need for an external bleed tube connection to a constant burning pilot since the bleed gas is consumed at the burner along with the main gas when the valve is opened. As illustrated in *Figure 9-49,* this valve has a *restrictor* in the pressure inlet. The restrictor serves to lower the gas pressure above the diaphragm when the *bleed control valve* opens.

Some diaphragm valves are known as *pilot* or *servo* control systems since they can have a small *sensing regulator* controlling the action of the diaphragm and main gas valve. As illustrated in *Figure 9-50,* the *bleed valve operator* controls the *on-off* action of the diaphragm valve as it would in a standard internal bleed type of valve. However, this valve has the additional feature of a sensing regulator in the bleed line that also controls the movement of the diaphragm which functions as a pressure regulator for the main gas.

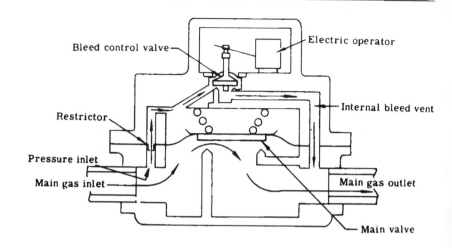

Figure 9-49: Internal bleed type of diaphragm valve.

Bleed control valve — Electric operator — Internal bleed vent — Restrictor — Pressure inlet — Main gas inlet — Main gas outlet — Main valve

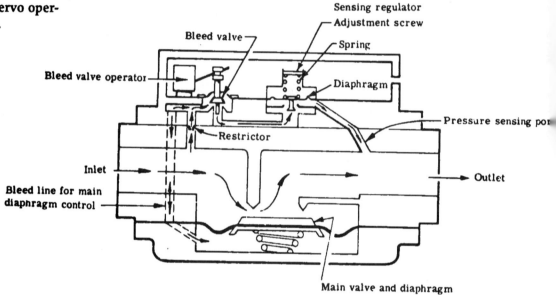

Figure 9-50: Pilot or servo operated diaphragm valve.

Sensing regulator — Adjustment screw — Bleed valve — Spring — Bleed valve operator — Diaphragm — Restrictor — Pressure sensing port — Inlet — Outlet — Bleed line for main diaphragm control — Main valve and diaphragm

The sensing regulator operates by by-passing some of the bleed line gas directly to the outlet of the valve. The amount of gas by-passed through the sensing regulator will determine the amount of bleed line gas pressure acting upon the underside of the diaphragm of the main valve. The movement or travel of the diaphragm is therefore controlled indirectly by the sensing regulator which is spring set to control the desired downstream pressure. Therefore, the diaphragm valve acts not only as an *on-off* valve under the control of a thermostat but also acts as a main gas pressure regulator under the control of the small sensing regulator located in the bleed line.

Diaphragm gas valves are well adapted to high capacity application because the valve area can be made as large as practical to obtain low pressure drops for high capacity applications.

Figure 9-51 illustrates a diaphragm control valve coil being energized by a thermopile when the thermostat contacts are being

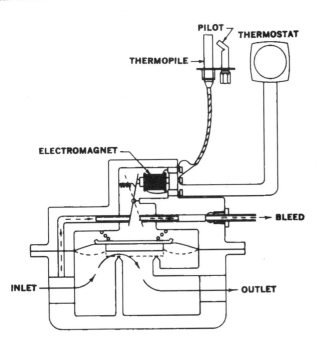

Figure 9-51: Diaphragm valve used in a self-generating control system.

closed by a call for heat. This is a good example of a *self-energizing* or *generating* control system in which the power supply to operate the circuit is provided by the thermopile.

The Combination Control Valve

The combination control valve, as illustrated in F*igures 9-52 and 9-53* is the major control mechanism found on the burner manifold line. All of the necessary control components are provided in one body assembly.

Figure 9-54 is an exposed view of the components that go to make up a combination control valve. *Figure 9-55* illustrates the piping and tubing connections for a combination control valve.

The *lighting procedure* or *lightoff*, using the three way manual valve of the combination control valve, is shown in *Figure 9-56.*

Figure 9-52: 24 volt combination control valve.

Figure 9-53: Powerpile type combination control valve used for a millivolt control system.

Figure 9-54: Components of a combination control valve.

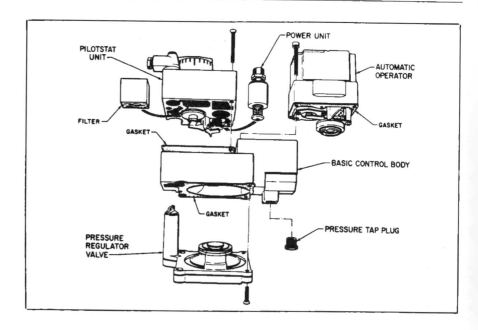

Figure 9-55: Piping and tubing connections for a combination control valve.

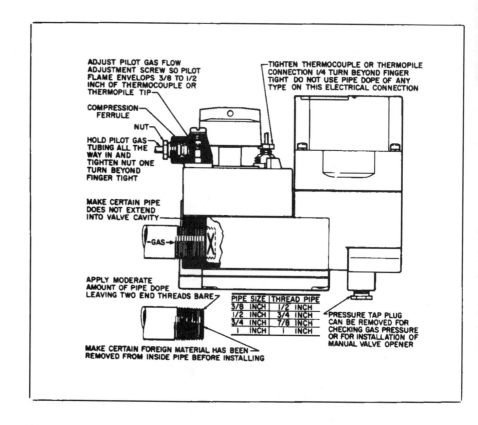

LIGHTING PROCEDURE

1. Turn to PILOT. Press dial in and light pilot. Hold for 60 seconds and release.

2. Turn dial counter-clockwise to ON. Use this position for thermostat control. Set thermostat for desired room temperature.

3. Press dial in and turn clockwise to OFF. Use this position when complete shutdown is necessary. (Use PILOT position for temporary or seasonal shutdown.)

NOTE: When valve is turned off, dial on models equipped with Safety-Lock cannot be turned to PILOT for relighting until after three minutes. Do not attempt to force dial.

Figure 9-56: Lighting procedure.

Figures 9-57, 9-58 and 9-59 illustrate the wiring arrangements for the combination control valve for low voltage wiring, line voltage wiring and powerpile or millivolt wiring.

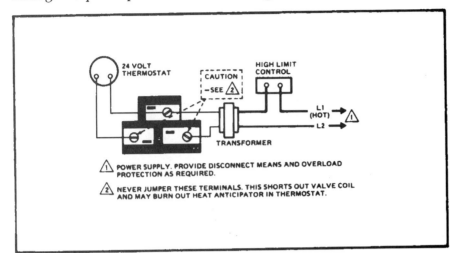

Figure 9-57: Low voltage wiring.

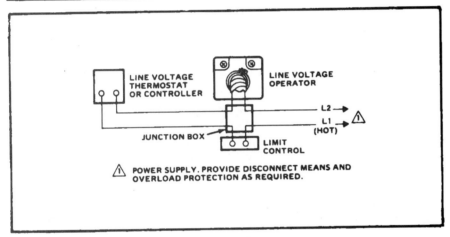

Figure 9-58: Line voltage wiring.

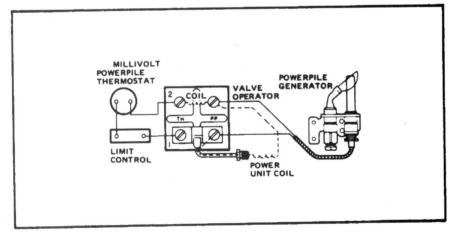

Figure 9-59: Power pile wiring.

Control Circuits

The following are pictorial and schematic wiring diagrams for typical gas fired forced warm air furnaces having 24 volt and millivolt control circuits.

Figure 9-60: Pictorial/schematic wiring diagram of a typical forced warm air furnace having a 24 volt control circuit.

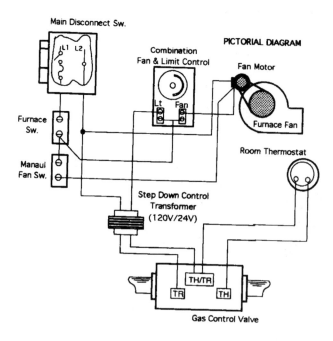

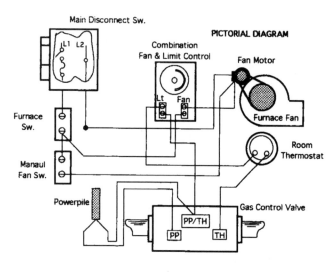

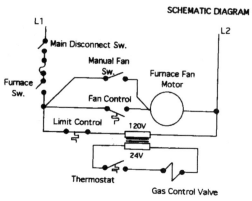

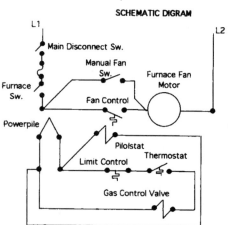

Figure 9-61: Pictorial/schematic wiring diagrams of a typical forced warm air furnace having a millivolt control circuit

Trouble Shooting

Figure 9-62 illustrates the checking of the 24 volt thermostat and gas valve circuit, while *Figure 9-63* illustrates the expected readings of a typical millivolt system.

Figure 9-62

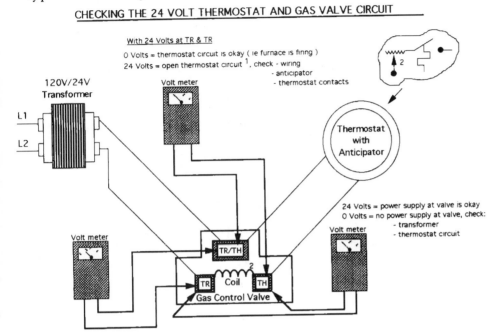

CHECKING THE 24 VOLT THERMOSTAT AND GAS VALVE CIRCUIT

With 24 Volts at TR & TR
0 Volts = thermostat circuit is okay (ie furnace is firing)
24 Volts = open thermostat circuit [1], check - wiring
  - anticipator
  - thermostat contacts

Thermostat with Anticipator

24 Volts = power supply at valve is okay
0 Volts = no power supply at valve, check:
  - transformer
  - thermostat circuit

120V/24V Transformer

L1
L2

Volt meter

Volt meter

Volt meter

TR/TH

TR Coil TH
Gas Control Valve

24 Volts = Power supply to circuit is okay (ie transformer okay)
0 Volts = No power supply, check - transformer
  - 120 V circuit (ie high limit switch)

Footnote: 1. Zero volts across TH & TH when thermostat is open indicates a break in the valve coil circuit (burned out coil)
2. Do not jumper the valve coil out of the circuit since it will burn out the thermostat heat anticipator. The heat anticipator is set as to the amperage drawn by the valve coil.

Figure 9-63

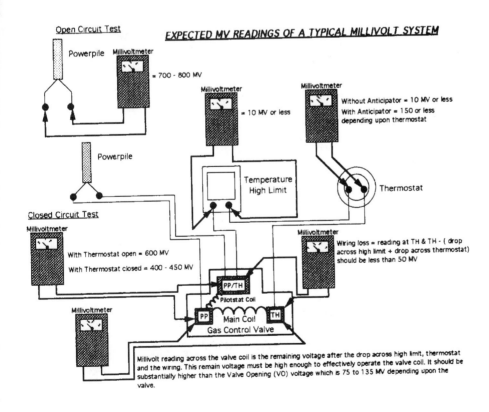

Open Circuit Test

EXPECTED MV READINGS OF A TYPICAL MILLIVOLT SYSTEM

Powerpile Millivoltmeter

= 700 - 800 MV

Millivoltmeter
= 10 MV or less

Millivoltmeter
Without Anticipator = 10 MV or less
With Anticipator = 150 or less depending upon thermostat

Powerpile

Temperature High Limit

Thermostat

Closed Circuit Test

Millivoltmeter
With Thermostat open = 600 MV
With Thermostat closed = 400 - 450 MV

Millivoltmeter
Wiring loss = reading at TH & TH - (drop across high limit + drop across thermostat) should be less than 50 MV

Millivoltmeter

PP/TH
Pilotstat Coil

PP Main Coil TH
Gas Control Valve

Millivolt reading across the valve coil is the remaining voltage after the drop across high limit, thermostat and the wiring. This remain voltage must be high enough to effectively operate the valve coil. It should be substantially higher than the Valve Opening (VO) voltage which is 75 to 135 MV depending upon the valve.

Figure 9-64

Figure 9-64 is a trouble-shooting flow chart that can be used to eliminate various problems that can occur in gas control systems.[3]

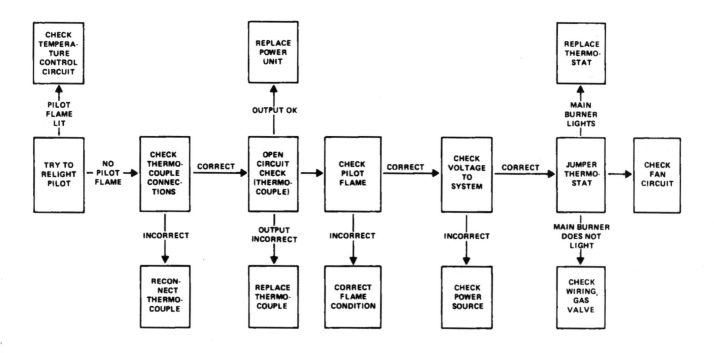

[3] Also see *Appendix IV* for general check list for residential no heat call.

202

Assignment

1. Define the following terms:

   a) Thermocouple
   b) Thermopile
   c) Power pile
   d) Pilot generator
   e) Power Unit
   f) Pilotstat
   g) Extra low voltage
   h) Millivolt system

2. Give the purpose of the following tests:

   a) Open circuit test
   b) Closed circuit test
   c) Drop out test
   d) Response test

3. Give the values you would expect to get from a single thermo-couple from each of the tests given in question No. 2.

4. Define the following terms:

   a) Automatic pilot
   b) Non 100% pilot protection
   c) 100% pilot protection
   d) Aerated pilot
   e) Non-aerated pilot
   f) Incinerating pilot

5. State the advantages and disadvantages of the aerated and non-aerated pilots.

6. Give the causes and remedies for the various pilot conditions as illustrated in *Figure 9-65*.

Figure 9-65: Assignment — Question #6.

7. Briefly describe the *pilotstat* arranged as:

   a) A separate valve in the gas line.
   b) An electromagnetic switch or relay.
   c) A component of a combination control valve.

8. Briefly explain how gas pressure is utilized in operating:

   a) An external bleed type of diaphragm gas valve.
   b) An internal bleed type of diaphragm gas valve.

203

9. As illustrated in *Figure 9-66* state and give the function for each of the operating components found in a typical combination control valve.

Figure 9-66: Assignment — Question #9.

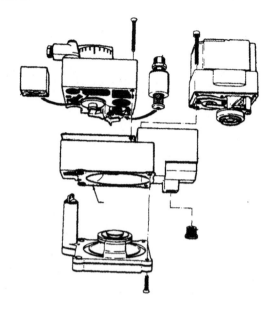

10. Draw and label a schematic wiring diagram of:

    a) a forced warm air furnace having a standard 24 volt control circuit,

    b) a forced warm air furnace having a millivolt control circuit.

11. Draw and label a pictorial wiring diagram of:

    a) a forced warm air furnace having a standard 24 volt control circuit,

    b) a forced warm air furnace having a millivolt control circuit.

12. A burner installation having a millivolt control system is experiencing problems in that the burner does not always come on. The thermostat has a heat anticipator. The millivolt gas valve opens when tapped. Explain why the burner is not operating normally.

    The millivolt readings for the system are:

    1. Close circuit or supply voltage to system from powerpile = 269 M.V.

    2. Valve opening voltage = 75 M.V.

    3. Drop across thermostat and thermostat wiring = 190 M.V.

    4. Drop across thermostat only = 30 M.V.

    5. Drop across high limit control = 2 M.V.

    6. Voltage drop across valve when operating = 77 M.V.

Principles of Gas Controls
—Part II—
Non-Electric Controls

Non Electrical Control Systems

Non electrical control systems are used on heating appliances that are designed to be self-contained, independent of any electrical requirements. The temperature control and valve functions are together in one unit often called a *thermostatic control unit*.

Non electrical controls used on space heaters are *hydraulic* in nature, working on the principle of fluid expansion caused by a temperature change. *Figure 10-1* is an illustration of a hydraulic operated control valve. Note that the temperature dial is marked with a series of numbers starting with one. Each number corresponds to a specific temperature setting. *Figure 10-2* illustrates the application of this valve on a typical space heater.

Gas fired hot water heaters use a non electric control system based on the application of *rod and tube* temperature sensing. *Figure 10-3* is an illustration detailing the operating component of such a control system.

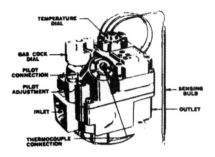

Figure 10-1: Hydraulic operated control valve.

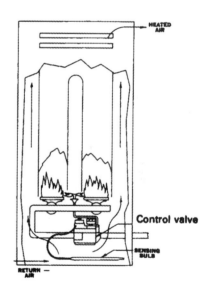

Figure 10-2: Application of a hydraulic operated control valve on a typical space heater.

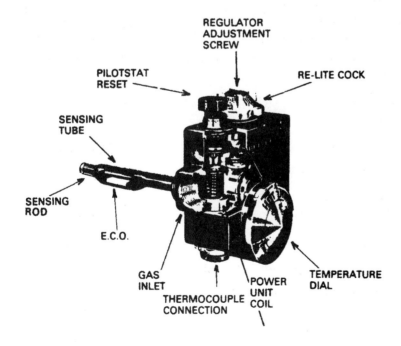

Figure 10-3: Operating components of a thermostatic hot water (heater) control valve.

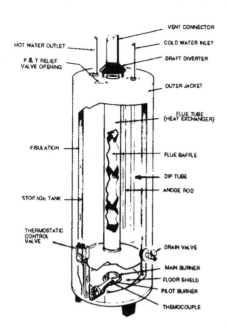

Figure 10-4: Application of a thermostatic control valve to a hot water heater.

Figure 10-4 illustrates the application of this control system to a hot water heater by which the temperature is controlled non electrically.

When the hot water is drawn from the top of the water heater tank, cold water enters the lower part of the tank as discharge from the dip tube. This lowers the water temperature near the bottom of the tank; water which was previously near the bottom is displaced towards the top. The cooler water from the dip tube is sensed by the *insertion element* of the *thermostatic control valve* which turns on the main burner. The main burner flame is established by constant pilot ignition and water temperature will increase throughout the tank. When the water temperature rises to the control setting, the main burner shuts off.

Hydraulic Control System

As illustrated in *Figure 10-5*, a hydraulic or fluid expansion type of control consists of a bulb connected by a hollow tube called a *capillary* to a flexible bellows which can expand or contract. The system is filled with fluid and sealed.

When the bulb is heated, the fluid inside the system expands and creates a fluid pressure. This fluid pressure is transmitted through the fluid expanding the bellows. This is illustrated in *Figure 10-6*.

As the bellows expand inside the valve housing, the valve disc attached to the bellows will move closing off the valve opening as illustrated in *Figure 10-7*.

Figure 10-5

Figure 10-6

Figure 10-7

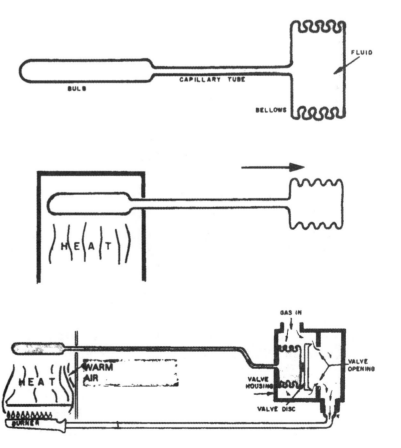

Snap-acting control (on-off control)

It is often desirable to provide a snap-acting control in which the gas flow to the burner is either fully on or fully off. A *snap disc* can be used to provide this type of action with a fluid expansion system. Such an arrangement is shown in *Figure 10-8*.

The system is filled with a fluid which has a high co-efficient of thermal expansion. A rise in temperature is sensed by the bulb causing an expansion of the fluid and a rise in its pressure, thus causing the bellows to expand. The amount of movement of the bellows depends on the temperature change being sensed and as such provides for the temperature calibration of the system.

The bellows are normally spring loaded in compression. The resulting movement caused by a change in temperature is utilized for operating the snap mechanism for valve opening and closing according to the temperature setting on the temperature dial.

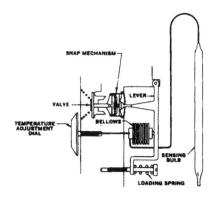

Figure 10-8: The application of a "Snap disc" to a fluid expansion control system giving snap acting control (on-off control).

Modusnap control (modulating-off control)

The modusnap control provides a modulating burner input control from a minimum burner input or firing position. Burner input modulation achieves a closer temperature control giving less temperature override.

The valve will *snap open* on minimum flame position, then *modulate* between minimum and maximum flames in proportion to the demand for heat. If the minimum flame position exceeds the heat load or demand, the valve will *snap closed*, preventing the burner from firing with an input below its minimum turndown position. *Figure 10-9* is an illustration of a modusnap control valve.

Figure 10-9: Modusnap control valve.

Remote Dial Application

Some hydraulic operated valves have a remote temperature dial which can be mounted on the outside of the appliance cabinet for convenient temperature setting. Also, a remote dial application protects the temperature dial from excessive ambient temperatures that can occur around the appliance firing area. *Figure 10-10* is a typical hydraulic operated valve having a remote temperature setting dial.

Rod and Tube Temperature Sensing

The principle of expansion and contraction of a metal in response to changes in temperature is used in the operation of automatic controls for gas appliances.

One such application is the *rod and tube* control where a rod of a material which has a low co-efficient of thermal expansion is inserted into a tube constructed of a material that has a high co-efficient of thermal expansion. *See Figure 10-11.*

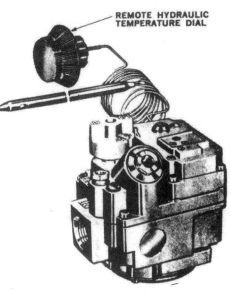

Figure 10-10: A hydraulic operated valve having a remote temperature setting dial.

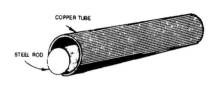

Figure 10-11

Figure 10-12

Figure 10-13: Thermostatic valve in the open position.

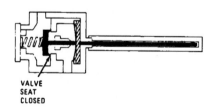

VALVE
SEAT
CLOSED

Figure 10-14: Thermostatic valve in the closed position.

A simple but efficient temperature control device can be developed based on the rod and tube application, as illustrated in *Figure 10-12*. End "B" of a copper tube is attached to a valve housing and a valve disc is attached to the steel or Invar rod at "A".

When the tube is heated, end "C" of the copper tube will move away from the valve housing. As a result the valve disc, which is attached to the steel rod, will move toward the valve opening "D" and close the valve.

A snap-action control function can be added to the basic rod and tube control by the addition of a spring and snap-acting or *clicker* disc. We now have a snap-acting *thermostat* valve giving an *on-off* control function actuated by a rod and tube sensor as illustrated in *Figures 10-13 and 10-14*.

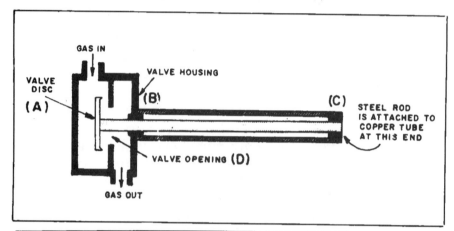

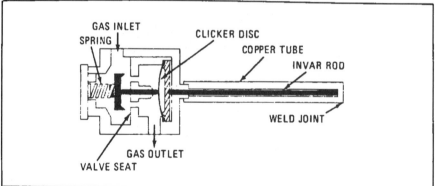

Domestic Hot Water Control System

The Thermostatic Hot Water (Heater) Control Valve
Figures 10-16 and 10-17 are illustrations of a thermostatic valve used to provide temperature control for gas fired hot water heaters. The valve consists of the following components, all housed in one compact unit as illustrated in *Figure 10-3*:

1. Water heater thermostatic control.
2. 100% automatic pilot protection.
3. Built-in high temperature *energy cut-off* device.

Figure 10-15: Domestic water heater control system.

TEMPERATURE
CONTROL
MECHANISM

SAFETY SHUTOFF CIRCUIT

Key to component functions:

1. Pilot burner
2. Thermocouple
3. Power unit
4. Safety shut off valve
5. Pilot gas adjustment
6. Snap disc
7. Rod & Tube sensor
8. Main valve
9. Main burner

Figure 10-16: Thermostatic valve use to provide temperature control for gas fired hot water heater (angle view).

Figure 10-17: Thermostatic valve used to provide temperature control for gas fired hot water heaters (top view).

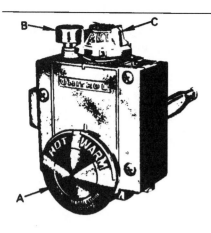

Key to operating functions:
a. Thermostatic valve
b. Automatic pilot valve
c. Manual gas valve

Figure 10-18: The hot water thermostatic control valve.

4. Main gas pressure regulator.
5. Pilot filter.
6. Pilot regulator (non adjustable).
7. Main and pilot gas cocks.

Operating Components of the Hot Water Thermostatic Control Valve

Thermostatic Valve

The thermostatic valve function is obtained by the combination of the *shank assembly* with the *clicker snap mechanism* and the main *thermostatic valve* component in the control body. Temperature setting adjustment is obtained by rotation of the front thermostat dial acting through a threaded adjustment nut and adjustment stem. The axial movement of the adjustment stem acting on a lever, which transfers force and movement from the shank assembly to the clicker mechanism, acts to change the temperature at which the thermostatic valve opens and closes. *Figures 10-19 and 10-20* illustrate the operation of this control in its closed and open positions.

Figure 10-19: Thermostatic valve in the closed position.

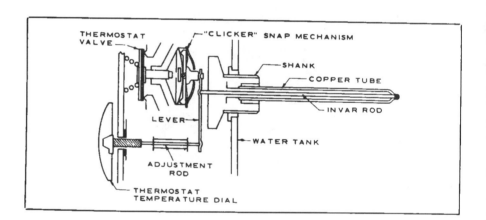

Figure 10-20: Thermostatic valve in the open position.

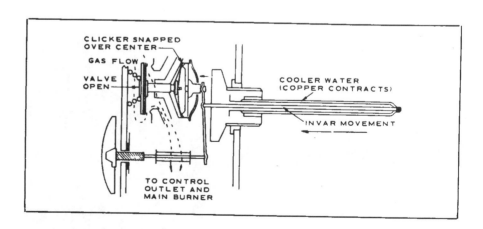

Automatic Pilot Valve (100% Safety Shut off or Pilot Protection)
The automatic pilot valve on the thermostatic valve is first in the automatic control sequence. Gas must pass through the automatic pilot valve before going to the other control functions within the control. The automatic pilot valve function is to shut off all gas to the water heater in case of pilot outage. A constant burning pilot at the main burner performs the dual function of main burner ignition and thermocouple energization. *Figures 10-21, 10-22 and 10-23* illustrate the component operation under pilot lighting (or manual reset) conditions, normal operating conditions and under conditions of pilot outage.

Manual Gas Valve (Re-lite Cock)
The manual gas valve on combination controls, such as the hot water thermostatic control valve, provides for manual control of both main gas and pilot gas. Also, in combination with the automatic pilot valve *reset* operation, it provides for safe lighting. Safe lighting is the mechanism which ensures that only the pilot gas is provided during the light up operation so as to avoid the possibility of main burner ignition during the light up operation. The manual valve on the thermostatic valve consists of a tapered conical plug type valve in a matching conical cavity in the control body. The main gas enters through a side opening in the plug and exits from the bottom of the plug through a passage in the center of the plug. Pilot gas is routed through porting that is connected in *pilot* and on positions of the valve through grooves on the outside of the tapered plug. A retainer type of assembly provides means for a gas cock spring to exert pressure on the plug so that the plug's position is maintained in the cavity against the force of the internal gas pressure. The dial of the manual gas cock contains a cut-out portion which allows the depressing of the adjacent reset button for the automatic pilot valve when the gas cock dial is in the *pilot* position *(see Figures 10-18 and 10-25)*. This interlocking feature between the manual valve and the reset mechanism provides for a safe light up. *Figure 10-24* illustrates the operation of the manual gas valve (or relite cock) as to its:

1. on-position ....both pilot and main gas are flowing
2. pilot-position..........only pilot gas is flowing
3. off-position ....both main gas and pilot gas are off

Field Adjustments for the Thermostatic Hot Water Control Valve

Pressure Regulator Adjustment
The main burner pressure regulator adjustment screw slot is filled to seal the factory pressure setting; the regulator should never need readjustment. If, however, adjustment should be necessary, proceed as follows:

Figure 10-21: Pilot lighting (or manual reset) conditions.

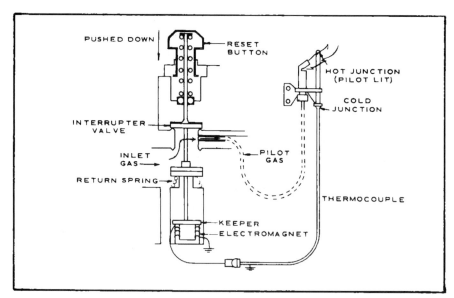

Figure 10-22: Normal operating conditions.

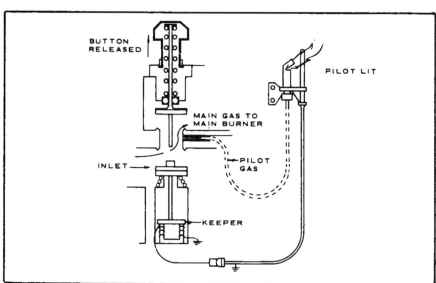

Figure 10-23: Condition of pilot outage.

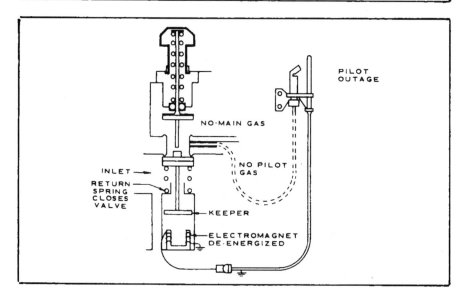

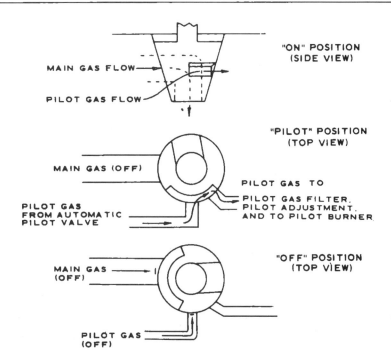

MAIN GAS FLOW →
PILOT GAS FLOW →

"ON" POSITION
(SIDE VIEW)

MAIN GAS (OFF)

PILOT GAS
FROM AUTOMATIC
PILOT VALVE

"PILOT" POSITION
(TOP VIEW)

PILOT GAS TO
PILOT GAS FILTER,
PILOT ADJUSTMENT,
AND TO PILOT BURNER

MAIN GAS
(OFF)

"OFF" POSITION
(TOP VIEW)

PILOT GAS
(OFF)

Figure 10-24: Operation of the manual gas valve.

1. Remove regulator adjustment cap by inserting screwdriver in slot and rotating counter-clockwise (see Figure 10-25).
2. With small screwdriver, remove sealant from adjustment screw slot, if necessary.
3. Rotate adjustment screw "clockwise" to increase or "counter-clockwise" to decrease pressure.
4. Replace regulator adjustment cap.

Note: Pilot pressure regulator is non adjustable.

To Recalibrate Thermostat
The thermostat is built to the most exacting standards and is a precision instrument which should never need recalibration. If, however, through misuse, tampering, or other conditions, the thermostat is found to be more than the 20°F (11°C) out of calibration, recalibrate as follows:

1. Determine water temperature at the drain valve of the tank.
2. Turn *Temperature Dial* to correspond to the actual water temperature and remove *Dial*, being careful not to rotate dial during removal. Mark location of *Stop* for reference and replace *Dial*.
3. Turn *Dial* slowly until the control snaps *Off*, remove *Temperature Dial*. Holding *Stop*, to prevent rotation, carefully loosen *Stop Adjustment Nut*. (See Figure 10-26.)
4. Taking care not to move *Temperature Adjusting Screw*, turn *Stop* until it corresponds with reference mark previously made.
5. Hold *Stop* and tighten *Stop Adjustment Nut*.
6. Replace *Temperature Dial*, recheck *Off* temperature.

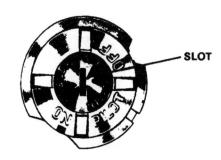

SLOT

Figure 10-25: Pressure regulator adjustment cap.

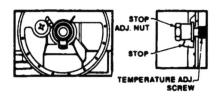

STOP
ADJ. NUT

STOP

TEMPERATURE ADJ.
SCREW

Figure 10-26

213

Note: Temperature dial marking.

160° Control (71°C.)
Mid-Zone Notch = 140° (60°C.)
Hot = 160° (71°C.)

180°Control (82°C.)
Warm = 120° (49°C.)
Normal = 140° (60°C.)
Very Hot 180° (82°C.)

CAUTION—TEMPERATURE DIAL TYPES MUST NOT BE INTERCHANGED
SINCE E.C.O. TEMPERATURES ARE MATCHED TO DIAL TYPE

Energy Cut-Off "ECO"

A bi-metallic seal thermostatic switch is installed within the copper tube along side the regular invar sensing rod of the thermostat and is called an *energy cut-off* switch *(see Figure 10-3).* The ECO switch is wired in series with the thermocouple and the power unit coil inside the thermostatic control valve. It is calibrated to open and take control at a temperature range above the thermostat control range. Both main and pilot gas are thereby shut off when this limit is reached. *Figure 10-27* illustrates the operation of the ECO.

Figure 10-27: Operation of the energy cut-off mechanism.

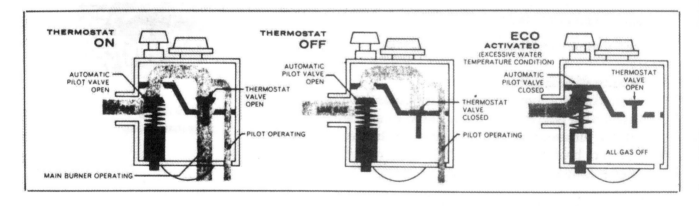

Domestic Water Heater Service Analysis Chart

Figure 10-28 is a service analysis chart that can be used to isolate various problems that can occur in domestic hot water heaters.

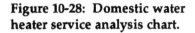

Figure 10-28: Domestic water heater service analysis chart.

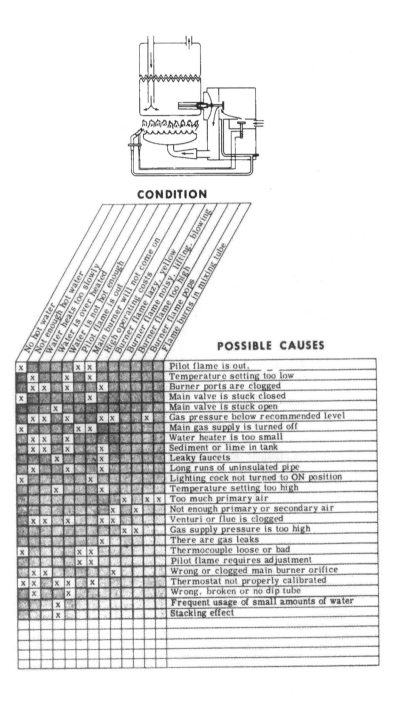

CONDITION

Conditions:
- No hot water
- Not enough hot water
- Water heats too slowly
- Water is over heated
- Water is not hot enough
- Pilot flame is out
- Main burner will not come on
- High operating costs
- Burner flame lazy, yellow
- Burner flame noisy, lifting, blowing
- Burner flame too high
- Burner flame pops
- Flame burns in mixing tube

POSSIBLE CAUSES

- Pilot flame is out.
- Temperature setting too low
- Burner ports are clogged
- Main valve is stuck closed
- Main valve is stuck open
- Gas pressure below recommended level
- Main gas supply is turned off
- Water heater is too small
- Sediment or lime in tank
- Leaky faucets
- Long runs of uninsulated pipe
- Lighting cock not turned to ON position
- Temperature setting too high
- Too much primary air
- Not enough primary or secondary air
- Venturi or flue is clogged
- Gas supply pressure is too high
- There are gas leaks
- Thermocouple loose or bad
- Pilot flame requires adjustment
- Wrong or clogged main burner orifice
- Thermostat not properly calibrated
- Wrong, broken or no dip tube
- Frequent usage of small amounts of water
- Stacking effect

Assignment

1. Define the following terms:

    a) Hydraulic or fluid expansion control system
    b) Snap acting control
    d) Remote dial
    e) Rod and tube sensing control
    f) ECO

2. Identify the components of a hydraulic operated control valve illustrated in Figure *10-29*.

Figure 10-29: Assignment — Question #2

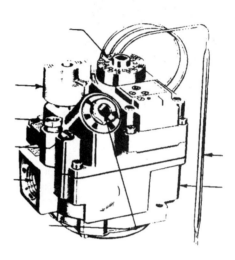

3. Give a brief description of the operation of a hydraulic sensor and actuating system used for a snap acting control illustrated in *Figure 10-30*.

Figure 10-30: Assignment — Question #3

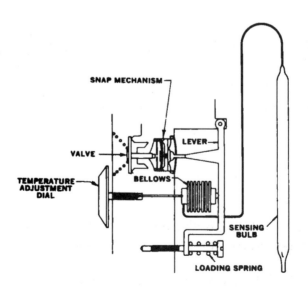

4. Identify the components of a hot water thermostatic control valve illustrated in *Figure 10-31*.

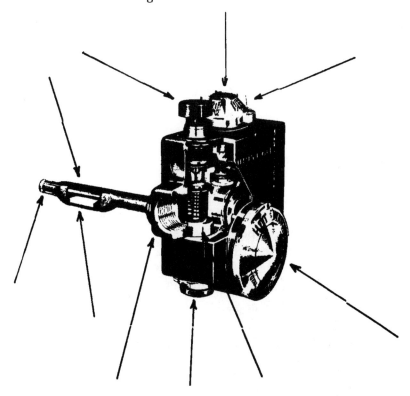

Figure 10-31: Assignment — Question #4

5. Give a brief description of the operation of a thermostatic control valve utilized to control water temperature in a hot water heater illustrated in *Figure 10-32*.

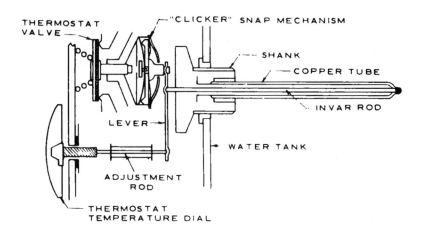

Figure 10-32: Assignment — Question #5

6. Briefly describe the procedure taken to calibrate a thermostatic control valve used to control water heater temperature.

7. State how the ECO functions to provide protection against excessive temperature conditions in the hot water heater.

11 Principles of Gas Controls —Part III— Automatic Ignition Systems

Automatic Ignition System

In the past, automatic ignition systems were mainly used on light commercial heating equipment where access to the pilot was difficult or where environmental factors, such as wind and rain, caused frequent pilot outage that often involved expensive service calls. These automatic ignition systems were mainly designed to *re-light* standing or constant pilots by either an electrical spark or a *glow coil*.[1] Typical automatic applications were duct heaters, unit heaters, and outdoor heating units such as roof top units.

Today automatic ignition systems for residential and light commercial gas heating equipment are the following:

Direct Spark Ignition (DSI)
An automatic ignition system in which the burner flame is directly ignited by an ignition spark upon each call for heat.

Intermittent Pilot (IP)
An automatic ignition system in which the burner flame is ignited by a pilot flame that is established, usually by an ignition spark, upon each call for heat.

Hot Surface Ignition (HSI)
An automatic ignition system in which the burner flame is ignited by a hot surface igniter upon each call for heat.

Unlike the older systems that mainly provided a relight function upon failure of a standing or constant pilot, DSI, IP and HSI systems are energized upon each call for heat. Also, these systems employ electronic flame sensing which has radically reduced the flame sensing response time as compared to thermal sensing via the application of a thermocouple.

---

[1] A glow coil is a high resistance wire that becomes very hot when an electrical current is applied across it, hot enough to provide an assured source of pilot ignition—sometimes referred to as *hot wire ignition*.

As with the older systems, DSI, IP and HSI systems provide the same application for appliances having remote location or where environmental conditions make automatic lighting desirable. However, the rising cost of energy and the recognition for the need to conserve fuel has provided a new impetus in the application of DSI, IP and HSI systems. These systems are especially effective with high efficiency gas appliances as we will see in the chapters dealing with high efficiency gas furnaces.

Terminology

The following are terms that are associated with the function and application of DSI, IP and HSI systems:

Trial for Ignition Time: maximum time allowed the ignition control module to establish flame upon burner start up from a call for heat.[2]

Flame Failure Response Time: time it takes the ignition control module to react to the presence or absence of the flame.[3]

Lock-out or Safety Shut-off: the process of the ignition control module shutting down upon failure to establish flame during the ignition cycle. A manual reset is required to restart the control.

Remote Reset: resetting the ignition control module by turning down the room thermostat to interrupt the 24 volt power supply to the module.

Recycling: the process of the ignition control module repeating the ignition sequence upon lost of flame detection during the burner's running cycle.

Safe Start Check: a feature of most ignition control modules that prevents it from starting if it is experiencing a real or simulated flame condition prior to the call for heat.

Prepurge: a feature of the ignition control module that allows the operation of an induced draft fan or burner fan to purge the appliance combustion chamber during the period between the thermostat's initial call for heat and the beginning of the module's ignition cycle.

Retry: a feature of the ignition control module that allows the control to repeat the ignition sequence if the burner flame is undetected after the first try for ignition.[4]

[2] Also called flame establishing period or safety switch timing.

[3] Codes require 90 seconds for systems under 400,000 Btuh. Most thermocouples will give a flame failure response time of 60 to 90 seconds. DSI, IP and HSI automatic ignition systems will usually have a 0.8 second flame failure response time.

[4] A control that has this feature will usually be equipped with a set number of retries before locking out into safety.

Direct Spark Ignition Systems

Direct spark ignition or DSI is a method of burner ignition in which ignition is directed to main flame by a high voltage electrical spark rather than by a pilot flame. As illustrated in *Figure11-1*, the DSI system consists of the following components:

- System Control (Ignition Control Module)
- Spark Igniter
- Flame Sensor
- Gas Control Valve
- Auxiliary Controls (i.e., temperature controller, high limit, transformer, etc.)

Figure 11-1: System component of a DSI system.

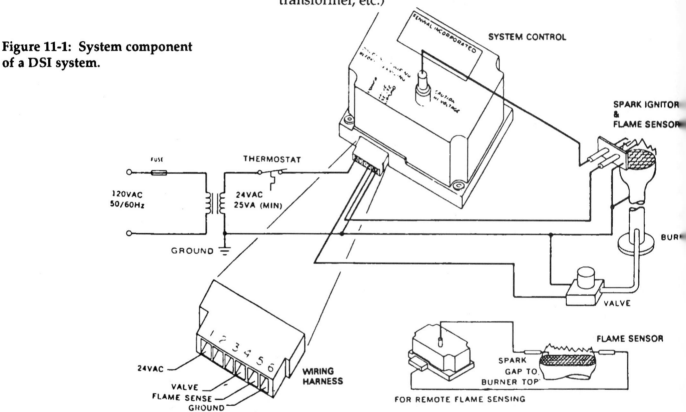

System Control Module

The system or ignition control module controls system operations. It also provides a control wiring panel, terminal strip(s) or harness for wiring of external operating controls.

The system control module is usually powered by a 24 VAC transformer and is activated by a temperature controller (i.e., thermostat).

The following functions are usually provided by the system control module:

1. Provides a *safe-start-check* before each start up. When a false flame condition is present (i.e., short to ground) before start up, the control module will not initiate the burner start up. *Note:* All DSI, as well as IP and HSI systems have this feature.

2. Provides power to operate the gas control valve.

3. Generates a high *open circuit voltage* at the spark igniter for direct ignition of the main burner flame.

4. Discontinues ignition spark when flame is established or goes into *safety lock out* if flame fails to ignite on burner start up.

5. Protects against both flame out and momentary interruption of electrical power supply.

Spark Igniter

The spark igniter consists of an inner electrode (insulated rod) and an outer *ground* electrode that may be a normal electrode or the top of the burner. The tip of the spark electrode extends into the path of the main burner gas, arcing the ignition spark across the *spark gap* igniting the main flame.

Gas Control Valve

DSI, IP and HSI systems employ *valve redundancy*. As illustrated in *Figure 11-2*, the control valve consists of two *in line* main valves that provide added protection against valve failure. This ensures positive gas shut off in the event dirt or debris lodges on one of the valve seats.

The operation of the control valve is very similar to that of a standard control valve. On a call for heat, gas enters the control through the manual on-off valve, past the solenoid operated first main valve and flows through the servo pressure operated second main valve.

On intermittent pilot systems (IP), the first main valve is energized when the thermostat calls for heat and gas is allowed to flow to the pilot burner. The second main valve is not energized until the pilot flame is proven.

On DSI and HSI systems, both the first and second main valves are energized when the thermostat calls for heat.

Flame Sensor

The flame sensor works on the principle of *flame conduction* and *rectification*. In the presence of the burner flame, a very small AC signal current is sent to the flame sensor (often called the *flame rod*) from the system or ignition control module. This very small AC signal current is conducted and rectified through the flame to a DC signal current.[5] The DC signal current returns through the system

---

[5] Air and gas molecules between the flame sensor (i.e., the flame rod) and the grounded area of the burner head become *ionized* and are able to conduct an electrical current. The current through the flame flows mostly in one direction because of the size difference between the flame sensor and ground areas, and results in a pulsing direct current (i.e., flame rectification principle).

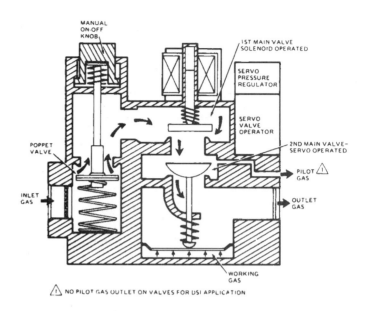

Figure 11-2: Schematic diagram of a control valve equipped with two in line main valves giving valve redundancy.

ground to the control module thus proving the presence of the main flame. The flame sensor and the control module continuously monitor the flame during the burner on period or duty cycle. The signal or *flame current* is an extremely small current in the microampere range (i.e., 1,000,000 microamps (UA) = 1 ampere).

Sequence of Operation

Upon a call for heat, the system or ignition control module energizes the spark igniter and at the same time opens the gas valve. Once burner ignition has been achieved, flame sensor detection terminates the *trial for ignition period* and interrupts the ignition spark. The burner will operate until the demand for heat is satisfied and the thermostat de-energizes the system.

In the event of a flame out, some DSI systems will lock out immediately; others will retry for ignition before locking out on safety. Several reset options are available. If the system should lock out, some systems can be *recycled* from the thermostat, while others have a manual reset button on the body of the system control module. In either case, the reset function provides timing protection to initiate safety lock out action upon component malfunction. Any false flame signal, including an electrical short to ground, will result in a safety shut down of the DSI system.

Sequence Diagram
Figure 11-3, illustrates the general sequence of operation of a DSI system. *Note:* The unshaded areas show normal operation whereas the shaded areas show a system malfunction.

222

Figure 11-3: Sequence diagram of a DSI system.

Contents of diagram:

TEMPERATURE CONTROL CALLS FOR HEAT

SPARK ON → IF NO SPARK—INTO LOCKOUT — SEE NOTE /1\

VALVE OPENS → FAILURE TO IGNITE —INTO LOCKOUT — SEE NOTE /1\

BURNER IGNITES —SPARK CUTS OFF

IF POWER INTERRUPTED—SYSTEM SHUTS OFF UNTIL POWER IS RESTORED

IF FLAMEOUT OCCURS —SPARK RETURNS FOR REIGNITION — SEE NOTE /2\

TEMPERATURE CONTROL SATISFIED - BURNER OFF

/1\ CORRECTION AND SYSTEM RESET NECESSARY.

/2\ IF BURNER DOES NOT REIGNITE, SYSTEM GOES INTO SAFETY LOCKOUT. CORRECTION AND SYSTEM RESET IS NECESSARY.

Honeywell DSI Systems

Specifications

1. Trial for ignition period or time (i.e., safety lock out timing): 4, 6, 11 or 21 seconds depending upon the system control module.

2. Flame failure response time: 0.8 seconds.

3. Flame current signal:
   4 UA min. for S825 system control module.
   1.5 UA min. for S87 system control module.

4. Reset time:
   S825 and S87 system control modules utilize remote reset, the system is reset from a lock out condition by turning the temperature controller down, no call for heat, for 30 seconds.

Installation Requirements

Spark Igniter and Flame Sensor Location
The location of the spark igniter and flame sensor are determined by the appliance manufacturer, and field alterations are not recommended. Changing the position of either the spark igniter or flame sensor could create poor ignition characteristics and inadequate

Figure 11-4: Honeywell DSI system components showing S825 and S87 system control modules, VR8450 dual valve combination gas control valve, Q330 spark igniter, Q354 flame sensor, and Q347 combined spark igniter-flame sensor.

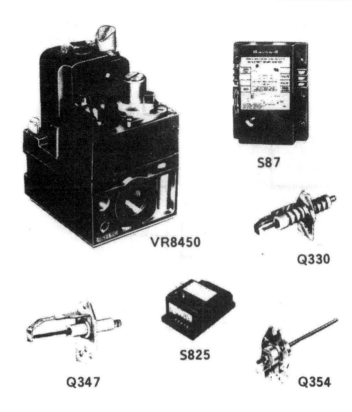

Figure 11-5: Wiring arrangements for Honeywell S87C DSI system.

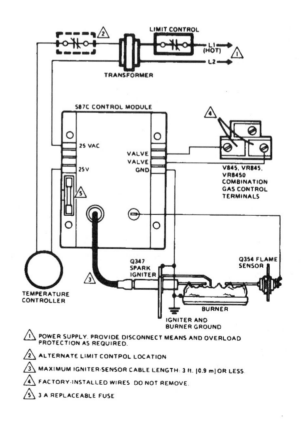

flame current readings resulting in nuisance shut down. However, if adjustments are required due to replacement of defective components, the following should be considered:

a) The spark igniter should be positioned so that only the tips of the electrodes are immersed in the burner flame so that the burner will ignite smoothly. This is usually accomplished by mounting the igniter at a location relative to the main burner where the electrode gap will be approximately 1/4" (6.4 mm) above the burner and with the igniter positioned so that gas is allowed to flow into one of the three open sides of the spark gap (i.e., where the outer electrode does not block the gas entrance). *(See Figure 11-6.)*

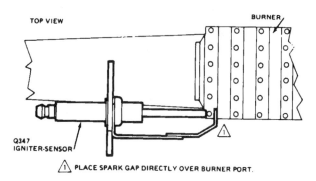

Figure 11-6: Q347 igniter-sensor location on main burner.

b) The flame sensor, likewise, should be mounted at a fixed location relative to the main burner so that only the tip of the flame rod is positioned in the burner flame—usually about 1" (25.4 mm). It may be mounted on the same bracket as the igniter or on a separate bracket. The distance from the flame sensor rod to the burner surface is dependent on the type of flame sensor, the type of burner and the flame configuration. However, the position selected must produce a constant sensor current for the flame monitoring circuit in the control module.

Grounding DSI Systems
For DSI systems to operate properly, the spark igniter, flame sensor, control module, and L2 side of the transformer must all share a common ground with the main burner *(see Figure 11-5)*. Therefore, it is important to ensure that all grounded connections are clean and tight to provide a trouble free system.

Note:
Systems with S825 control modules must be grounded to earth ground. Systems with S87 control modules must be grounded to the main burner, but it is not necessary that the burner be earth grounded.

Component Checks

Control Module Spark Ignition Circuit

Figure 11-7: Checking spark ignition circuit.

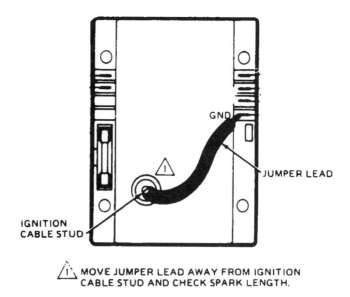

GND

JUMPER LEAD

IGNITION
CABLE STUD

⚠ 1 MOVE JUMPER LEAD AWAY FROM IGNITION
CABLE STUD AND CHECK SPARK LENGTH.

To check the spark ignition circuit proceed as follows:

a) Shut off gas supply to gas control valve.

b) Disconnect the ignition cable at the control module stud terminal to isolate the circuit from the igniter or igniter sensor.

c) Prepare a short jumper lead using heavy insulated wire, such as
ignition cable.

d) Touch one end of the jumper firmly to the GND terminal on the
system control module. *Do not* remove the existing ground
lead. Slowly move the other end of the jumper wire toward the
stud terminal on the control module to establish a spark.

e) Pull the wire away from the stud and note the length of gap at
which spark discontinues.

f) A spark length of 1/8" (3.2 mm) for the S87 and 3/16" (4.8 mm)
for the S825 or more indicates satisfactory voltage output. If no
arc can be established or the maximum spark is less than indicated above and power to the control module input terminals
was proven, the control module should be replaced.

Flame Current Check
If the flame signal is less than the required minimum or is unsteady,
the system will lock out.

To check the actual flame current signal from the flame sensor to the system control module, proceed as follows:

a) Connect a meter (DC micro ammeter scale) in series with the flame signal ground wire *(see Figure 11-8)*. Disconnect the ground wire at the control module. Connect the rod (positive) lead of the meter to the free end of the ground wire. Connect the black (negative) meter lead to the quick-connect ground terminal on the control module.

b) Restart the system and read the meter. The flame sensor current must be at least 1.5 UA for the S87 and 4 UA for the S825. The reading must be steady. If the reading is below the value designated above or is unsteady, check the burner flame, flame sensor (igniter-sensor) location and electrical connections as follows:

Figure 11-8: Flame current measurement for S87 DSI system.

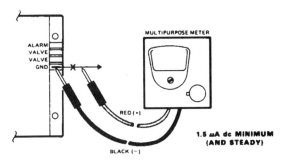

FLAME SENSOR CURRENT CHECK—USE μA SCALE

Burner Flame: The flame sensor must be constantly immersed in flame. Check burner flame conditions as shown in *Figure 11-9*. If necessary, improve the flame condition or relocate the flame sensor to a place on the main burner where flame conditions are better.

Flame Sensor: The flame sensor is best when about 1" (25.4 mm) of flame rod is immersed in the burner flame. A bent flame rod or mounting bracket can affect flame signal. Bend the flame rod back to the correct position if necessary.

Excess temperature at the ceramic flame rod insulator may cause leakage to ground, decreasing the flame signal. Replace the flame sensor if the ceramic insulator is cracked and relocate the sensor to an area of lower ambient temperature if necessary.

Electrical Connections, Shorts: Connections at the flame sensor or igniter-sensor must be clean and tight. If wiring needs replacement, use moisture resistant number 18 wire rated for continuous duty up to 221°F (105°C).

Figure 11-9: If flame current is under the required minimum for the system control module, check for the following burner flame conditions.

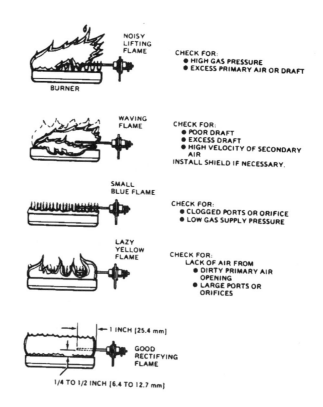

Trouble Shooting Guide for S87 DSI System

The following is a trouble shooting guide for the S87 DSI system. To use the guide, start the system by setting the temperature controller to call for heat. Observe the system response and establish the type of problem from the normal operations using *Figure 11-10*.

To effectively use a trouble shooting guide, each step should be completed in the proper sequence, performing whatever test or checks are suggested. After the completion of each test or check, the guide will indicate the next logical step in the trouble shooting procedure, based on the results of the previous check.

Note: Components should be replaced *only* when suggested by the trouble shooting guide, and *only* after completing each check in the required sequence.

Intermittent Pilot Systems

Intermittent pilot systems (IP) differ from DSI and HSI systems in that a spark ignited pilot is established to ignite the main flame upon each burner start up. The flame sensor continuously monitors the pilot flame which remains on during the burner running cycle. The elements of a typical IP system are illustrated in *Figure 11-11*.

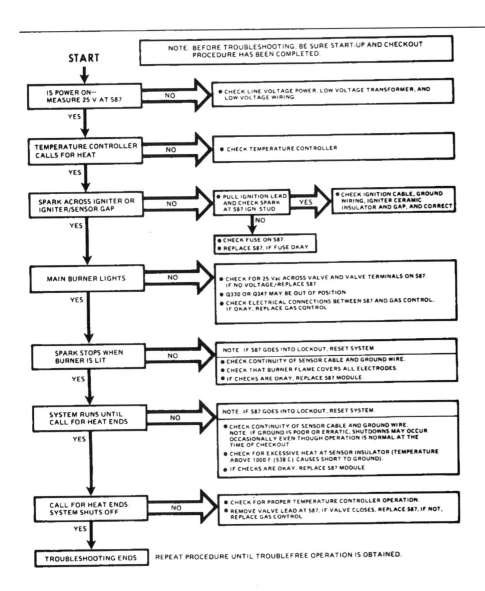

START

NOTE: BEFORE TROUBLESHOOTING, BE SURE START-UP AND CHECKOUT PROCEDURE HAS BEEN COMPLETED.

IS POWER ON— MEASURE 25 V AT S87 — NO → ● CHECK LINE VOLTAGE POWER, LOW VOLTAGE TRANSFORMER, AND LOW VOLTAGE WIRING

YES

TEMPERATURE CONTROLLER CALLS FOR HEAT — NO → ● CHECK TEMPERATURE CONTROLLER

YES

SPARK ACROSS IGNITER OR IGNITER/SENSOR GAP — NO → ● PULL IGNITION LEAD AND CHECK SPARK AT S87 IGN STUD — YES → ● CHECK IGNITION CABLE, GROUND WIRING, IGNITER CERAMIC INSULATOR AND GAP, AND CORRECT

NO ↓

● CHECK FUSE ON S87.
● REPLACE S87, IF FUSE OKAY

YES

MAIN BURNER LIGHTS — NO → ● CHECK FOR 25 Vac ACROSS VALVE AND VALVE TERMINALS ON S87. IF NO VOLTAGE, REPLACE S87.
● Q330 OR Q347 MAY BE OUT OF POSITION
● CHECK ELECTRICAL CONNECTIONS BETWEEN S87 AND GAS CONTROL. IF OKAY, REPLACE GAS CONTROL

YES

SPARK STOPS WHEN BURNER IS LIT — NO → NOTE: IF S87 GOES INTO LOCKOUT, RESET SYSTEM
● CHECK CONTINUITY OF SENSOR CABLE AND GROUND WIRE.
● CHECK THAT BURNER FLAME COVERS ALL ELECTRODES.
● IF CHECKS ARE OKAY, REPLACE S87 MODULE.

YES

SYSTEM RUNS UNTIL CALL FOR HEAT ENDS — NO → NOTE: IF S87 GOES INTO LOCKOUT, RESET SYSTEM.
● CHECK CONTINUITY OF SENSOR CABLE AND GROUND WIRE. NOTE: IF GROUND IS POOR OR ERRATIC, SHUTDOWNS MAY OCCUR OCCASIONALLY EVEN THOUGH OPERATION IS NORMAL AT THE TIME OF CHECKOUT
● CHECK FOR EXCESSIVE HEAT AT SENSOR INSULATOR (TEMPERATURE ABOVE 1000 F (538 C) CAUSES SHORT TO GROUND).
● IF CHECKS ARE OKAY, REPLACE S87 MODULE.

YES

CALL FOR HEAT ENDS. SYSTEM SHUTS OFF — NO → ● CHECK FOR PROPER TEMPERATURE CONTROLLER OPERATION.
● REMOVE VALVE LEAD AT S87. IF VALVE CLOSES, REPLACE S87, IF NOT, REPLACE GAS CONTROL

YES

TROUBLESHOOTING ENDS   REPEAT PROCEDURE UNTIL TROUBLEFREE OPERATION IS OBTAINED.

Figure 11-10: Trouble shooting guide for the S87 DSI system.

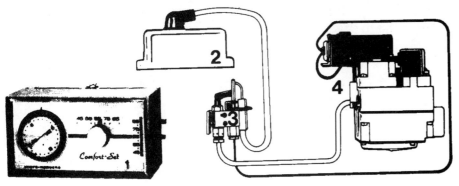

Figure 11-11: The basic elements of a typical IP system: (1) temperature controller; (2) solid state igniter; (3) pilot assembly incorporating the igniter and flame sensor and (4) gas control valve.

With reference to *Figure 11-11*, we can see the essentials of the operating sequence of an intermittent pilot system. When the thermostat (1) calls for heat, it signals the solid state igniter (2) to establish an ignition spark and pilot gas at the pilot assembly (3). The flame sensor, incorporated in the pilot assembly, senses the pilot flame and activates the main valve within the gas control valve (4) to bring on the main flame.

229

Intermittent pilot systems are growing in popularity as a method for eliminating standing pilots. Their growth in application has led to a variety of different systems with similarities and differences between them.

All intermittent pilot systems will incorporate a safe-start-check and will employ valve redundancy in controlling gas flow. Nearly all have a 0.8 second flame failure response time. Systems having 100% safety shut off will utilize *remote reset,* using the thermostat or main operating controller to reset the system, if system lock out occurs.

Some IP systems are designed to give only non 100% safety shut off when used for natural gas operation.[6] These systems require the addition of a *lock out timer* or *module* to give complete 100% safety shut off. Other systems are designed having internal circuitry that provides for 100% safety shut off. Also, some systems have the capacity to give a system prepurge as a feature in their start up sequence when used with power blower combustion systems such as an induced draft fan. This eliminates the need for an external prepurge timing device.

Because of the variety of IP systems in use today, this chapter can not hope to cover all the various systems. As a result, this chapter will examine the following two systems that give a good representation of current IP technology and application.

1. White Rodgers Cycle Pilot System

2. Honeywell S8660D Intermittent Pilot Ignition System

White Rodgers Cycle Pilot System

The White Rodgers cycle pilot system is an intermittent pilot system consisting of the following components as illustrated in *Figure 11-12.*

Gas Control Valve
The gas control valve incorporates the following features:

i)   Pilot/redundant solenoid valve *(see Figure 11-13).*

ii)   Integral pressure switch to sense incoming gas pressure *(see Figure 11-13).*

iii) Relay operated main valve *(see Figure 11-13).*

iv)   Socket to accept plug in mercury flame sensor *(see Figure 11-14).*

---

[6] Complete 100% safety shut off is required for propane gas operation due to the higher specific gravity or relative density of propane gas.

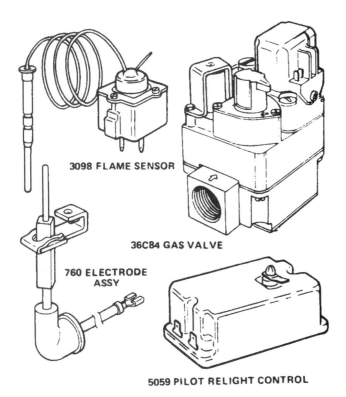

3098 FLAME SENSOR

36C84 GAS VALVE

760 ELECTRODE ASSY

5059 PILOT RELIGHT CONTROL

Figure 11-12: White Rodgers cycle pilot system showing the flame sensor, gas valve, electrode assembly and pilot relight control.

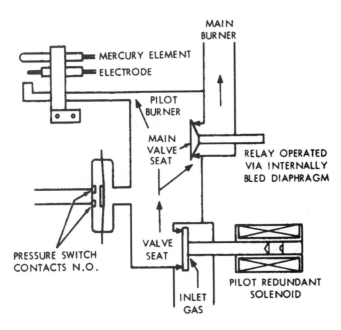

MERCURY ELEMENT
ELECTRODE

MAIN BURNER

PILOT BURNER

MAIN VALVE SEAT

RELAY OPERATED VIA INTERNALLY BLED DIAPHRAGM

PRESSURE SWITCH CONTACTS N.O.

VALVE SEAT

PILOT REDUNDANT SOLENOID

INLET GAS

Figure 11-13: A schematic diagram of the White Rodgers cycle pilot gas control valve showing pilot/redundant solenoid operated pilot valve, relay operated main valve and normally open (NO) pressure switch.

The pilot valve is solenoid operated and is controlled directly by the room thermostat. Pilot gas is taken from between the two valves. The main valve is energized when the flame sensor that is plugged into the valve (*see Figure 11-14*) has received sufficient heat from the pilot flame.

The pressure switch, shown in *Figure 11-13*, is used to sense incoming gas pressure. The switch is normally wired so that an interruption in gas pressure causes the switch to de-energize the pilot solenoid valve, stopping all gas flow. When gas supply pressure is restored, the system will resume its normal function. *Figure 11-15* illustrates the location of the pressure switch on the valve body as well as the pin/socket arrangement for the mercury switch plug in.

Figure 11-14: Mercury flame sensor being plugged into the valve.

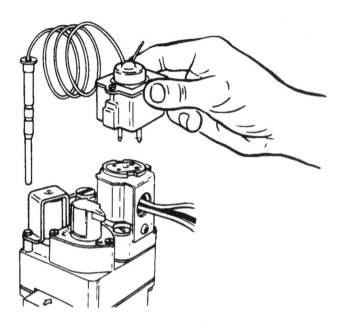

Figure 11-15: Pressure switch location and mercury switch pin/socket arrangement on the White Rodgers cycle pilot gas control valve.

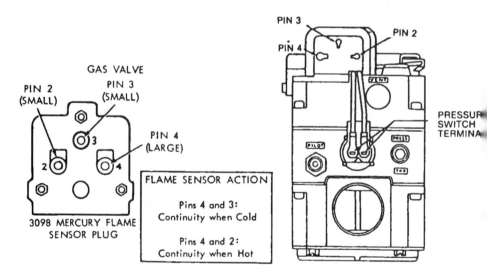

GAS VALVE

PIN 2 (SMALL)

PIN 3 (SMALL)

PIN 4 (LARGE)

3098 MERCURY FLAME SENSOR PLUG

FLAME SENSOR ACTION

Pins 4 and 3:
Continuity when Cold

Pins 4 and 2:
Continuity when Hot

PIN 3

PIN 2

PIN 4

PRESSURE SWITCH TERMINAL

Figure 11-16 illustrates a method of testing the pilot gas valve. By laying a flat steel rule or small screw driver blade across the top of the pilot solenoid coil, you can determine if the coil is energized or de-energized by the magnetic pull.

The Flame Sensor
The flame sensor is a mercury filled sensing bulb connected by a

capillary to a diaphragm assembly. When the pilot flame heats the bulb, increasing mercury pressure activates the diaphragm assembly to make or break a *snap switch* that is mechanically coupled to the diaphragm assembly.

The flame usually responds to the presence of flame heat within 30 to 40 seconds. It takes approximately 20 seconds for a sensor to cool and switch back to the *cold* position. For the flame sensor to operate effectively, the upper 3/4" (19 mm) of the sensing bulb should be engulfed in the pilot flame.

Figure 11-16: Testing the pilot solenoid coil.

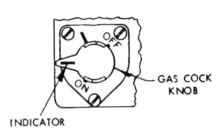

The Pilot Relight Control
The pilot relight control is energized by the room thermostat. It generates a high ignition voltage to establish an ignition spark at the pilot assembly. Once pilot flame is established, it detects the presence of the pilot flame by the process of flame rectification and will de-energize the ignition spark within 0.8 seconds.

Because of the quick flame failure response time, the relight control can detect the loss of a flame within 0.8 seconds and begin generating ignition spark to re-establish the pilot flame. The flame rectification circuit uses the pilot burner and relight chassis to provide a path for the returning *flame current*. This means that all relight controls must be properly grounded to operate. Some relight controls are equipped with metal mounting bosses that help ensure a good ground. If the relight control generates a spark, but does not stop sparking once a flame is present, a bad ground should be suspected.

Some pilot relight controls will incorporate a *lock out timer*. For natural gas application non 100% safety shut off (i.e., pilot protection) is adequate because of the self-venting nature of the gas due to its low specific gravity or relative density. However, for heavier fuel gases, such as propane, the pilot relight control must incorporate a lock out timer to give 100% safety shut off.

233

The lock out timer is used to de-energize the gas valve in the event that a pilot flame or main burner flame is not established within the specified timing (i.e., trial for ignition time). The timer is controlled by the flame sensor, and keeps track of the amount of time that elapses before the main valve is energized. It is usually a *warp switch heater* that is energized by the thermostat and is de-energized when the flame sensor switches to turn on the main valve.[7]

The lock out timer is wired in series with both the pilot and main gas valves. If the warp switch opens, both valves are de-energized. To reset the timer, the thermostat circuit must be interrupted (i.e., thermostat turned back) for 3–5 minutes.

Figure 11-17: Electrode mounting on the pilot burner.

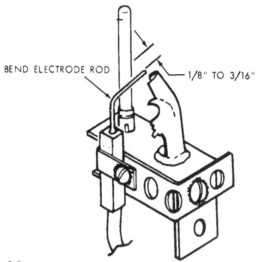

BEND ELECTRODE ROD

1/8" TO 3/16"

Electrode Assembly
The ignition and cable assembly are designed to be attached directly to the pilot burner without modification of the burner. As illustrated in *Figure 11-17*, adjust the electrode rod by bending so that the spark will jump to the mercury element and the rod tip will be in the pilot flame. Spark gap from the rod tip to mercury element must be from 1/8" to 3/16" (3 mm to 4.75 mm). The spark must jump through the pilot gas, not to the pilot burner or bracket.

The cable is made of high temperature insulation surrounding a stranded conductor. Both ends of the cable are usually terminated with quick connect terminals. One terminal is designed to fit the ignition electrode, while the other fits the relight control.

The ignition electrode function is to deliver the high voltage spark and detect the rectified flame current for the ignition circuit. Most problems that are encountered with poor or erratic ignition are due to misapplication of the ignition electrode or damaged or loose cable assemblies.

[7] A warp switch heater is a small resistance heating element which when powered in a circuit will heat and activate a heat sensitive bi-metal switch called the warp switch.

Sequence of Operations

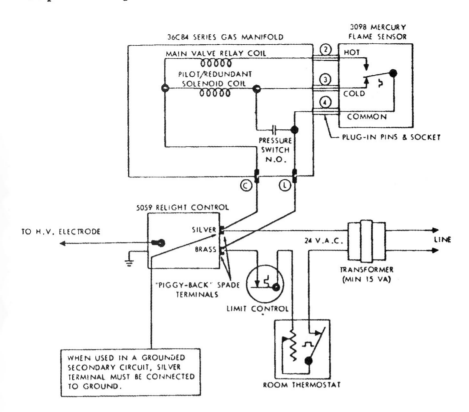

Figure 11-18: Wiring schematic of the White Rodgers cycle pilot system for natural gas operation (i.e., non 100% safety shut off).

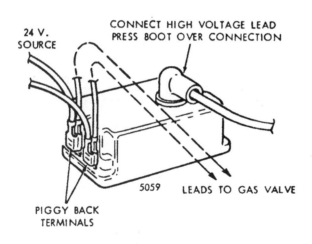

Figure 11-19: Piggy back terminals on pilot relight control facilitating power connection to gas control valve.

The following is a description of the normal start up sequence for the White Rodgers cycle pilot system as illustrated in *Figure 11-18*.

1. When the thermostat calls for heat, a circuit is completed through the limit control to the relight control. Also, via piggy back terminal connections at the relight control, the gas valve is powered at terminals L and C (*see Figure 11-19*).

2. During the first instant the system is energized, the pressure switch contacts remain open, forcing the circuit to be completed through the mercury flame sensor terminals 4 and 3, the pilot solenoid coil, and terminal C at the gas valve.

3. At this time, the pilot gas valve is energized and the relight control initiates sparking at the pilot assembly.

4. A pilot flame is established which is detected by the ignition circuit of the relight control which terminates the sparking.

5. When the pilot solenoid valve opens, gas pressure is allowed into the main valve cavity, closing the pressure switch to provide a holding circuit for the pilot solenoid coil.

6. The pilot flame heats the flame sensor and after approximately 5 seconds causes the sensor to switch to the hot position energizing the main valve relay coil.

7. The main flame is established and is discontinued only when:
   i)   thermostat is satisfied
   ii)   interruption of power supply
   iii)   incoming gas pressure falls below the setting of the pressure switch–5"wc (1.25 kPa).

Trouble Shooting
Figures 11-20, 11-21, 11-22, and 11-23 are trouble shooting guides that provide a systematic method for isolating equipment problems associated with White Rodgers cycle pilot systems—natural gas system.

Figure 11-20

NATURAL GAS SYSTEMS

NO SPARK

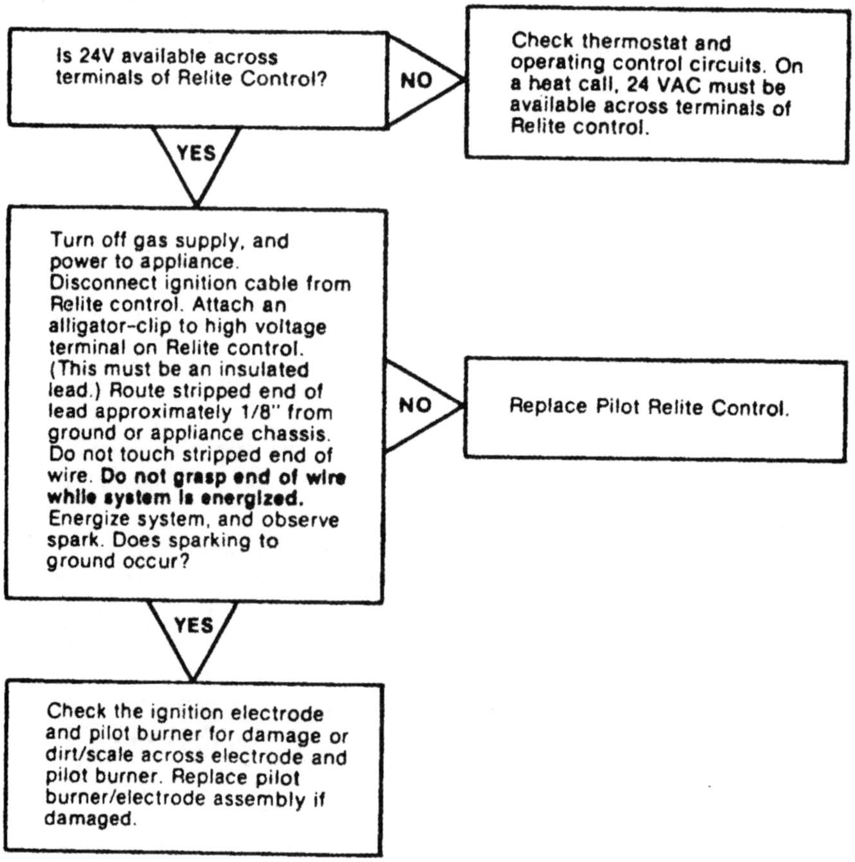

Is 24V available across terminals of Relite Control? — **NO** → Check thermostat and operating control circuits. On a heat call, 24 VAC must be available across terminals of Relite control.

YES ↓

Turn off gas supply, and power to appliance. Disconnect ignition cable from Relite control. Attach an alligator-clip to high voltage terminal on Relite control. (This must be an insulated lead.) Route stripped end of lead approximately 1/8" from ground or appliance chassis. Do not touch stripped end of wire. **Do not grasp end of wire while system is energized.** Energize system, and observe spark. Does sparking to ground occur? — **NO** → Replace Pilot Relite Control.

YES ↓

Check the ignition electrode and pilot burner for damage or dirt/scale across electrode and pilot burner. Replace pilot burner/electrode assembly if damaged.

236

Figure 11-21

NATURAL GAS SYSTEMS

SPARK IS PRESENT — PILOT WILL NOT LIGHT

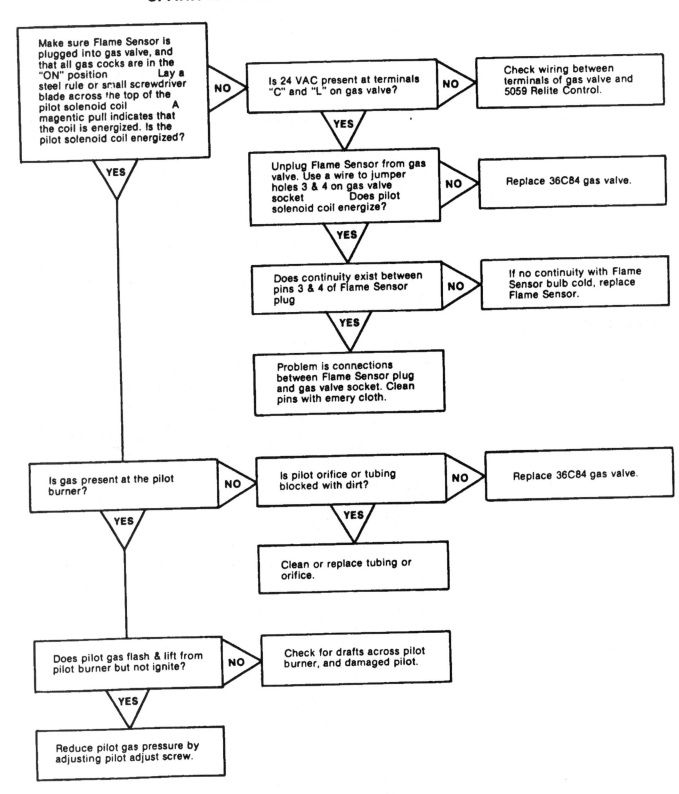

Make sure Flame Sensor is plugged into gas valve, and that all gas cocks are in the "ON" position. Lay a steel rule or small screwdriver blade across the top of the pilot solenoid coil. A magentic pull indicates that the coil is energized. Is the pilot solenoid coil energized?

NO → Is 24 VAC present at terminals "C" and "L" on gas valve?

NO → Check wiring between terminals of gas valve and 5059 Relite Control.

YES → Unplug Flame Sensor from gas valve. Use a wire to jumper holes 3 & 4 on gas valve socket. Does pilot solenoid coil energize?

NO → Replace 36C84 gas valve.

YES → Does continuity exist between pins 3 & 4 of Flame Sensor plug

NO → If no continuity with Flame Sensor bulb cold, replace Flame Sensor.

YES → Problem is connections between Flame Sensor plug and gas valve socket. Clean pins with emery cloth.

YES (from first box) → Is gas present at the pilot burner?

NO → Is pilot orifice or tubing blocked with dirt?

NO → Replace 36C84 gas valve.

YES → Clean or replace tubing or orifice.

YES → Does pilot gas flash & lift from pilot burner but not ignite?

NO → Check for drafts across pilot burner, and damaged pilot.

YES → Reduce pilot gas pressure by adjusting pilot adjust screw.

Figure 11-22

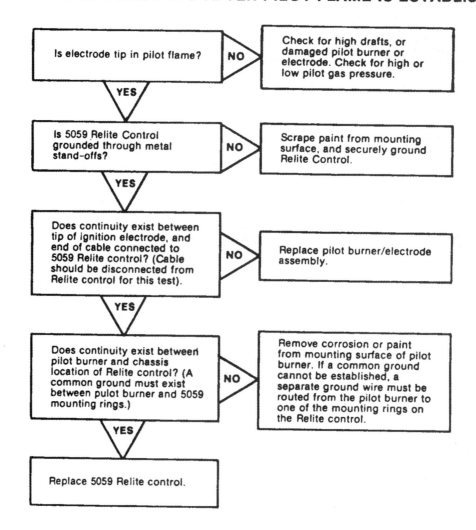

NATURAL GAS SYSTEMS

SPARK WILL NOT SHUT-OFF AFTER PILOT FLAME IS ESTABLISHED

Is electrode tip in pilot flame?	NO → Check for high drafts, or damaged pilot burner or electrode. Check for high or low pilot gas pressure.
↓ YES	
Is 5059 Relite Control grounded through metal stand-offs?	NO → Scrape paint from mounting surface, and securely ground Relite Control.
↓ YES	
Does continuity exist between tip of ignition electrode, and end of cable connected to 5059 Relite control? (Cable should be disconnected from Relite control for this test).	NO → Replace pilot burner/electrode assembly.
↓ YES	
Does continuity exist between pilot burner and chassis location of Relite control? (A common ground must exist between pulot burner and 5059 mounting rings.)	NO → Remove corrosion or paint from mounting surface of pilot burner. If a common ground cannot be established, a separate ground wire must be routed from the pilot burner to one of the mounting rings on the Relite control.
↓ YES	
Replace 5059 Relite control.	

Figure 11-23

NATURAL GAS SYSTEMS

PILOT LIGHTS, OR CYCLES "ON" AND "OFF" — NO MAIN BURNER IGNITION

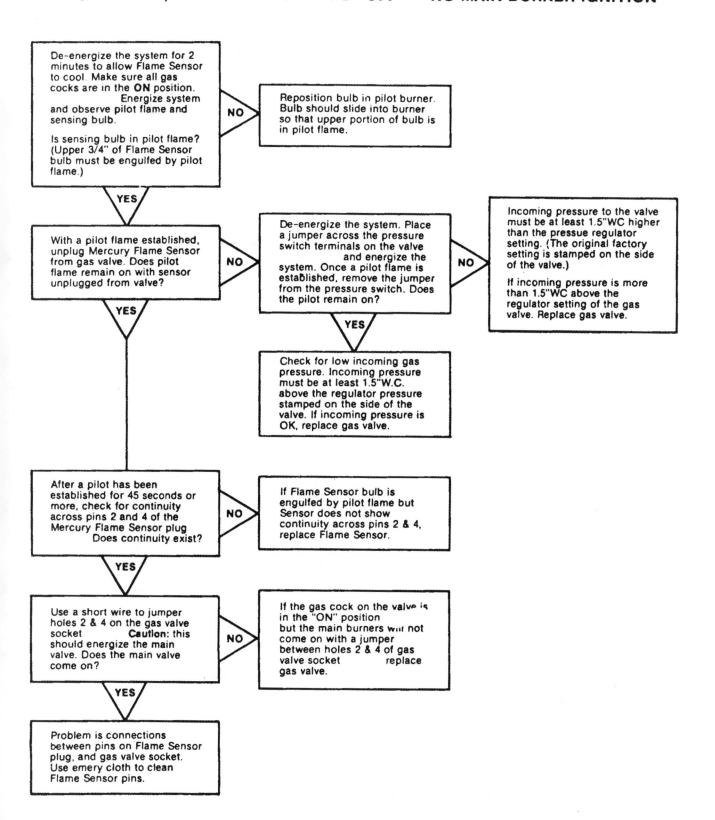

De-energize the system for 2 minutes to allow Flame Sensor to cool. Make sure all gas cocks are in the **ON** position. Energize system and observe pilot flame and sensing bulb.

Is sensing bulb in pilot flame? (Upper 3/4" of Flame Sensor bulb must be engulfed by pilot flame.)

NO → Reposition bulb in pilot burner. Bulb should slide into burner so that upper portion of bulb is in pilot flame.

YES

With a pilot flame established, unplug Mercury Flame Sensor from gas valve. Does pilot flame remain on with sensor unplugged from valve?

NO → De-energize the system. Place a jumper across the pressure switch terminals on the valve and energize the system. Once a pilot flame is established, remove the jumper from the pressure switch. Does the pilot remain on?

NO → Incoming pressure to the valve must be at least 1.5"WC higher than the pressue regulator setting. (The original factory setting is stamped on the side of the valve.)

If incoming pressure is more than 1.5"WC above the regulator setting of the gas valve. Replace gas valve.

YES

Check for low incoming gas pressure. Incoming pressure must be at least 1.5"W.C. above the regulator pressure stamped on the side of the valve. If incoming pressure is OK, replace gas valve.

YES

After a pilot has been established for 45 seconds or more, check for continuity across pins 2 and 4 of the Mercury Flame Sensor plug Does continuity exist?

NO → If Flame Sensor bulb is engulfed by pilot flame but Sensor does not show continuity across pins 2 & 4, replace Flame Sensor.

YES

Use a short wire to jumper holes 2 & 4 on the gas valve socket **Caution:** this should energize the main valve. Does the main valve come on?

NO → If the gas cock on the valve is in the "ON" position but the main burners will not come on with a jumper between holes 2 & 4 of gas valve socket replace gas valve.

YES

Problem is connections between pins on Flame Sensor plug, and gas valve socket. Use emery cloth to clean Flame Sensor pins.

Figure 11-24: Honeywell S8660D control module.

Honeywell S8660D Intermittent Pilot Ignition System

The Honeywell S8660D intermittent pilot ignition system is a flame rectification type intermittent pilot system that provides 100% safety shut off and system prepurge. The complete system consists of:

1. S8660D control module *(see Figure 11-24)*

2. VR8440 dual automatic combination control valve (or VR8520 two stage dual automatic combination control valve for high low fire operation of the main burner). *(See Figure 11-25.)*

3. Q345 pilot burner/igniter-sensor assembly. *(See Figure 11-26.)*

Note: Other assemblies that are available are Q346 and Q348.

Figure 11-25: Top view of the Honeywell VR8440 dual automatic combination control valve.

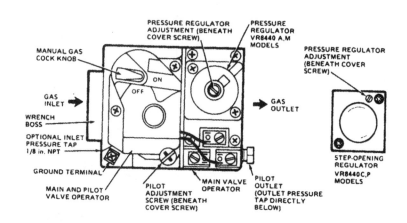

Specifications

1. Trial for ignition period or time (i.e., safety lock out time): 15 or 90 seconds depending on model.

2. Flame failure response time: 0.8 seconds maximum.

3. Prepurge time: 45 seconds.

4. Reset time: 60 seconds.

Wiring Arrangements for the S8660D Intermittent Pilot System
Figures 11-27, 11-28 and 11-29 illustrate typical external wiring arrangements for S8660D intermittent pilot system.

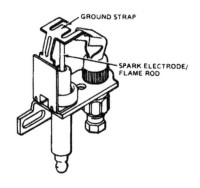

Figure 11-26: Honeywell Q345 pilot burner/igniter-sensor assembly.

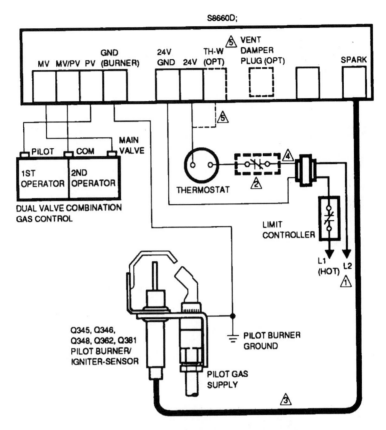

$\triangle$ 1 POWER SUPPLY. PROVIDE DISCONNECT MEANS AND OVERLOAD PROTECTION AS REQUIRED.

$\triangle$ 2 ALTERNATE LIMIT CONTROLLER LOCATION.

$\triangle$ 3 MAXIMUM CABLE LENGTH 3 ft [0.9 m].

$\triangle$ 4 CONTROLS IN 24V CIRCUIT MUST NOT BE IN GROUND LEG TO TRANSFORMER.

$\triangle$ 5 FOR MODULE WITH TH-W TERMINAL AND VENT DAMPER PLUG, CONNECT THERMOSTAT TO TH-W. LEAVE 24V OPEN. DO NOT REMOVE VENT DAMPER PLUG.

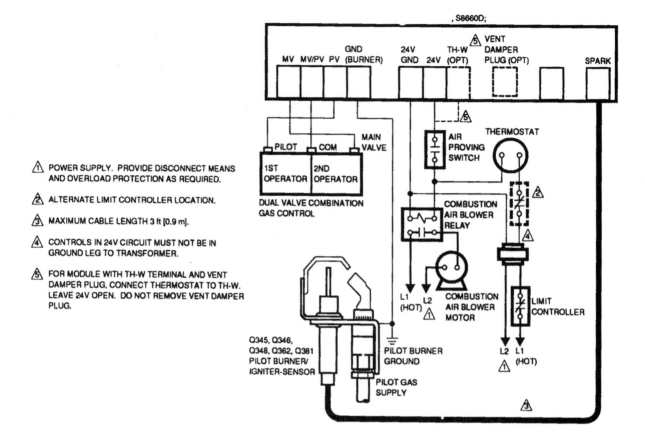

① POWER SUPPLY. PROVIDE DISCONNECT MEANS AND OVERLOAD PROTECTION AS REQUIRED.

② ALTERNATE LIMIT CONTROLLER LOCATION.

③ MAXIMUM CABLE LENGTH 3 ft [0.9 m].

④ CONTROLS IN 24V CIRCUIT MUST NOT BE IN GROUND LEG TO TRANSFORMER.

⑤ FOR MODULE WITH TH-W TERMINAL AND VENT DAMPER PLUG, CONNECT THERMOSTAT TO TH-W. LEAVE 24V OPEN. DO NOT REMOVE VENT DAMPER PLUG.

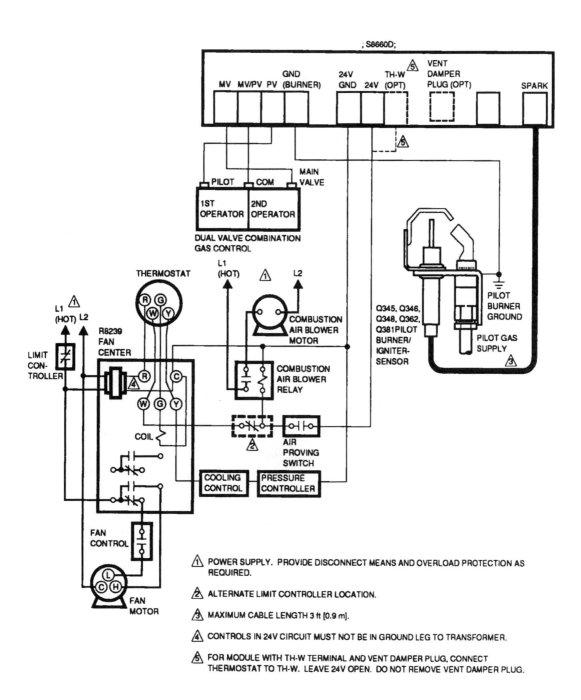

△1 POWER SUPPLY. PROVIDE DISCONNECT MEANS AND OVERLOAD PROTECTION AS REQUIRED.

△2 ALTERNATE LIMIT CONTROLLER LOCATION.

△3 MAXIMUM CABLE LENGTH 3 ft [0.9 m].

△4 CONTROLS IN 24V CIRCUIT MUST NOT BE IN GROUND LEG TO TRANSFORMER.

△5 FOR MODULE WITH TH-W TERMINAL AND VENT DAMPER PLUG, CONNECT THERMOSTAT TO TH-W. LEAVE 24V OPEN. DO NOT REMOVE VENT DAMPER PLUG.

Installation Requirements

1. Pilot burner/igniter-sensor assemblies are conventional style pilot burners which have been fitted with an insulated rod and grounding strap to provide for igniting and sensing the presence of the pilot flame *(see Figure 11-26)*. The recommended spark gap between the igniter sensor and grounding strap is 1/8" (3.2 mm).

2. As illustrated in *Figure 11-30* the pilot flame should envelop 3/8 to 1/2" (9.5 to 12.7 mm) of the tip of the insulated rod or igniter.

Figure 11-30: Proper pilot flame adjustment.

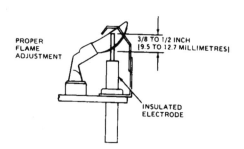

3. A common ground is required for the pilot burner/igniter-sensor mounting bracket, and the GND-burner terminal of the S8660D control module. If ground is poor or erratic, safety shut down may occur. Also, excessive temperatures at the ceramic flame rod insulator will permit electrical leakage to the ground. Examine the flame rod and mounting bracket and correct if bent out of position. Replace pilot burner/igniter-sensor if insulator is cracked.

Operating Sequence

The S8660D control module performs the following basic functions:

1. Provides a 45 second system prepurge.

2. Opens and closes the first main valve (pilot) operator of the gas control valve.

3. Provides a spark for igniting the pilot burner.

4. Allows a 90 second (maximum) trial for ignition period before system lock out.

5. Senses the pilot burner flame.

6. Shuts off the spark after pilot flame is lit.

7. Opens and closes the second main valve operator of the gas control valve.

These functions occur in the following stages:
   system prepurge
   trial for pilot ignition
   main burner operation

With reference to *Figures 11-31 and 11-32* the following is the operating sequence for the S8660D intermittent pilot system.

Figure 11-31: Sequence diagram illustrating the normal operating sequence of the S8660D intermittent pilot system.

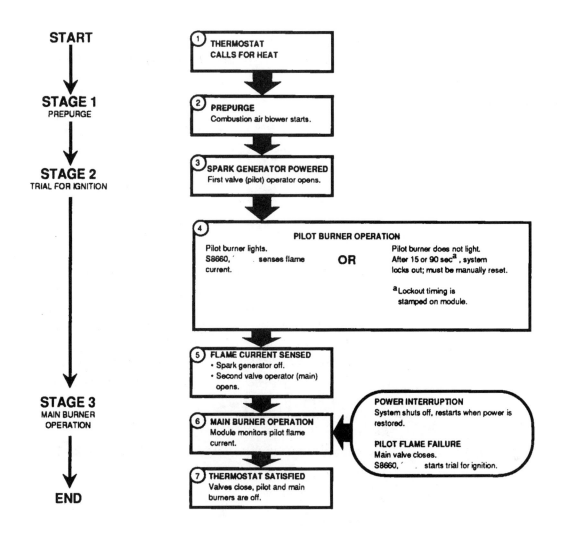

245

Figure 11-32: Simplified internal schematic diagram of the S8660D intermittent pilot system fan assisted application.

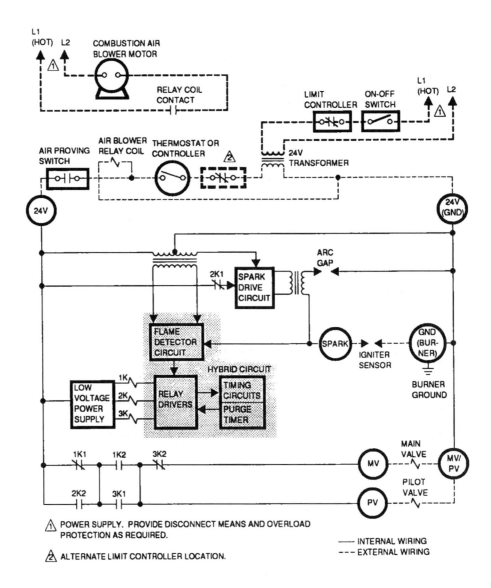

⚠️ POWER SUPPLY. PROVIDE DISCONNECT MEANS AND OVERLOAD PROTECTION AS REQUIRED.

⚠️ ALTERNATE LIMIT CONTROLLER LOCATION.

—— INTERNAL WIRING
--- EXTERNAL WIRING

System Prepurge

On every call for heat (system start) the S8660D will allow the furnace combustion air blower (i.e., induced draft fan) to operate and provide a 45 second system prepurge. After prepurge, the pilot ignition system is energized.

Trial for Pilot Ignition

After the prepurge sequence, the S8660D will energize the first main valve (pilot) operator of the gas control valve, which allows gas to flow to the pilot burner. At the same time, the electronic spark generator in the S8660D produces a high voltage spark pulse output. This voltage produces a spark at the igniter-sensor rod which ignites the pilot burner.

If the pilot flame does not light or the presence of the pilot flame is not detected back through the flame rod, the S8660D will not energize the second main valve operator of the gas control valve. The S8660D will continue to spark only until the timed trial for ignition period is over and then will go into safety lock out, which closes the first main valve and requires the system to be reset from the thermostat.

Main Burner Operation

When the pilot flame is established, a flame rectification circuit is completed to the burner ground. The S8660D flame sensing circuit detects the flame current, shuts off the spark generator and energizes the second main valve operator in the gas control valve to allow gas to flow to the main burner. The pilot flame ignites the main burner conventionally. The flame current also holds the safety lock out timer in reset (normal) operating condition.

Safety Lock Out Timer

The safety lockout timer circuit starts timing the moment the trial for pilot ignition starts. When the timing period runs out, the trial for pilot ignition ends, and the control module goes into lock out. On the S8660D, the spark stops when it goes into safety lock out.

Before another attempt to start the system can be made, the S8660D must be reset. Reset is performed by turning the thermostat down, below call for heat (or turning the power off) for one minute.

Component Checks

Spark Ignition Circuit

The S8660D module provide spark ignition at high voltages. The circuit can be checked at the S8660D as follows:

i)   Turn off the manual gas cock to prevent the flow of gas.

ii) Disconnect the ignition cable at the S8660D spark terminal to isolate the circuit from the pilot burner/igniter-sensor. Prepare a short jumper lead using heavily insulated wire, such as ignition cable.

iii) Energize the S8660D and touch one end of the jumper firmly to the S8660D ground terminal (GND-burner). After the pre-purge, move the free end slowly toward the spark terminal to establish a spark and then pull the lead wire slowly away from the terminal; note the length of the gap at which arcing discontinues.

iv) An arc length of 1/8" (3.2 mm) or more indicates satisfactory voltage output. If no arc can be established or the maximum arc is less than 1/8" (3.2 mm)—and fuse was okay, and power to the S8660D input terminal was proven—the S8660D should be replaced.

Flame Current Circuit

The nominal flame current reading for the S8660D control is approximately 1.0 UA. Generally, the flame current circuit is tested the same way as the Honeywell S87 DSI system—see *Figure 11-8*. To check the actual flame current signal from the flame sensor to the control module proceed as follows:

i) Connect a meter (DC micro ammeter scale) in series with the flame signal ground wire. Disconnect the ground wire at the control module (i.e., GND-burner terminal). Connect he red (positive) lead of the meter to the free end of the ground wire. Connect the black (negative) meter lead to he quick-connect ground terminal on the control module.

ii) Restart the system and read the meter. The flame sensor current must be approximately 1.5 UA and steady. If the flame signal is less than the required or is unsteady, check for required pilot flame position or poorly grounded points in the flame current circuit.

Trouble Shooting

Figure 11-33 is a trouble shooting guide that provides a systematic method for isolating equipment problems associated with the Honeywell S8660D intermittent pilot system.

Figure 11-33

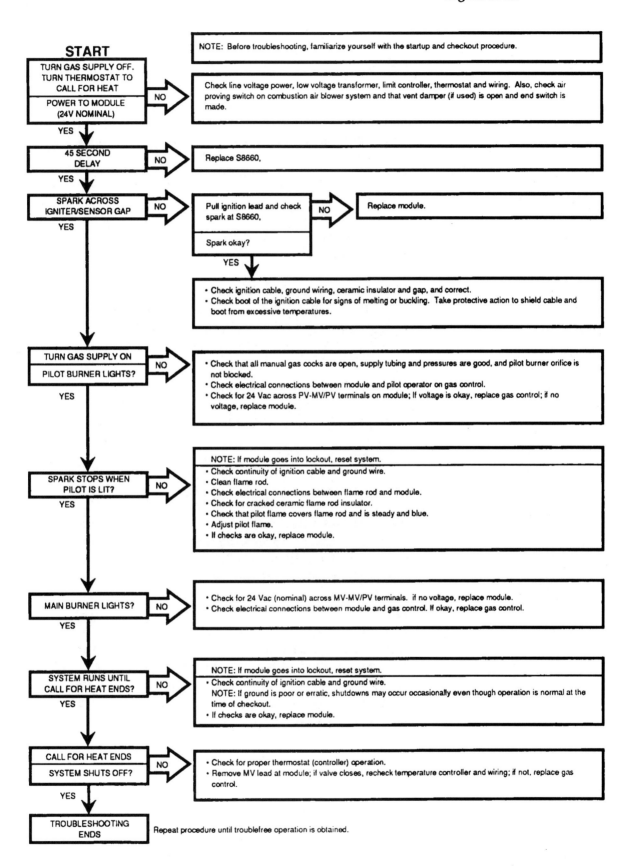

START

TURN GAS SUPPLY OFF.
TURN THERMOSTAT TO
CALL FOR HEAT

POWER TO MODULE
(24V NOMINAL)

NO → NOTE: Before troubleshooting, familiarize yourself with the startup and checkout procedure.

Check line voltage power, low voltage transformer, limit controller, thermostat and wiring. Also, check air proving switch on combustion air blower system and that vent damper (if used) is open and end switch is made.

YES

45 SECOND DELAY — NO → Replace S8660,

YES

SPARK ACROSS IGNITER/SENSOR GAP — NO →

Pull ignition lead and check spark at S8660,

Spark okay? — NO → Replace module.

YES

• Check ignition cable, ground wiring, ceramic insulator and gap, and correct.
• Check boot of the ignition cable for signs of melting or buckling. Take protective action to shield cable and boot from excessive temperatures.

YES

TURN GAS SUPPLY ON

PILOT BURNER LIGHTS? — NO →

• Check that all manual gas cocks are open, supply tubing and pressures are good, and pilot burner orifice is not blocked.
• Check electrical connections between module and pilot operator on gas control.
• Check for 24 Vac across PV-MV/PV terminals on module; If voltage is okay, replace gas control; if no voltage, replace module.

YES

SPARK STOPS WHEN PILOT IS LIT? — NO →

NOTE: If module goes into lockout, reset system.
• Check continuity of ignition cable and ground wire.
• Clean flame rod.
• Check electrical connections between flame rod and module.
• Check for cracked ceramic flame rod insulator.
• Check that pilot flame covers flame rod and is steady and blue.
• Adjust pilot flame.
• If checks are okay, replace module.

YES

MAIN BURNER LIGHTS? — NO →

• Check for 24 Vac (nominal) across MV-MV/PV terminals. if no voltage, replace module.
• Check electrical connections between module and gas control. If okay, replace gas control.

YES

SYSTEM RUNS UNTIL CALL FOR HEAT ENDS? — NO →

NOTE: If module goes into lockout, reset system.
• Check continuity of ignition cable and ground wire.
NOTE: If ground is poor or erratic, shutdowns may occur occasionally even though operation is normal at the time of checkout.
• If checks are okay, replace module.

YES

CALL FOR HEAT ENDS

SYSTEM SHUTS OFF? — NO →

• Check for proper thermostat (controller) operation.
• Remove MV lead at module; if valve closes, recheck temperature controller and wiring; if not, replace gas control.

YES

TROUBLESHOOTING ENDS

Repeat procedure until troublefree operation is obtained.

Hot Surface Ignition System (HSI)

The hot surface ignition system (HSI), like the DSI system, provides direct ignition to the burner flame. Like the IP and DSI systems, the HSI system components *(see Figure 11-34)* will include the following:

Ignition Control Module
Ignition control module is a microcomputer control that governs the ignition sequence of the system. The ignition control module can be equipped with the following features:

i) *Prepurge*
    Allows the operation of an induced draft fan to purge the combustion chamber during the period between the thermostat's initial call for heat and the beginning of the ignition cycle.

ii) *Retry*
    Allows the control to re-initiate an ignition sequence if the burner flame is undetected after the first try for ignition.

iii) *Recycle*
    Allows the control to repeat the ignition sequence upon loss of flame detection during the burner's running cycle.

The module can be facilitated with a diagnostic light that simplifies troubleshooting if there is a fault.[8]

Redundant Gas Valve
The gas control valve consists of two in line valves (i.e., the main valve and the redundant valve) that provide valve redundancy.

Flame Sensor
The flame sensor provides the remote sensing of the burner flame. Like the DSI and IP systems, the sensor is a flame rod that utilizes the principles of flame conductivity and rectification.

Igniter
The igniter is a silicon carbide igniter which is heated to give a hot surface that ignites the burner flame. The igniter provides a reliable source of ignition. The relatively large surface area of the igniter ensures that it is not position sensitive as an ignition spark. Also, the igniter provides approximately three times more ignition energy than that of a standard pilot burner.

---

[8] The light is a LED (light emitting diode). HSI ignition control modules that are equipped with a diagnostic light are polarity sensitive and may lock out if the 120 volt service wiring is reversed.

White Rodgers Hot Surface Ignition System

Figure 11-34: White Rodgers
Hot Surface Ignition System

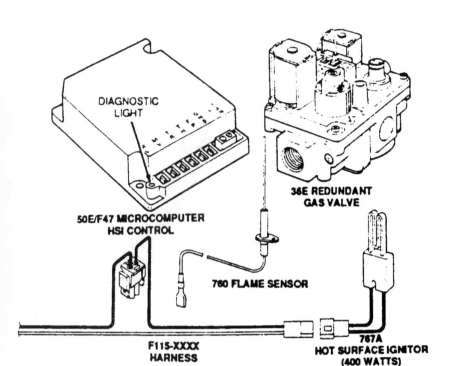

DIAGNOSTIC LIGHT

50E/F47 MICROCOMPUTER HSI CONTROL

36E REDUNDANT GAS VALVE

760 FLAME SENSOR

F115-XXXX HARNESS

767A HOT SURFACE IGNITOR (400 WATTS)

As illustrated in *Figure 11-34*, the White Rodgers HSI System consist of a line voltage 767A Series Silicon Carbide Igniter, 760 Series Flame Sensor, 50E/F47 Ignition Control Module, 36EXX Redundant Gas Valve and an F115-XXXX Harness.

The following are the main features of the White Rodgers HSI System:

Flame Current
Minimum current to ensure flame detection is 1 microamp (DC)
Note: The flame current is measured with a DC microammeter in the flame probe lead (*see Figure 11 -35*).

Prepurge Time *(if so equipped)*
    50E47 ————— 30 seconds
    50F47 ————— 17 seconds

Ignition Activation Period
    Standard is 1 second while the optional is 4 seconds

Trial for Ignition Time
    Standard is 4 seconds while the optional is 7 seconds

Flame Failure Response Time
    0.8 seconds

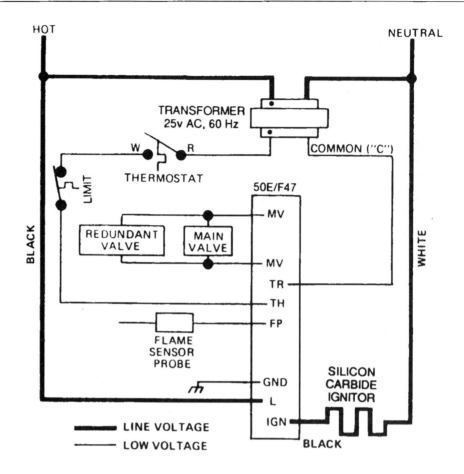

Figure 11-35 Typical system wiring diagram for the White Rodgers HSI system.

HOT

NEUTRAL

TRANSFORMER
25v AC, 60 Hz

COMMON ("C")

W   R

THERMOSTAT

LIMIT

BLACK

WHITE

50E/F47

MV

REDUNDANT VALVE   MAIN VALVE

MV

TR

TH

FP

FLAME SENSOR PROBE

GND

L

IGN

SILICON CARBIDE IGNITOR

BLACK

━━━ LINE VOLTAGE
─── LOW VOLTAGE

Terminal Legend
MV – Main Valve
TR – Transformer
TH – Thermostat
FP – Flame Probe
GND – Burner Ground
L – Line
iGN – Ignitor

Operating Sequence

Normal Sequence
The thermostat calls for heat to energize the HSI ignition control module. If the module is equipped with a prepurge, a prepurge cycle is initiated prior to the ignition cycle. After the prepurge cycle is completed, the silicon carbide igniter is activated to start its warm-up period (17 or 45 seconds depending upon the control model). At the end of the igniter warm-up time, both main and redundant valves within the gas control valve are energized. The burner flame is established, however, the igniter will remain on for a short period of time (*Ignition Activation Period*). The flame is detected by the flame sensor, and the burner continues to operate until the thermostat is satisfied.

Abnormal Sequence
The flame must be detected within the trial for ignition period. If the flame is not detected, then both valves within the control valve will shut off. The igniter will be turned off and the ignition control module goes into lockout.

At this point the diagnostic light indicates whether the fault is internal (steady light) or external (flashing light) to the control module. If the fault is indicated to be external to the control, then the control can be reset by momentary interrupting either the line power or the 24 volt thermostat power.

The ignition control module may be equipped with a *retry* option. With this option the control will not lock out upon failure to establish flame upon burner startup. The control will provide a 60 second wait (90 seconds if the control has prepurge) to retry for burner flame ignition.[9] If this ignition attempt is unsuccessful, one more retry will be made before the control module will lockout.

If the burner flame is established for more than 10 seconds after ignition, then any loss of flame will cause the control to recycle.[10] The control will recycle to restart the ignition sequence after a 60 second delay.

Reading the Diagnostic Light

Flash on-off
On start up, the light on the control module will flash once to indicate that the control is functional.

Steady Light
A continuous light indicates a dysfunctional control. To make sure, reset the control by momentary interrupting line or 24 volt thermostat power. If light is still on continuously, then an internal fault is indicated and the control should be replaced.

Flashing Light
A flashing light indicates an external problem located in the wiring or the external components (refer to the trouble shooting charts).

Trouble Shooting Charts

Figures 11-36, 11-37 and 11-38 are trouble shooting charts that provide a logical method for identifying equipment problems associated with the White Rodgers HSI System.

---

[9] After this wait, the ignition cycle is restarted with an additional 10 seconds of igniter warm-up time.

[10] After 10 seconds into the burner running cycle the retry counter of the ignition control module is cleared.

Figure 11-36

CHART 1
50D/E/F47 FIRST VISUAL CHECK
(Does ignitor glow bright red?)

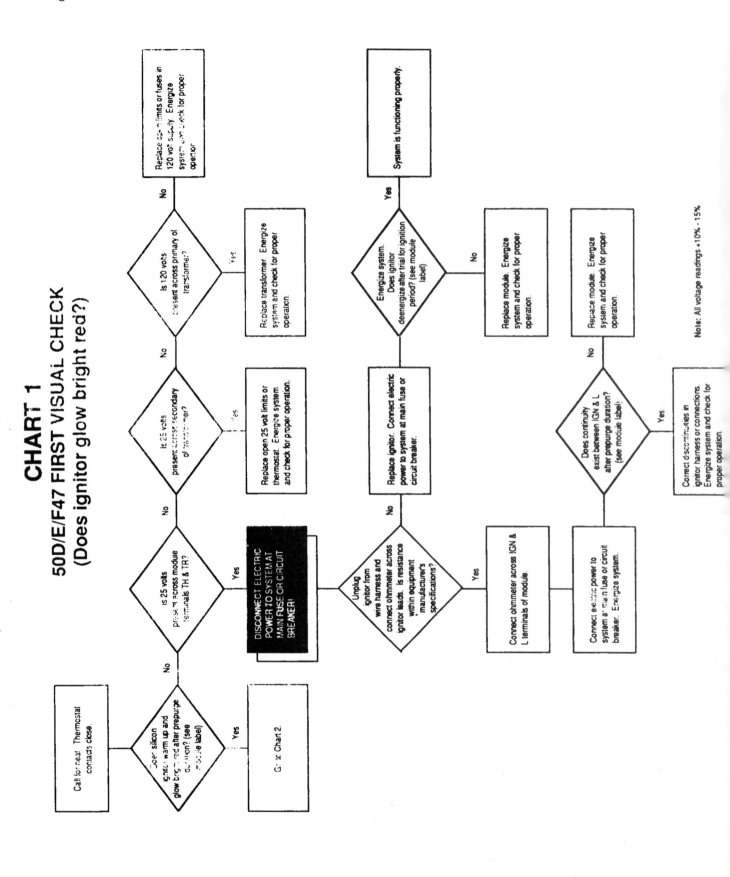

Call for heat. Thermostat contacts close.

Does silicon ignitor warm up and glow bright red after prepurge duration? (see module label)

Yes → Go to Chart 2.

No → Is 25 volts present across module terminals TH & TR?

No → Is 25 volts present across secondary of transformer?

Yes → Replace open 25 volt limits or thermostat. Energize system and check for proper operation.

No → Is 120 volts present across primary of transformer?

Yes → Replace transformer. Energize system and check for proper operation.

No → Replace open limits or fuses in 120 volt supply. Energize system and check for proper operation.

Yes → DISCONNECT ELECTRIC POWER TO SYSTEM AT MAIN FUSE OR CIRCUIT BREAKER!

Unplug ignitor from wire harness and connect ohmmeter across ignitor leads. Is resistance within equipment manufacturer's specifications?

No → Replace ignitor. Connect electric power to system at main fuse or circuit breaker.

Yes → Connect ohmmeter across IGN & L terminals of module.

Does continuity exist between IGN & L after prepurge duration? (see module label)

Yes → Correct discontinuities in ignitor harness or connections. Energize system and check for proper operation.

No → Connect electric power to system at main fuse or circuit breaker. Energize system.

Replace module. Energize system and check for proper operation.

Energize system. Does ignitor deenergize after trial for ignition period? (see module label)

Yes → System is functioning properly.

No → Replace module. Energize system and check for proper operation.

Note: All voltage readings +10% - 15%

254

CHART 2
50D/E/F47 SECOND VISUAL CHECK
(Does main burner ignite?)

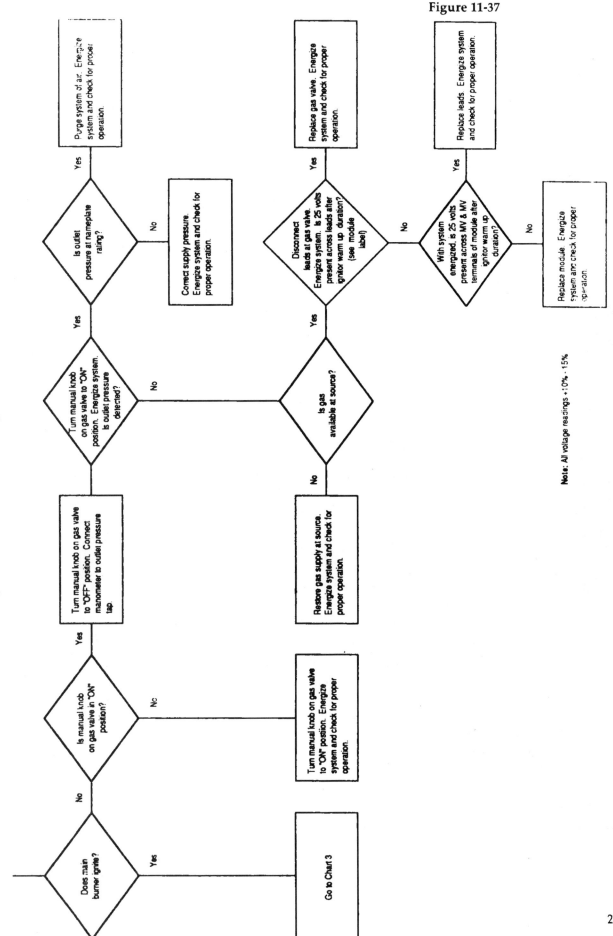

Figure 11-37

Note: All voltage readings +10% - 15%

CHART 3

50D/E/F47 THIRD VISUAL CHECK
(Does main burner remain lit?)

Figure 11-38

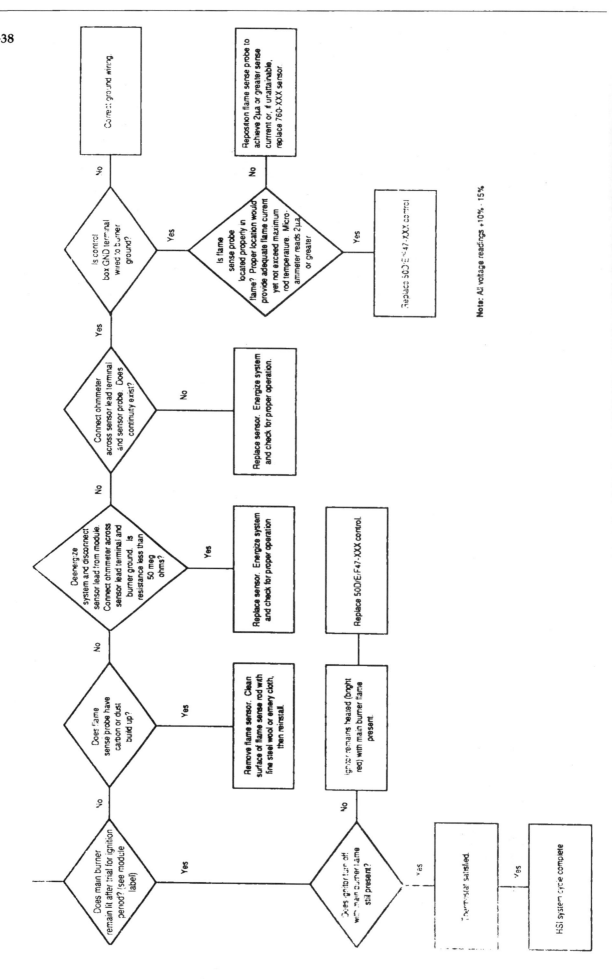

Note: All voltage readings +10% - 15%

Integrated Furnace Control

The integrated furnace control *(see Figure 11-39)* is an expanded automatic ignition control that contains a microprocessor that governs the following furnace functions:

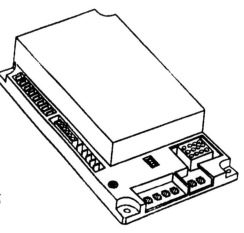

Figure 11-39: Integrated furnace control.

- burner ignition sequence
- burner flame detection
- control of furnace blower operation for the desired heating and cooling speeds
- control of furnace blower operation for *delay-to-blower-on* and *delay-to-blower-off* periods for both heating and cooling modes
- control of the induced draft fan operation
- control of the power humidifier
- control of the electronic air cleaner

The control will sequence the operation of the furnace blower, induced draft fan, power humidifier and electronic air cleaner. The control has all of the features of a HSI system such as prepurge, retry, and recycling that facilitates the control's ignition sequence.

Also, the control may be equipped with a diagnostic light that provides quick identification of system faults. The control continuously monitors its own operation and the operation of the system. If a failure occurs, the diagnostic light on the control will flash a failure code.

Figures 11-40 and 11-41 illustrate the White Rodgers series 50A50 Integrated Furnace Control's typical system wiring diagram and typical system wiring table.

Assignment

1. Define the following terms:
   a) intermittent pilot
   b) direct spark ignition
   c) hot surface ignition
   d) safe-start check
   e) valve redundancy
   f) trial for ignition
   g) flame failure response time
   h) prepurge
   i) safety lock out
   j) flame current
   k flame rectification
   l) remote reset
   m) micro amps
   n) lock out module

Figure 11-40: White Rodgers series 50A50 Integrated
Furnace Control's typical system wiring diagram.

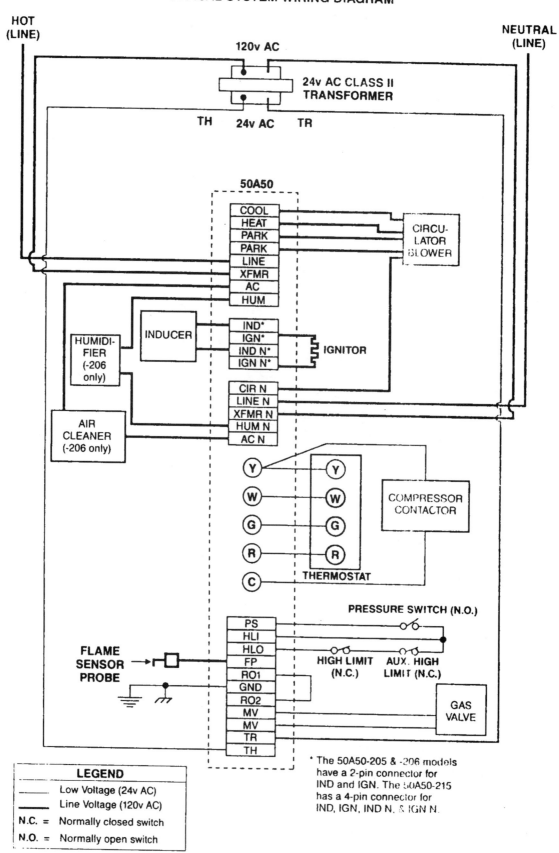

TYPICAL SYSTEM WIRING DIAGRAM

TYPICAL SYSTEM WIRING TABLE

50A50 TERMINAL	TERMINAL TYPE	SYSTEM COMPONENT CONNECTION
W	captive screw	low voltage thermostat W terminal (or equivalent)
G	captive screw	low voltage thermostat G terminal (or equivalent)
R	captive screw	low voltage thermostat R terminal (or equivalent)
Y	captive screw {	low voltage thermostat Y terminal (or equivalent) / 2nd wire from Y terminal goes to 24vAC HOT side of compressor contactor coil
C	captive screw	24v AC COMMON side of compressor contactor coil
MV (2 terminals)		gas valve (both gas valve solenoids are connected in parallel)
TR		24v AC transformer (low voltage COMMON SIDE)
TH		24v AC transformer (low voltage HIGH SIDE)
RO1		rollout switch OUTPUT
RO2	12-pin connector & harness	rollout switch INPUT
FP		flame sensor probe*
PS		pressure switch INPUT
HLI		high limit INPUT
HLO		high limit OUTPUT
GND		MUST BE RELIABLY GROUNDED TO CHASSIS
(unused terminal)		
IND	2-pin connector & harness	inducer HOT side
IGN		ignitor HOT side
IND		inducer HOT side
IGN	4-pin connector & harness	ignitor HOT side
IND N		inducer NEUTRAL side
IGN N		ignitor NEUTRAL side
COOL	spade terminal	circulator blower COOL SPEED terminal
HEAT	spade terminal	circulator blower HEAT SPEED terminal
PARK (2 terminals)	spade terminal	unused circulator blower terminals
LINE	spade terminal	input voltage (120v AC) HOT SIDE
XFMR	spade terminal	24v AC transformer line voltage HOT SIDE
AC (optional)	spade terminal	air cleaner HOT side
HUM (optional)	spade terminal	humidifier HOT side
CIR N	spade terminal	circulator blower NEUTRAL terminal
LINE N	spade terminal	input voltage (120v AC) NEUTRAL SIDE
XFMR N	spade terminal	24v AC transformer line voltage NEUTRAL SIDE
HUM N (optional)	spade terminal	humidifier NEUTRAL side
AC N (optional)	spade terminal	air cleaner NEUTRAL side

-205 & -206 models only (IND, IGN)

-215 model only (IND, IGN, IND N, IGN N)

* maximum recommended flame probe wire length is 36 inches.

2. Give the functions that are usually provided by a DSI system control module.

3. Give a brief explanation how a flame sensor, based on the principle of flame rectification, detects the presence of a gas flame.

4. Draw and label a sequence diagram illustrating the general operation of a DSI system.

5. Give the major similarities and differences between various IP systems.

6. Using *Figure 11-18*, describe the start up sequence for the White Rodgers cycle pilot system.

7. For the system described in *Question 6*, a *good* pilot flame has been established for at least 45 seconds, however, main flame cannot be established. Give the various causes why main flame cannot be established—how would you test for each cause?

8. Describe the method for checking the spark ignition circuit for the Honeywell S8660D IP system.

9. Draw and label a wiring schematic for a fan assisted forced warm air furnace with the Honeywell S8660D IP system. (*Note:* Use *Figure 11-28* as a guide in drawing your wiring schematic.)

10. During the pilot trial for ignition for a Honeywell S8660D IP system, the pilot flame is established, however, the ignition spark is *not* terminated:

    a) What will be the likely result?
    b) What would you check to ensure a normal start up?

11. Draw and label a wiring schematic for a fan assisted forced warm air furnace having the White Rodgers hot surface ignition system. (*Note:* Use *Figure 11-35* as a guide in drawing your wiring schematic.)

12. Give the condition indicate by the following flash sequences of the diagnostic light found on the White Rodgers HSI system:

    a) Flash on-off
    b) Steady light
    c) Flashing light

13. Give the furnace functions that are controlled by an integrated furnace control.

Conversion Burners
—Part I—
The Fan Assisted Burner

12

Conversion burners are unit gas burners used to convert heating appliances which were originally designed for another fuel such as coal or oil. The heating appliance may be a boiler or a warm air furnace.

In the past, conversions were usually coal and oil firing boilers and furnaces that were converted to gas using either an atmospheric upshot burner *(see Figure 8-9)* or an atmospheric inshot burner *(see Figure 8-8)*. Most conversions today are from oil to gas. An up to-date oil boiler or forced warm air furnace can be easily converted using a fan assisted type of gas conversion burner *(see Figure 12-1)*.

The Fan Assisted Conversion Burner

The fan assisted burner utilizes a burner fan to provide the burner's air supply. The burner creates the same general firing pattern as a gun type oil burner. Like the original oil burner, the fan assisted conversion burner only develops sufficient air pressure to overcome the restriction through the burner and must rely on the natural draft developed by the appliance chimney to draw the flue gas through the appliance and the horizontal vent connector.

Therefore, draft developed at the base of the chimney is required in order to:

Figure 12-1: Typical fan assisted gas conversion burner.

i) Overcome the resistance of the lateral or horizontal vent connector;
ii) Overcome the internal resistance of the appliance;
iii) Provide a slight negative overfire draft condition (i.e., .01 to .02"wc or 2.5 to 5 Pa) in the combustion chamber of the appliance to assist the burner fan in its air delivery. This required overfire draft is controlled by the application of a double acting barometric draft control.[1]

Since these burners have the added advantage of a close control of the air supply, the following can be achieved as compared to the older atmospheric upshot and inshot conversion burners.

---

[1] Furnaces and boilers that have an updraft design in which there is very little internal resistance can be fired with a fan assisted burner by which a neutral overfire draft condition is maintained by a vertical or horizontal draft diverter or hood.

1. A greater degree of combustion control and hence better combustion efficiency.

2. Reduction in the volume of combustion space required.

The installation requirements for the fan assisted type of conversion burner are illustrated by *Figures 12-2 and 12-3.*

Figure 12-2: A fan assisted burner installation in a hot water or steam boiler.

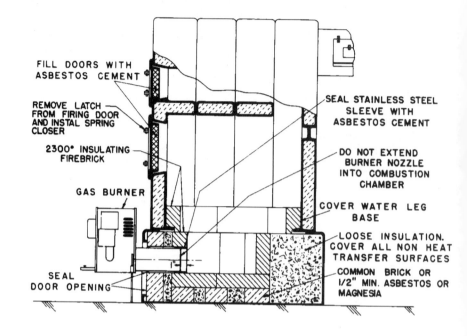

Figure 12-3: A fan assisted burner installation in a forced warm air furnace.

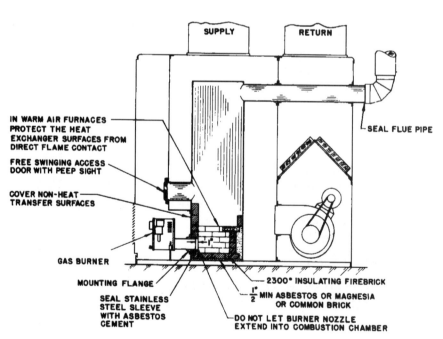

Many oil furnaces cannot easily be converted. The following is a list of some of the important factors to keep in mind when contemplating oil furnace conversions:

1. Furnaces having multi-tube or multi-pass secondary heat exchangers on the suction side of the furnace fan or blower should not be converted since a crack in the secondary heat exchanger would allow flue gases into the warm air stream.

2. Furnaces with a single cylindrical flue pipe passing directly from the primary heat exchanger through the suction side of the furnace to the flue collar (see Figure 12-3) may be converted, provided that all joints are continuously welded and gas tight, and that there are no gaskets in any part of the heat exchanger within the suction zone or fan compartment of the furnace.

3. A furnace having a single cylindrical flue extension showing signs of corrosion or deterioration of any nature must not be converted.

4. The minimum combustion chamber size of oil furnace to be converted to natural gas utilizing a fan assisted burner is 10 inches (254 mm) in diameter.

Sizing the Fan Assisted Conversion Burner

Coal Conversion
Warm air furnaces and boilers that are to be converted from a coal or wood firing are sized according to the allowable combustion space provided for the gas conversion burner.

The ashpit area is used to determine the available space for combustion. Based on the ashpit floor area the fan assisted conversion burner is sized at:

> 200,000 Btuh per sq.ft. of available ashpit floor area

OR

> 630.72 kW per m^2 of available ashpit floor area

Oil Conversion
The Btuh input requirement for the fan assisted gas conversion burner used to convert an oil firing furnace or boiler can be determined by the nozzle size used by the existing oil burner.

Oil burner nozzle size in gallons per hour	X	Heat content of No.2 fuel oil	=	Gas burner input in Btuh

For example, if the oil unit to be converted has a nozzle size of 1.25 gph, then the required gas burner input would be:

1.25 X 140,000 = 175,000 Btuh

Note: 1. Oil burner nozzles are rated in U.S. gallons/hour (gph).
       2. The heat content of No.2 fuel oil (grade of fuel oil used in home heating) is 140,000 Btu/U.S. gallon.

Limit Control Setting

The following are maximum limit control settings recommended for converted central heating systems:

Gravity hot water	180°F	82°C
Forced hot water	200°F	93°C
Gravity warm air	350°F	177°C
Forced warm air	250°F	121°C
Steam	Off @ 3 lbs. ——— on @ 1 lb.	
	(cut in 1 lb. differential 2 lbs.)	

Burner Control Circuits

Residential fan assisted burners can have the following control systems:

1. 24 volt combustion control circuit

2. 110 volt burner motor circuit

3. 110 volt furnace fan motor circuit

4. 24V/110V burner blower motor starting relay

5. Gas valve and burner blower motor interlock—usually an air switch

The following electrical diagrams illustrate the above control systems as utilized by a power or fan assisted burner:

1. *Figure 12-4*—Electrical block diagram for a typical fan assisted burner.

2. *Figure 12-5*—Electrical schematic diagram for a fan assisted burner.

3. *Figure 12-6*—Electrical schematic diagram for a fan assisted burner oil furnace conversion.

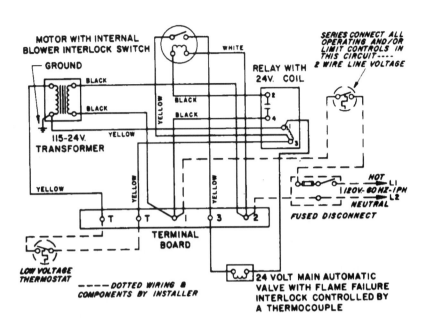

Figure 12-4: Electrical block diagram for a typical fan assisted burner.

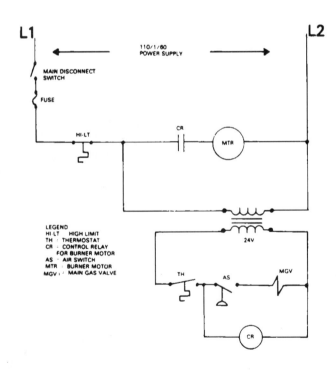

Figure 12-5: Electrical schematic diagram for a fan assisted burner.

The following is a *trouble shooting chart* for the fan assisted conversion burner utilized to isolate a problem that may occur in the burner system. Refer to *Figures 12-4, 12-5 and 12-16* when viewing the trouble shooting chart.

Figure 12-6: Electrical schematical diagram for a fan assisted burner oil furnace conversion.

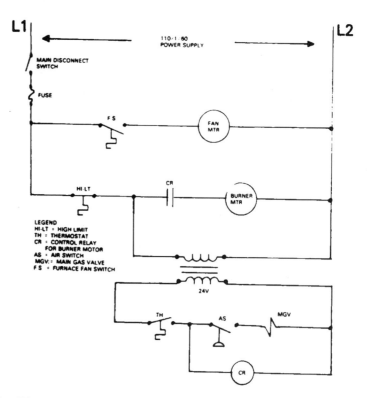

LEGEND
HI-LT = HIGH LIMIT
TH = THERMOSTAT
CR = CONTROL RELAY
     FOR BURNER MOTOR
AS = AIR SWITCH
MGV = MAIN GAS VALVE
F S = FURNACE FAN SWITCH

Trouble Shooting Chart

Symptom		Cause
1. Pilot will not light	a)	Air in gas line
	b)	Low gas pressure
	c)	Clogged pilot orifice
	d)	Extreme draft
	e)	Defective lighter valve
	f)	Defective lighter tube
	g)	Valve dial "A" not depressed in the pilot position
	h)	Pilot adjustment "D" incorrectly set
2. Pilot goes out frequently	a)	Lint in pilot
	b)	Clogged pilot orifice
	c)	Low or high gas pressure
	d)	Extreme draft
	e)	Reverse or no draft
	f)	Nozzle extending into combustion chamber
	g)	Defective thermocouple
	h)	Defective pilot safety element in valve
	i)	Pilot adjustment "D" incorrectly set
	j)	Clogged pilot filter in combination valve

3. Motor continues to run Pilot is on but no main flame	a) Defective valve operator
	b) Defective blower interlock
	c) Slow motor

3. Motor continues to run Pilot is on but no main flame
   a) Defective valve operator
   b) Defective blower interlock
   c) Slow motor

4. Spasmodic or no start
   a) Loose wiring
   b) Defective wiring
   c) Defective burner transformer
   d) Defective relay
   e) Defective thermostat

5. Short flame
   a) Wrong main orifice
   b) Low gas pressure
   c) Air shutter misadjusted
   d) Regulator misadjusted

6. Long hazy flame
   a) Wrong main orifice
   b) High gas pressure
   c) Dirty blower wheel
   d) Air shutter misadjusted
   e) Regulator misadjusted
   f) Shelf gasket missing or damaged

7. Gas fails to shut off
   a) Dirt on valve seat
   b) Defective main valve

Assignment

1. Define the fan assisted burner in terms of its chimney draft requirements.

2. Give two advantages that conversion using a fan assisted conversion burner may have compared to a conversion using the older atmospheric upshot or atmospheric inshot conversion burner.

3. List some of the types of oil furnace designs that cannot be converted.

4. Determine the required fan assisted burner input for the following:

   a) A coal fired boiler having an available ashpit floor diameter of 14".
   b) An oil fired forced warm air furnace having a 1.75 gph nozzle.

5. State the limit control settings for the following:

   a) Gravity hot water
   b) Forced hot water
   c) Gravity warm air
   d) Forced warm air
   e) Steam

6. Draw and label a schematic wiring diagram for a typical warm air furnace being converted by a fan assisted gas conversion burner.

Conversion Burners —Part II—Flue Gas Analysis and Combustion Efficiency

13

The installation of conversion burners is governed by two objectives:
1. The installation will be safe as to the combustion process of the new fuel.
2. Maximum operating efficiency will be achieved and maintained by the installation.

Setting the Fan Assisted Conversion Burner

The fan assisted conversion burner is the burner of choice when converting present day oil furnaces and boilers. Like the original oil burner that it replaces, the fan assisted burner is set to fire against a slightly negative *overfire draft* of about .02"wc (5 Pa). This overfire draft is necessary since chimney draft is required to draw the products of combustion through the boiler or furnace.

Combustion air is supplied by the burner's fan, which is sufficient to supply adequate air for any normal furnace or boiler firing. The burner air shutter is adjustable to provide a quiet, soft flame—blue at the burner nozzle with well defined orange and yellow tips.[1]

For the burner operation, the barometric damper is the most commonly used draft control. It should be of the double swing or acting type which opens freely outward to afford downdraft protection irrespective of the settings made to the balancing weights for updraft control. As illustrated in *Figure 13-1* the barometric damper is set to give a .02"wc (5 Pa) reading (negative overfire draft when the burner is firing at the required rated input).

Setting the Barometric Draft Control

To efficiently control draft, the barometric damper must be properly sized. If it is too large, it will float in the nearly closed position making precise control difficult. If it is too small, it will float in the wide open position most of the time, serving as no better than an open hole in the flue pipe. For a chimney of recommended height by the burner manufacturer, the damper can be sized to cover an area from 80 to 100% of the flue pipe area.

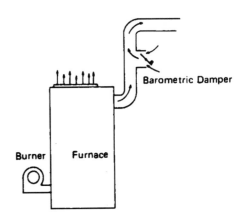

Figure 13-1: A fan assisted burner installation in which a barometric damper controls the overfire draft.

---

[1] For propane gas with well defined yellow tips.

Figure 13-2: Locating the barometric draft control.

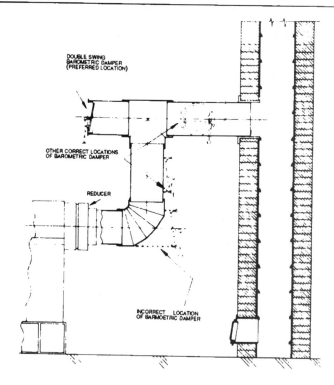

DOUBLE SWING
BAROMETRIC DAMPER
(PREFERRED LOCATION)

OTHER CORRECT LOCATIONS
OF BAROMETRIC DAMPER

REDUCER

INCORRECT LOCATION
OF BARMOETRIC DAMPER

The barometric damper is best placed in the flue pipe between the boiler and the chimney. In no case should the damper be located so that the velocity pressure of the flue gases interferes with its operation. *Figure 13-2* illustrates the various possible locations for the damper.

Flue Gas Analysis and Combustion Efficiency

The conversion burner must be set to achieve the maximum possible operating efficiency for the furnace or boiler that it has converted. To that end, the burner installation is subjected to combustion testing to ensure peak combustion efficiency.

Flue Gas Analysis

Combustion can be defined as a process in which a fuel is rapidly combined with oxygen to produce light and heat. By analyzing the products of combustion, we can determine the type and quality of the combustion process that is taking place in the furnace or boiler. There are three types of combustion processes, each depending upon the initial air supply to determine its type:

1. Perfect combustion
2. Complete combustion
3. Incomplete combustion

Perfect Combustion

Perfect combustion is the complete burning of the fuel with the *exact* amount of air (theoretical or ideal air supply) for the combustion process. The resulting products of combustion are:

Carbon Dioxide	CO_2
Water Vapour	H_2O
Nitrogen	N_2
Heat	

The reaction for perfect combustion is the following:

$$CH_4 + 2O_2 + + 8N_2 \longrightarrow CO_2 + 2H_2O + 8N_2 + Heat$$

1 cu. ft. + 10 cu. ft.	$\longrightarrow$	11 cu. ft. of products of combustion
fuel of air		or flue gases

In the above reaction there is 0% carbon monoxide and 0% oxygen (excess air) in the products of combustion. This indicates that sufficient air was supplied for the combustion process and that all of the air is used up in the burning of the fuel.

If the amount of water vapour is extracted from the flue gases, then the amount of carbon dioxide (CO_2) in the *dry base flue gases* is 12%. This amount of carbon dioxide is only obtained at perfect combustion and is called the *ultimate % CO_2*.[2] Thus, any amount of carbon dioxide below the ultimate 12% indicates either incomplete or complete combustion is taking place depending upon the initial air supply. Therefore, we can test for the percentage of carbon dioxide in the flue gases to determine the type and quality of the combustion process.

Figure 13-3 is a graphic illustration showing the ultimate % of CO_2 occurring at perfect combustion with declining amounts of carbon dioxide occurring at both incomplete and complete combustion.

[2] Depending upon its composition, the ultimate percentage of CO_2 for natural gas can vary from 11.8% to 12.2%. Twelve percent (12%) is usually accepted as the nominal value for the ultimate percentage of CO_2 for natural gas.

Figure 13-3: Ultimate % of CO_2 occurring at perfect combustion with declining amounts of CO_2 occurring at both incomplete and complete combustion.

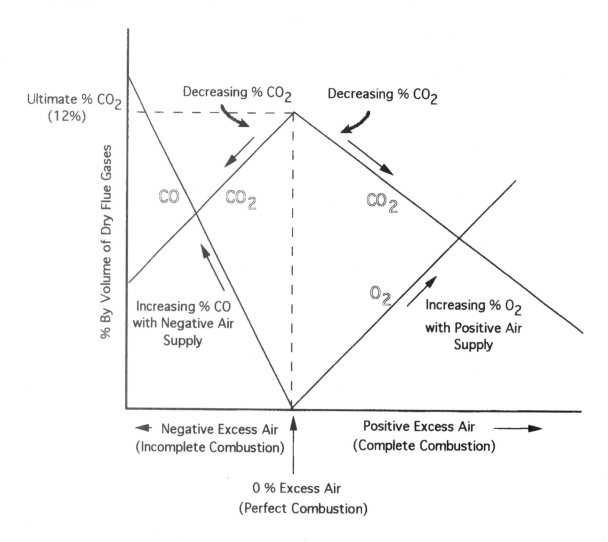

Complete Combustion

Complete combustion is the complete burning of the fuel; however, *excess air* (oxygen) is found in the flue gases as a result of an initial air supply greater than that required for perfect combustion. The resulting products of combustion are:

Carbon Dioxide	CO_2
Water Vapour	H_2O
Nitrogen	N_2
Excess Air	O_2
Heat	

Excess air is defined as an air supply to the combustion process in excess of the theoretical amount and is found in the products of combustion.

To ensure the complete combustion of the fuel, a burner must be fired with some excess air as determined by the burner's air supply. However, increasing the amount of excess air in the flue gases increases the *stack* or *flue losses* of the furnace or boiler and results in lower *combustion efficiency*. The higher amounts of excess air in the flue gases absorb heat from the combustion reaction and this heat is passed out through the furnace or boiler stack rather than in the warm air or water to be heated.

The amount of excess air in the flue gases can be determined by the following expression:

$$\text{Percentage of excess air} = \frac{\text{ULTIMATE \% } CO_2 - \text{OBSERVED \% } CO_2}{\text{OBSERVED \% } CO_2} \times 90$$

Note: 90 is a constant for most common fuel gases; ultimate % of CO_2 for natural gas being 12%.

Example
The amount of excess air for an 8% CO_2 reading in the flue gases would be:

$$\% \text{ excess air} = \frac{12 - 8}{8} \times 90$$

$$= 4/8 \times 90$$

$$= 45\% \text{ excess air}$$

Incomplete Combustion

Incomplete combustion occurs when fuel is not completely burned due to insufficient air supply. We have a *negative* excess air condition in which carbon monoxide is found in the flue gases. Since carbon monoxide (CO) is a fuel in itself, additional air will complete its combustion giving carbon dioxide and heat:

$$CO + 1/2\, O_2 \longrightarrow CO_2 + \text{Heat}$$

The importance of preventing a condition of incomplete combustion is twofold:

1. The formation of CO prevents the full release of the heat of combustion from the partially burnt fuel.

2. CO is an extremely toxic gas.

In all three types of combustion processes (perfect, complete and incomplete), the presence of carbon dioxide in the flue gases indicates not only the type of combustion process, but quality of the combustion process as well. Thus, the percentage of CO_2 in the flue gases is a component in determining the combustion efficiency of the furnace or boiler.

Heat Absorption of the Heating Plant

Figure 13-4: Flue gas temperature rise across the heating appliance.

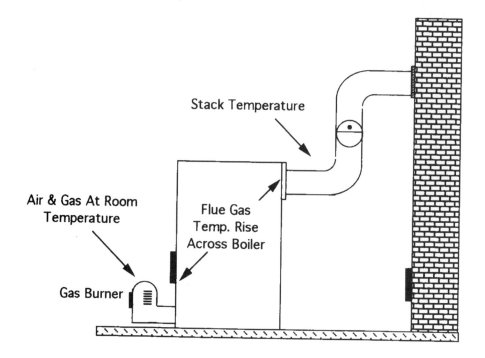

Stack Temperature

Air & Gas At Room Temperature

Flue Gas Temp. Rise Across Boiler

Gas Burner

As illustrated in *Figure 13-4* the furnace or boiler *stack* temperature is an indication of the ability of the heating plant to absorb heat. For the appliance to be 100% efficient in absorbing the heat from the combustion process, the temperature at the stack would have to equal the room temperature. In this case, there would be no *flue gas temperature rise* across the furnace or boiler, indicating that all of the heat generated by the combustion process was imparted to the warm air or boiler water. However, a moderate stack temperature is required to:

1. prevent condensation of the water vapour in the flue gases; and
2. develop sufficient chimney draft to remove the products of combustion through the appliance, appliance vent connector and chimney.

Thus, every heating appliance will experience some degree of stack loss associated with a flue gas temperature rise across the furnace or boiler. This stack loss must be kept to a minimum in order to obtain good combustion efficiency from the furnace or boiler.

Therefore, the second component for combustion efficiency is stack temperature or specifically *net stack temperature*. The net stack temperature is the actual temperature rise of the flue gases across the furnace or boiler. The actual temperature at the stack is called *gross stack temperature*. To obtain net stack temperature, use the following calculation:

NET STACK TEMPERATURE =
GROSS STACK TEMPERATURE - ROOM TEMPERATURE

Factors That Affect Stack Temperature
The following are factors that tend to elevate the stack temperature of the furnace or boiler and thereby lead to a lowering of the combustion efficiency of the heating appliance:

1. Overfiring of the burner;

2. Increasing the amount of air supply giving high amounts of excess air in the flue gases which absorb heat from the combustion process creating higher stack losses;

3. High overfire draft which increases the velocity of the flue gases across the furnace or boiler, thereby reducing the time for effective heat transfer within the heating plant;

4. Dirty heat exchanger surface which insulates and prevents effective heat transfer.

Combustion Efficiency of the Heating Appliance

As illustrated in *Figure 13-5*, the combustion efficiency of the heating appliance can be simply expressed as:

$$\text{Combustion Efficiency of Appliance} = \frac{\text{Appliance Btuh Output}}{\text{Appliance Btuh Input}}$$

Note that the appliance Btuh output is equal to the appliance Btuh input minus the appliance stack or flue losses.[3]

[3] The appliance stack or flue loss as indicated in *Figure 13-6* is calculated as the sum of the heat above room temperature carried by the flue gases. For the purpose of the calculation, for non-condensing type appliances, water in the combustion products is assumed to exist as a vapour above room temperature, condensation occurring at room temperature.

However, where the water vapour is condensed, as in a condensing appliance, the percentage of the flue or stack loss must be corrected as determined by the following formula: — continued next page

Figure 13-5: Combustion efficiency of heating appliance.

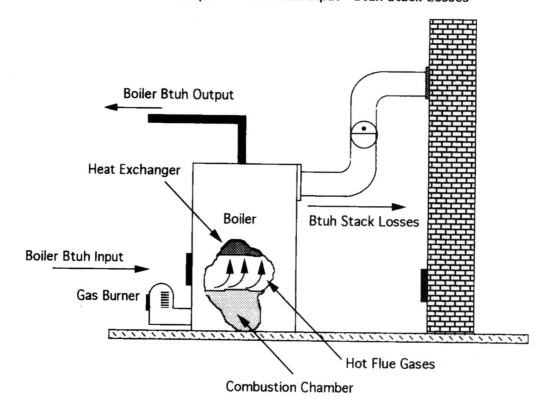

BOILER COMBUSTION EFFICIENCY = BOILER Btuh OUTPUT/BOILER Btuh INPUT

Note: Boiler Btuh Output = Boiler Btuh input - Btuh Stack Losses

Boiler Btuh Output

Heat Exchanger

Boiler Btuh Input

Gas Burner

Boiler

Btuh Stack Losses

Hot Flue Gases

Combustion Chamber

$$\% \text{ flue loss} = \text{uncorrected flue loss from } \textit{Figure 13-6} - \frac{1059 \times C_1}{Q1} \times 100\%$$

OR

$$\% \text{ flue loss} = \text{uncorrected flue loss from } \textit{Figure 13-6} - \frac{0.68435 \times C_2}{Q_2} \times 100\%$$

Where $C_1 (C_2)$ = condensation rate, lbs/hr (kg/hr)

$Q_1 (Q_2)$ = gas input rate, Btuh (kW)

NOTE: C_1 and C_2 = 0 for non-condensing type appliances

Figure 13-6: Chart for determining flue loss with natural gas.

CO$_2$ IN FLUE GASES (%)

FLUE LOSS (%)

FLUE GAS TEMP. MINUS ROOM TEMP. °F (°C)	2.0	2.5	3.0	3.5	4.0	4.5	5.0	5.5	6.0	6.5	7.0	7.5	8.0	8.5	9.0	9.5	10.0	10.5	11.0	11.5
20 (11)	11.8	11.5	11.2	11.0	10.9	10.8	10.7	10.7	10.6	10.5	10.5	10.5	10.4	10.4	10.4	10.4	10.3	10.3	10.3	10.3
30 (17)	12.8	12.3	11.9	11.6	11.4	11.3	11.1	11.0	11.0	10.9	10.8	10.8	10.7	10.7	10.6	10.6	10.6	10.6	10.5	10.5
40 (22)	13.8	13.1	12.6	12.2	11.9	11.7	11.6	11.4	11.3	11.2	11.1	11.1	11.0	10.9	10.9	10.9	10.8	10.8	10.7	10.7
50 (28)	14.8	13.8	13.2	12.8	12.4	12.2	12.0	11.8	11.7	11.5	11.4	11.4	11.3	11.2	11.1	11.1	11.0	11.0	11.0	10.9
60 (33)	15.7	14.6	13.9	13.4	13.0	12.6	12.4	12.2	12.0	11.9	11.8	11.6	11.5	11.4	11.3	11.3	11.2	11.2	11.2	11.1
70 (39)	16.7	15.4	14.5	13.9	13.5	13.1	12.8	12.6	12.4	12.2	12.1	11.9	11.8	11.7	11.7	11.6	11.5	11.4	11.4	11.3
80 (44)	17.7	16.2	15.2	14.5	14.0	13.6	13.2	13.0	12.7	12.5	12.4	12.2	12.1	12.0	11.9	11.8	11.7	11.7	11.6	11.5
90 (50)	18.7	17.0	15.9	15.1	14.5	14.0	13.6	13.3	13.1	12.9	12.7	12.5	12.4	12.3	12.2	12.1	12.0	11.9	11.8	11.8
100 (56)	19.6	17.8	16.5	15.7	15.0	14.5	14.1	13.7	13.4	13.2	13.0	12.8	12.7	12.5	12.4	12.3	12.2	12.1	12.0	12.0
110 (61)	20.6	18.6	17.2	16.2	15.5	14.9	14.5	14.1	13.8	13.5	13.3	13.1	12.9	12.7	12.6	12.5	12.4	12.3	12.2	12.2
120 (67)	21.6	19.3	17.9	16.8	16.0	15.4	14.9	14.5	14.1	13.9	13.6	13.4	13.2	13.1	12.9	12.8	12.7	12.6	12.5	12.4
130 (72)	22.5	20.1	18.5	17.4	16.5	15.8	15.3	14.9	14.5	14.2	13.9	13.7	13.5	13.3	13.2	13.0	12.9	12.8	12.7	12.6
140 (78)	23.5	20.9	19.2	17.9	17.0	16.3	15.7	15.3	14.9	14.5	14.2	14.0	13.8	13.6	13.4	13.3	13.1	13.0	12.9	12.8
150 (83)	24.5	21.7	19.8	18.5	17.5	16.8	16.1	15.6	15.2	14.9	14.6	14.3	14.1	13.9	13.7	13.5	13.4	13.2	13.1	13.0
160 (89)	25.4	22.5	20.5	19.1	18.0	17.2	16.6	16.0	15.6	15.2	14.9	14.6	14.3	14.1	13.9	13.7	13.6	13.5	13.3	13.2
170 (94)	26.4	23.3	21.2	19.7	18.5	17.7	17.0	16.4	15.9	15.5	15.2	14.9	14.6	14.4	14.2	14.0	13.8	13.7	13.5	13.4
180 (100)	27.4	24.1	21.8	20.2	19.1	18.1	17.4	16.8	16.3	15.9	15.5	15.2	14.9	14.6	14.4	14.2	14.1	13.9	13.8	13.6
190 (106)	28.4	24.8	22.5	20.8	19.6	18.6	17.8	17.2	16.6	16.2	15.8	15.5	15.2	14.9	14.7	14.5	14.3	14.1	14.0	13.8
200 (111)	29.3	25.6	23.2	21.4	20.1	19.1	18.2	17.6	17.0	16.5	16.1	15.8	15.4	15.2	14.9	14.7	14.5	14.3	14.2	14.0
210 (117)	30.3	26.4	23.8	22.0	20.6	19.5	18.6	17.9	17.3	16.9	16.4	16.1	15.7	15.4	15.2	15.0	14.8	14.6	14.4	14.2
220 (122)	31.3	27.2	24.5	22.6	21.1	20.0	19.1	18.3	17.7	17.2	16.7	16.3	16.0	15.7	15.4	15.2	15.0	14.8	14.6	14.5
230 (128)	32.3	28.0	25.2	23.1	21.6	20.4	19.5	18.7	18.1	17.5	17.1	16.6	16.3	16.0	15.7	15.4	15.2	15.0	14.8	14.7
240 (133)	33.2	28.8	25.8	23.7	22.1	20.9	19.9	19.1	18.4	17.9	17.4	16.9	16.6	16.2	16.0	15.7	15.5	15.2	15.1	14.9
250 (139)	34.2	29.6	26.5	24.3	22.6	21.4	20.3	19.5	18.8	18.2	17.7	17.2	16.9	16.5	16.2	15.9	15.7	15.5	15.3	15.1
260 (144)	35.2	30.4	27.2	24.9	23.2	21.8	20.7	19.9	19.1	18.5	18.0	17.5	17.1	16.8	16.5	16.2	15.9	15.7	15.5	15.3
270 (150)	36.2	31.2	27.8	25.5	23.7	22.3	21.2	20.3	19.5	18.9	18.3	17.8	17.4	17.0	16.7	16.4	16.2	15.9	15.7	15.5
280 (156)	37.2	32.0	28.5	26.0	24.2	22.7	21.6	20.7	19.9	19.2	18.6	18.1	17.7	17.3	17.0	16.7	16.4	16.2	15.9	15.7
290 (161)	38.2	32.8	29.2	26.6	24.7	23.2	22.0	21.0	20.2	19.5	18.9	18.4	18.0	17.6	17.2	16.9	16.6	16.4	16.2	15.9
300 (167)	39.1	33.6	29.9	27.2	25.2	23.7	22.4	21.4	20.6	19.9	19.3	18.7	18.3	17.9	17.5	17.2	16.9	16.6	16.4	16.2
310 (172)	40.1	34.4	30.5	27.8	25.7	24.1	22.9	21.8	21.0	20.2	19.6	19.0	18.6	18.1	17.8	17.4	17.1	16.8	16.6	16.4
320 (178)	41.1	35.2	31.2	28.4	26.3	24.6	23.3	22.2	21.3	20.6	19.9	19.3	18.8	18.4	18.0	17.7	17.4	17.1	16.8	16.6
330 (183)	42.1	36.0	31.9	29.0	26.8	25.1	23.7	22.6	21.7	20.9	20.2	19.6	19.1	18.7	18.3	17.9	17.6	17.3	17.0	16.8
340 (189)	43.1	36.8	32.6	29.6	27.3	25.6	24.1	23.0	22.0	21.2	20.5	19.9	19.4	18.9	18.5	18.2	17.8	17.5	17.3	17.0
350 (194)	44.1	37.6	33.3	30.2	27.8	26.0	24.6	23.4	22.4	21.6	20.9	20.2	19.7	19.2	18.8	18.4	18.1	17.8	17.5	17.2
360 (200)	45.1	38.4	33.9	30.7	28.4	26.5	25.0	23.8	22.8	21.9	21.2	20.5	20.0	19.5	19.1	18.7	18.3	18.0	17.7	17.4
370 (206)	46.1	39.2	34.6	31.3	28.9	27.0	25.4	24.2	23.1	22.3	21.5	20.8	20.3	19.8	19.3	18.9	18.5	18.2	17.9	17.7
380 (211)	47.1	40.0	35.3	31.9	29.4	27.4	25.9	24.6	23.5	22.6	21.8	21.1	20.6	20.0	19.6	19.2	18.8	18.5	18.1	17.9
390 (217)	48.1	40.8	36.0	32.5	29.9	27.9	26.3	25.0	23.9	22.9	22.1	21.5	20.8	20.3	19.8	19.4	19.0	18.7	18.4	18.1
400 (222)	49.1	41.6	36.7	33.1	30.5	28.4	26.7	25.4	24.2	23.3	22.5	21.8	21.1	20.6	20.1	19.7	19.3	18.9	18.6	18.3
410 (228)	50.1	42.5	37.4	33.7	31.0	28.9	27.2	25.8	24.6	23.6	22.8	22.1	21.4	20.9	20.4	19.9	19.5	19.2	18.8	18.5
420 (233)	51.1	43.3	38.0	34.3	31.5	29.3	27.6	26.2	25.0	24.0	23.1	22.4	21.7	21.1	20.6	20.2	19.8	19.4	19.0	18.7
430 (239)	52.1	44.1	38.7	34.9	32.0	29.8	28.0	26.6	25.4	24.3	23.4	22.7	22.0	21.4	20.9	20.4	20.0	19.6	19.3	19.0
440 (244)	53.1	44.9	39.4	35.5	32.6	30.3	28.5	27.0	25.7	24.7	23.8	23.0	22.3	21.7	21.2	20.7	20.2	19.9	19.5	19.2
450 (250)	54.1	45.7	40.1	36.1	33.1	30.8	28.9	27.4	26.1	25.0	24.1	23.3	22.6	22.0	21.4	20.9	20.5	20.1	19.7	19.4
460 (256)	55.2	46.6	40.8	36.7	33.6	31.3	29.3	27.8	26.5	25.4	24.4	23.6	22.9	22.3	21.7	21.2	20.7	20.3	20.0	19.6
470 (261)	56.2	47.4	41.5	37.3	34.2	31.7	29.8	28.2	26.8	25.7	24.7	23.9	23.2	22.5	22.0	21.4	21.0	20.6	20.2	19.8
480 (267)	57.2	48.2	42.2	37.9	34.7	32.2	30.2	28.6	27.2	26.1	25.1	24.2	23.5	22.8	22.2	21.7	21.2	20.8	20.4	20.1
490 (272)	58.2	49.0	42.9	38.5	35.2	32.7	30.7	29.0	27.6	26.4	25.4	24.5	23.8	23.1	22.5	22.0	21.5	21.0	20.6	20.3
500 (278)	59.2	49.8	43.6	39.1	35.8	33.2	31.1	29.4	28.0	26.8	25.7	24.8	24.1	23.4	22.8	22.2	21.7	21.3	20.9	20.5
510 (283)	60.2	50.7	44.3	39.7	36.3	33.7	31.5	29.8	28.3	27.1	26.1	25.2	24.4	23.7	23.0	22.5	21.9	21.5	21.1	20.7
520 (289)	61.2	51.5	45.0	40.3	36.9	34.1	32.0	30.2	28.7	27.5	26.4	25.5	24.7	23.9	23.3	22.7	22.2	21.7	21.3	20.9
530 (294)	62.3	52.3	45.7	41.0	37.4	34.6	32.4	30.6	29.1	27.8	26.7	25.8	24.9	24.2	23.6	23.0	22.5	22.0	21.6	21.2

The two components that determine the amount of appliance stack or flue loss and hence the combustion efficiency of the appliance are:

1. The percentage CO_2 in the flue gases, indicating the type and quality of the combustion process.

2. The net stack temperature, indicating the ability of the heating plant to absorb the heat from the combustion process.

By combining the % of CO_2 in the flue gases with the net stack temperature, the appliance stack or flue loss and hence appliance combustion efficiency can be determined from charts such as *Figure 13-6*.

Example
A gas fired furnace has a net stack temperature of 300° and a CO_2 reading of 8%. What would be the furnace combustion efficiency?

Steps

1. The stack or flue loss of the furnace, as read from *Figure 13-6*, is 18.3%.

2. The furnace combustion efficiency would be 100%-18.3% = 81.7%.

Acceptable Limits
The following are acceptable limits that should be obtainable on residential gas heating equipment to ensure adequate combustion efficiency:

Atmospheric burners:	7.5% to 9.8% CO_2 or 3.5% to 8% O_2
Fan assist burners:	8.25% to 9.8% CO_2 or 3.5% to 6% O_2
Stack temperature before draft diverter:	350°F (177°C) to 450°F (235°C)

Combustion Testing

Combustion Gas Analyzers
Combustion gas analyzers may be separated into two categories:

a) those that utilize chemicals for taking a *momentary reading*, and
b) those that are electronic for taking a *continuous reading*.

Chemical analyzers may analyze carbon dioxide (CO_2) or oxygen (O_2); however, carbon dioxide is the most commonly analyzed combustion product. With the chemical type analyzer, the flue gases are introduced into the analyzer by means of a hand pump, after which the flue gases enter a liquid chemical. The chemical has the ability to absorb selectively the gas being analyzed and indicates the percentage of the gas absorbed by a volumetric change of the chemical fluid in a calibrated tube. *Figure 13-7* illustrates a typical chemical flue gas analyzer as a component of a combustion testing kit illustrated in *Figure 13-10.*

Electronic analyzers, as illustrated in *Figures 13-8 and 13-9* will vary a great deal in their method of determining the percentage of CO_2, CO, and O_2 in the flue gases.

The advantages of the chemical type of analyzers are their low cost and durability. The advantages of the electronic analyzers are their ability to continuously make a flue gas analysis while making burner air/fuel adjustments, their speed in analysis and not needing to keep fresh chemicals on hand.

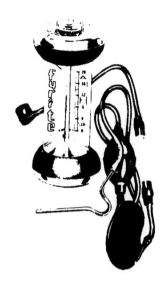

Figure 13-7: Typical chemical type of flue gas analyzer.

Process of Combustion Testing

Figure 13-11 illustrates the process of combustion testing. For most residential and light commercial applications, chemical type of flue gas analyzers are still being used. Usually they are a component of a *combustion testing kit,* illustrated in *Figure 13-10* consisting of:

> CO_2 & O_2 analyzer
> Stack thermometer
> CO tester
> Small pocket size draft gauge
> Combustion efficiency calculators[4]
> Manometer

Testing for Percentage of CO_2

As illustrated in *Figure 13-12 and 13-13* the percentage CO_2 can be tested either upstream or downstream of the draft diverter depending upon the design of the boiler or furnace. A 1/4" hole is drilled into the flue or stack to admit the probe of the analyzer and a sample of the flue gases is drawn into the analyzer. The percentage of CO_2 is determined as illustrated in *Figure 13-14.*

Testing For Net Stack Temperature

A stack thermometer is placed into the same hole of the flue where percentage of CO_2 was tested, to determine the gross stack temperature as illustrated in *Figure 13-15.* Once the gross stack temperature has been obtained, room temperature or ambient temperature is subtracted from the reading to obtain the net stack temperature or flue temperature rise across the furnace or boiler.

---

[4] Calculators are provide for natural gas, propane gas and fuel oil.

Figure 13-8: Electronic flue gas analyzer.

Figure 13-9: Small hand held electronic flue gas analyzer.

Figure 13-10: Combustion testing kit.

Figure 13-11: Combustion testing of heating appliance.

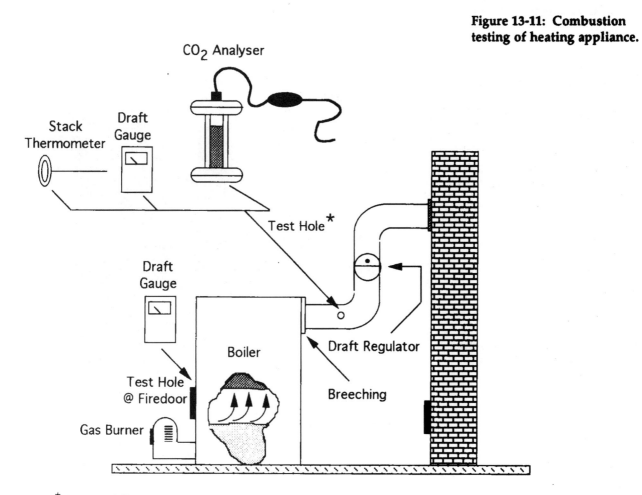

* Locate 1/4" test hole at least one flue pipe dia. upstream of draft regulator

Figure 13-12: Testing for percentage CO_2 upstream of draft diverter.

Figure 13-13: Testing for percentage of CO_2 downstream of draft diverter.

Figure 13-14: Determining the percentage of CO_2 in the flue gases.

  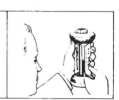

1. Push rubber connector down—then squeeze bulb 18 times.

2. Lift finger from rubber connector—this seals Fyrite.

3. Turn bottom side up and back again; twice on CO_2, four times on O_2.

4. Read fluid level on scale for percentage of gas.

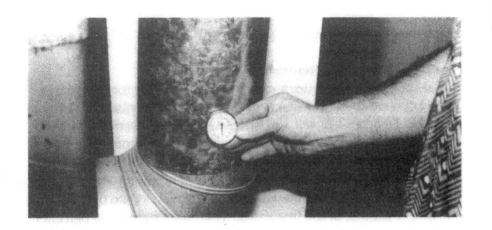

Figure 13-15: Determining the gross stack temperature.

Calculating Combustion Efficiency

As illustrated in *Figure 13-16*, the percentage of CO_2 and net stack temperature are entered into the combustion efficiency calculator which will read out the percentage of combustion efficiency.

Figure 13-16: Combustion efficiency calculator.

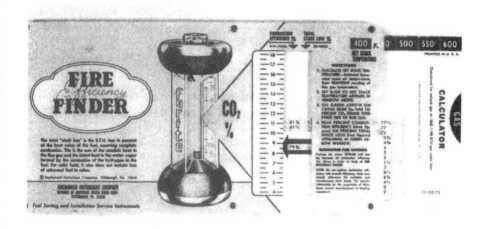

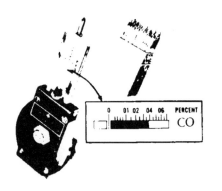

Figure 13-17: Checking CO with carbon monoxide indicator.

Draft Readings

A draft gauge can be utilized, as illustrated in *Figure 13-11*, to determine the overfire draft and the draft at the furnace or boiler stack.

Testing For Carbon Monoxide

Local codes and regulations usually require testing for percentage of CO content in the flue gases of the converted appliance. As illustrated in *Figures 13-17 and 13-18* the CO probe is inserted upstream from the draft diverter through the same opening from which the percentage of CO_2 was drawn. A sample of CO is drawn into the CO indicator and the percentage of CO is determined. *Note:* the gas industry standards limit the amount of CO to less than 0.04% CO in an air free sample of the flue gases. This is the maximum percent of carbon monoxide that will be tolerated. The equipment must be adjusted for less than 0.04%.[5]

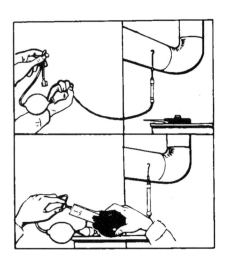

Figure 13-18: Determining the percentage of CO in flue gases.

[5] Since an air free sample is required, the percentage CO must be tested upstream from the appliance draft diverter to ensure that dilution air through the draft diverter's relief opening will not invalidate the reading.

Assignment

1. State the two objectives that govern the installation of conversion burners.

2. Give the required overfire draft needed to fire the fan assisted conversion burner effectively and state how this overfire draft is maintained.

3. Define the following terms:
   a) Perfect Combustion
   b) Complete Combustion
   c) Incomplete Combustion
   d) Ultimate % CO_2
   e) Excess Air
   f) Gross Stack Temperature
   g) Net Stack Temperature
   h) Combustion Efficiency
   i) Stack Losses

4. Give the acceptable limits that will ensure an adequate combustion efficiency for atmospheric and fan assisted burner application.

5. List the factors that affect the stack temperature of a boiler or furnace.

6. Combustion efficiency test was conducted on a converted boiler in which percentage of CO_2 was tested upstream of the draft diverter. The following readings were obtained:

CO_2	=	8%
Stack temperature	=	575°F
Room temperature	=	75°F
CO	=	NIL

   Find the following:

   a) the stack or flue loss;
   b) the combustion efficiency;
   c) the percentage of excess air.

14

High Efficiency Gas Furnaces —Part I

Since the early 1980's, residential gas furnace design has undergone a revolutionary change necessitated by the high cost of energy. Up until then, furnace design was mainly concerned with cost and durability and had little regard for fuel efficiency.

This design trend towards cost and durability rather than fuel efficiency is still evident in our present conventional natural draft gas furnaces. The conventional natural draft gas furnace consists of an atmospheric burner ignited by a standing pilot, a relatively inefficient sectional type heat exchanger (i.e., usually a clam shell type) and a fixed draft diverter or hood *(see Figure 8-12)*. The furnace employs conventional venting and buoyance of the hot flue gases within the venting system to remove the flue gases from the building. Draft diverter dilution, with its associated high amounts of excess air, is required to maintain a neutral overfire draft condition. This draft condition is required to maintain a consistent burner air supply and hence consistent furnace operating efficiency.

Steady State and Seasonal Efficiency

Until recently, gas furnace efficiency was always expressed in terms of *steady state efficiency*,[1] in which:

STEADY STATE EFFICIENCY = FURNACE HEAT OUTPUT / FURNACE HEAT INPUT

STEADY STATE EFFICIENCY = $\dfrac{\text{FURNACE HEAT OUTPUT}}{\text{FURNACE HEAT INPUT}}$

When the furnace has been firing for some time and all of the operating conditions are at a steady state (i.e., flue gas temperature rise across furnace).

The expected steady state efficiency for the conventional natural draft gas furnace is 75%. However, expressing efficiency in terms of the steady state does not take into account losses that are incurred when the furnace is not firing.

---

[1] Steady state efficiency is simply another term for combustion efficiency.

Since a gas furnace rarely operates continuously for extended periods but instead cycles on and off an average of 3 to 6 times per hour, its overall performance cannot be judged by its steady state efficiency. Therefore, we must view the furnace efficiency relative to the overall performance of the furnace as it operates through its on and off cycles. This overall performance rating is expressed as *seasonal efficiency*,[2] in which:

SEASONAL EFFICIENCY =	OVERALL ANNUAL EFFICIENCY OF THE FURNACE AS RECORDED FROM THE SUM OF THE FIRING CYCLES (I.E., STEADY STATE EFFICIENCY) MINUS THE OFF CYCLE LOSSES

Expected seasonal efficiencies for conventional natural draft appliances such as furnaces and water heaters are approximately:

Furnaces	45–58%
Water Heaters	30–45%

The difference between the steady state efficiency and seasonal efficiency is caused by the off cycle losses. Off cycle losses can be categorized as:

i)   Losses due to heated room air lost through appliance venting system via the draft diverter or hood relief opening and combustion air opening. *(See Figure 14-1.)*
ii) Gas consumption to maintain a standing pilot.
ii) Standby loss for water heaters and boilers.

Table 14-1 summarizes the general range of expected energy losses associated with conventional domestic gas appliances.

Improving the Seasonal Efficiency of the Conventional Furnace

As illustrated in *Figure 14-2*, the furnace manufacture can improve the seasonal efficiency of a conventional natural draft gas furnace by retro fitting the furnace with an automatic vent damper and an automatic ignition system.

---

[2] Also called annual fuel utilization efficiency (AFUE) in which:

$$AFUE = \frac{ENERGY\ INPUT - (ON\ TIME\ LOSSES + OFF\ TIME\ LOSSES)}{ENERGY\ INPUT}$$

Figure 14-1: Heated room air lost through appliance venting system via the draft diverter or hood relief opening and combustion air opening.

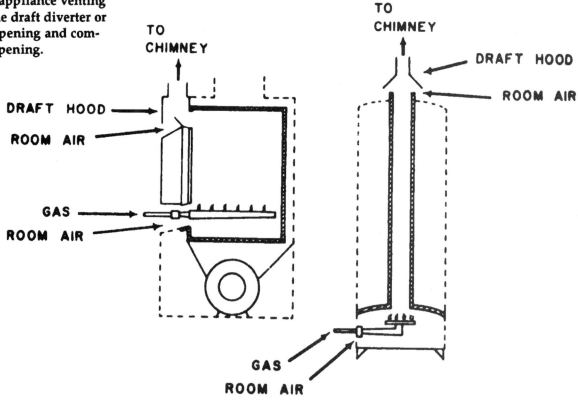

Table T14-1: Energy Losses of Domestic Appliances

TYPE OF LOSS	RESIDENTIAL FURNACE	RESIDENTIAL WATER HEATER
Flue gases[1]		
a) sensible	15-20%	18-23%
b) latent	10%	10%
Draft diverter & combustion air openings[2]	12-15%	20-25%
Standing pilot[2]	5-7%	2-4%
Standby[2]	0%	5-8%
Oversized unit[1]	0-3%	0%
Total	42-55%	55-70%

NOTE: 1 - steady state loss
2 - off cycle loss

Figure 14-2: Conventional natural draft gas furnace retro fitted with automatic vent damper and automatic ignition to improve seasonal efficiency.

DAMPER OPERATOR — WIRING HARNESS — STRAIN RELIEF CONNECTOR

The automatic vent damper decreases the off cycle losses associated with off time room air flow through the furnace draft diverter and combustion air openings. The automatic vent damper restricts stack flow when the furnace is not firing giving approximately 7% average reduction in off cycle losses. However, because of leakage across the damper (i.e., not a positive shut off device) it cannot completely eliminate this off cycle loss.[3]

The incorporation of an automatic ignition system, whether DSI, HSI or IP eliminates the loss associated with the standing pilot. This gives an approximate average reduction of 5% in the off cycle losses.

The retro fitted conventional natural draft furnace is classified as an *intermediate* or *mid-efficiency furnace*, having seasonal efficiencies of approximately 65–75%. However, retro fitting only reduces the off cycle losses and the best it can do to improve seasonal efficiency is to approach the steady state efficiency of the furnace.

To increase seasonal efficiency beyond the expected 75% steady state, the furnace would have to improve its steady state efficiency. However, its conventional design places constraints upon the ability of this furnace to improve its steady state efficiency. Because of gravity venting requirements, stack temperatures must be high enough to promote adequate venting of the flue gases through conventional chimneys and vents, preventing the maximization of heat transfer within the furnace. Also, because of draft diverter operation, the furnace is fired with relatively high amounts of excess air preventing improvements in its combustion efficiency (i.e., its steady state efficiency).

Improving Steady State Efficiency by Induced Draft Firing

The potential for increasing the steady state efficiency of a conventional natural draft furnace, retro fitted with an automatic vent damper and an automatic ignition system, is limited because of the requirements of stack temperature and draft diverter operation. Therefore, to improve seasonal efficiency the inherent constraints associated with natural draft firing must be removed.

Their removal is achieved through the application of *induced draft firing* in which the furnace is equipped with an induced draft fan or exhaust blower (i.e., power ventor). As illustrated in *Figure 14-3*, the furnace is still fired by an atmospheric burner; however, an ID fan or exhaust blower located at the flue outlet of the furnace provides a mechanical means of venting the flue gases.

[3] Some leakage is required to maintain stack flow so spillage does not occur because of a cold chimney when burner comes on.

Figure 14-3: Induced draft firing furnace.

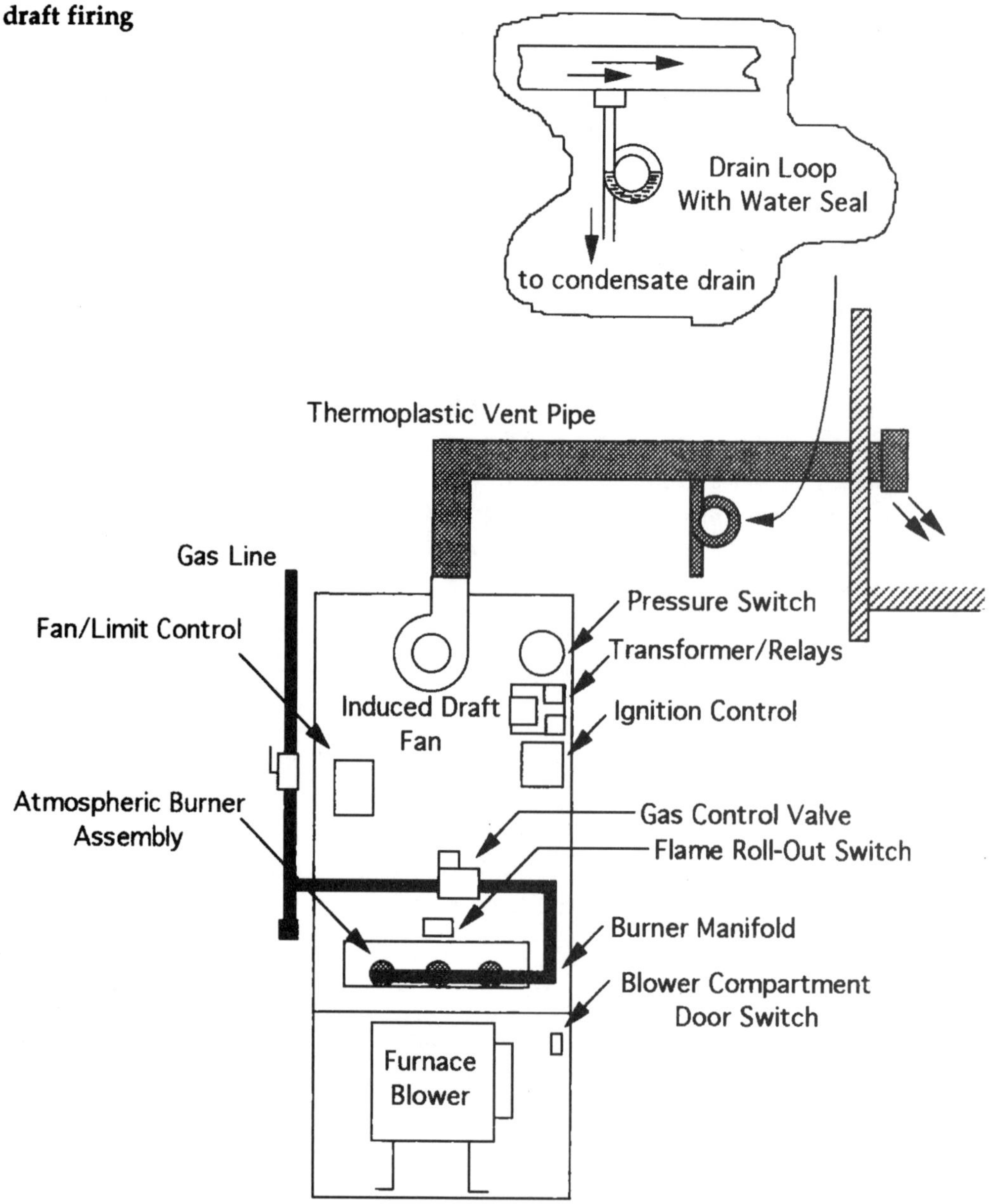

Drain Loop With Water Seal

to condensate drain

Thermoplastic Vent Pipe

Gas Line

Fan/Limit Control

Pressure Switch

Transformer/Relays

Induced Draft Fan

Ignition Control

Atmospheric Burner Assembly

Gas Control Valve

Flame Roll-Out Switch

Burner Manifold

Blower Compartment Door Switch

Furnace Blower

In induced draft firing, the furnace is fired by an atmospheric burner. However, instead of having gravity venting as you would have in natural draft firing, an induced draft fan *draws* the products of combustion across the furnace and *forces* the flue gases through the vent. *(See Figure 14-4.)*

As a result of induced draft firing, the overall seasonal efficiency of the furnace is increased by:

i)   Better control of excess air while the burner is firing since there is no dilution air required for draft diverter operation.

ii)   Elimination of stack temperature constraint associated with gravity venting, allowing a more restrictive heat exchanger design to maximize heat transfer.

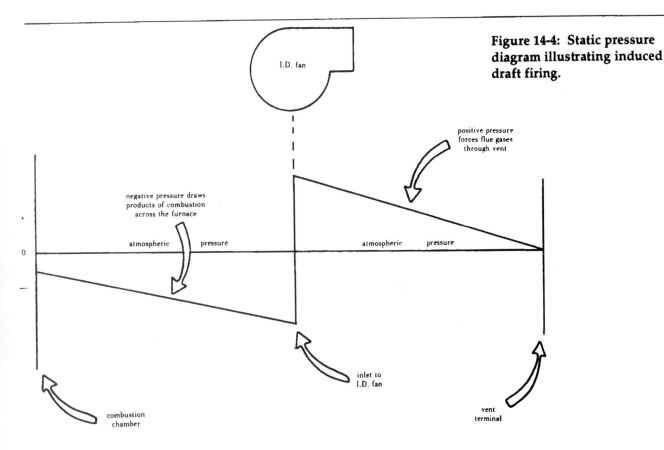

Figure 14-4: Static pressure diagram illustrating induced draft firing.

ii) Restrictive heat exchanger design plus ID fan off cycle restriction prevents room air flow across the furnace during the off cycle, together with automatic ignition, virtually eliminates off cycle losses.

As illustrated in *Figure 14-3*, induced draft firing necessitates additional control requirements aside from the standard fan and limit controls found on conventional furnace design. The following is a list of additional controls that provide extra control functions required by induced draft firing:

Components

Flame Roll-Out Switch
A manual reset thermal limit required to protect the furnace combustion air opening (i.e., burner's secondary air inlet pouch) from excessive heat and flame roll-out.

Pressure Switch
A negative pressure switch that proves ID fan operation. Negative pressure developed by the ID fan will trip the switch. This interlocks the ID fan operation with the combustion control circuit (i.e., the ignition control module) upon burner start up. The switch also serves to protect the furnace against a blocked vent condition since a blocked vent cannot develop sufficient negative ID fan pressure to trip the pressure switch.

Transformer/Relays
A step down control transformer provides 24 volt power for:

i)   a control relay that operates a 120 volt ID fan from thermostat command;

ii) a fan relay that operates a direct drive furnace fan or blower motor during a *manual on* mode and *cooling* mode.

Ignition Control
An IP, DSI or HSI ignition system will usually incorporate a pre-purge that will initiate the ID fan to run through a prepurge cycle prior to burner flame ignition. *Note:* prepurge is a requirement for induced draft and fan assisted furnaces and if the IP, DSI or HSI system does not have prepurge capability, then an external pre-purge timer is required.

Blower Compartment Door Switch
A switch that interlocks the furnace blower compartment door with the combustion control circuit (i.e. ignition control). The door must be closed for the switch to be closed to start the system.

Sequence of Operation

The following is the normal sequence of operation of a typical induced draft firing furnace as illustrated in *Figure 14-3*.

Normal Starting Sequence
1. Thermostat calls for heat.
2. Control relay is energized to start the ID fan.
3. Pressure switch will close to energize the ignition control module through the normal closed limit circuit that consist of the temperature high limit control and the flame roll-out switch.
4. Ignition control module will initiate a prepurge.
5. Upon the completion of the prepurge, ignition occurs (i.e., via spark ignited pilot, direct spark or hot surface igniter).
6. Main flame is established.

Stop Sequence
1. Thermostat is satisfied.
2. Main burner shuts down.
3. ID fan is de-energized.
4. Furnace fan or blower continues to operate until furnace temperature reaches fan control set point.
5. Furnace is on standby ready for the next thermostat call for heat.

Installation
As a category III vented appliance, the induced draft furnace can be vented horizontally through the wall of the building *(see Figure 14-3)*

using high temperature thermoplastic vent pipe.[4] Because the combustion products are under a positive vent pressure, vent pipe joints must be sealed using a high temperature sealant. Also, because of the possibility of condensation, a drain loop is usually installed in the vent pipe.

The Fan Assisted Furnace

The fan assisted furnace is a modified induced draft furnace that allows the gravity venting of the flue gases through a conventional vent (see Figure 14-5) such as type B vent or masonry chimney. The induced draft fan is calibrated to develop just the right amount of pull to move the products of combustion across the furnace. However, it does not establish a positive vent pressure in the flue pipe. The ID fan is prevented from developing a positive vent pressure due to the enlarging of the venting where the furnace flue collar is connected to the vent connector.

The fan assisted furnace has the same components as the induced draft furnace with the exception of the *vent safety switch (see Figures 14-5 and 14-6)*. The vent safety switch is a manual reset thermal limit switch. The switch will shut the furnace down upon excessive flue gas temperature as a result of a positive vent pressure caused by either a down draft condition or a blocked vent.

The induced draft firing and fan assisted furnaces operate with a stack temperature above that which will induce condensation. The furnaces are classified as *high efficiency non-condensing* giving seasonal efficiencies of approximately 75–85%.

To improve seasonal efficiencies beyond this level, the steady state efficiency must be raised by condensing the flue gases to recover the latent heat of condensation of the flue gases.

Improving Steady State Efficiency by Condensing the Flue Gases.

High efficiency condensing gas furnaces raise the steady state efficiency by condensing the flue gases. The condensing furnace employs a system of multiple heat exchangers; the first stage, of conventional design, captures sensible heat and the second stage, of a more restrictive design, captures latent heat.

Because the condensate from the flue gases is slightly acidic, the second stage heat exchanger is usually made from stainless steel. And, because of its restrictive design, a power combustion system must be utilized, with either induced draft firing or *pulse combustion* that draws or pushes the flue gases across the heating surface of the furnace.

4 Plastic vent material made from special resins which can withstand a flue gas temperature up to 480°F (249°C).

**Figure 14-5: The components of
a fan assisted furnace.**

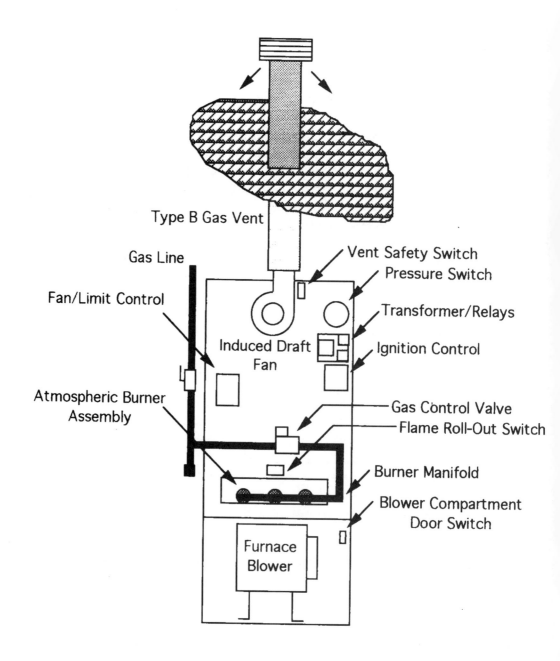

Type B Gas Vent

Gas Line

Fan/Limit Control

Vent Safety Switch
Pressure Switch

Transformer/Relays

Ignition Control

Induced Draft
Fan

Atmospheric Burner
Assembly

Gas Control Valve
Flame Roll-Out Switch

Burner Manifold

Blower Compartment
Door Switch

Furnace
Blower

At the end of the second stage, condensate is run to a drain. The
furnace may require a condensate pump if the drain is some distance from the furnace. Depending upon local codes, a *neutralizer*
may also be required because of the acidity of the condensate. The
amount of condensate is approximately 30–40 ml/min. at a steady
state for a full or completely condensating furnace.

LEGEND
DS = Door Switch
FR = Fan Relay
FS = Fan Switch
CR = Control Relay
VSS = Vent Safety Switch
TH = Thermostat
PS = Pressure Switch
MFS = Manual Fan Switch at
        Thermostat Subbase
LS= High Limit Control
FRS = Flame Roll-Out Switch
R = Thermostat Subbase Terminal
W= Thermostat Subbase Terminal
G = Thermostat Subbase Terminal
C = Thermostat Subbase Terminal

FURNACE BLOWER
L1   L2
DS
FR   FR
HI
MED
MED LOW
LOW
FS
CR
VSS
ID FAN
120V
Fuse   TRANSFORMER
24V
TH
R   W   CR
MFS
PS
CR
G   FR   C
LS   FRS   FLAME
SENSOR
IGNITOR   GAS VALVE
I L G F T T M M   IGNITION CONTROL
G 1 N P H R V V   MODULE
N   D

As illustrated in *Figure 14-7*, the high efficiency condensing furnace
employs a *counter flow design*. The restrictive second stage heat
exchanger, often called the *condensing heat exchanger*, is located next
to the cold air return since flue gas temperatures exiting from the
first stage are in the dew point range. This is the point where latent
heat is extracted from the flue gases, allowing the flue gases to condense. The first stage heat exchanger(s) is/are located at the supply
exit plenum to benefit from maximum temperature differential in
order to extract the sensible heat from the flue gases.

As illustrated in *Figure 14-8*, the condensed flue gases are vented
by an induced draft fan or power ventor, usually through the wall,
by a 2" diameter (51 mm) PVC plastic vent pipe.

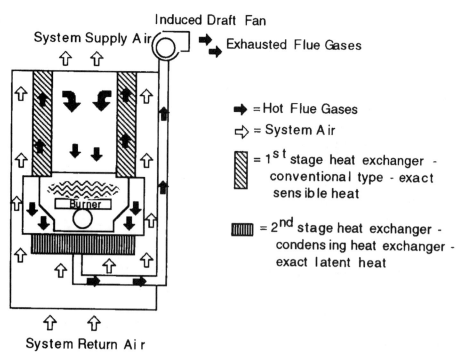

Figure 14-7: Counter flow design used by high efficiency condensing furnaces.

Induced Draft Fan

Exhausted Flue Gases

System Supply Air

→ = Hot Flue Gases

⇨ = System Air

▨ = 1st stage heat exchanger - conventional type - exact sensible heat

▥ = 2nd stage heat exchanger - condensing heat exchanger - exact latent heat

Burner

System Return Air

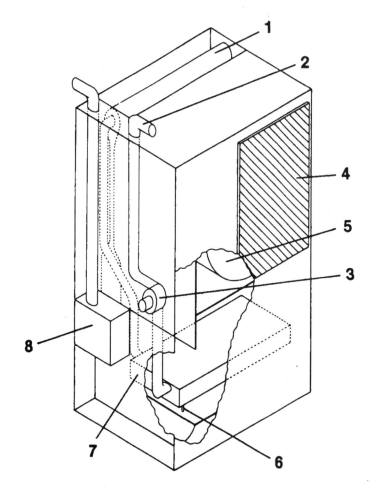

Figure 14-8: High efficiency condensing furnace showing—
(1) first stage heat exchanger;
(2) PVC plastic flue vent pipe;
(3) induced draft fan or power ventor;
(4) return air filter;
(5) furnace blower or fan;
(6) condensate drain;
(7) second state heat exchanger;
(8) burner and control compartment.

Assignment

1. Define the following terms:

   a) steady state efficiency
   b) seasonal efficiency
   c) off cycle losses
   d) induced draft firing
   e) fan assisted furnace
   f) counter flow design
   g) condensing Heat Exchanger
   h) neutralizer
   i) sensible heat
   j) latent heat

2. Give the off cycle losses and describe how they are reduced by retro fitting the conventional natural draft furnace.

3. Describe how the induced draft firing non-condensing furnace raises the seasonal efficiency above that of an intermediate efficiency furnace.

4. Describe and give the function for the following controls required for induced draft firing and fan assisted furnaces

   a) flame roll-out switch
   b) door switch
   c) pressure switch
   d) transformer/relays
   e) vent safety switch

5. Using *Figure 14-6*, describe the start up sequence of a typical fan assisted furnace.

6 Briefly describe the condensing gas furnace.

15 High Efficiency Gas Furnaces —Part II— Condensing Furnaces

Condensing gas furnaces generally fall into two major groups depending on the combustion system that they use. The first group employs induced draft firing, the same firing system used by the majority of high efficiency non-condensing gas furnaces. Because of the shared combustion system, many of the controls found on non-condensing and condensing gas furnaces are the same. The second group of condensing furnaces utilizes the principle of *pulse combustion* in which the burning process generates the pressure to exhaust the products of combustion.

As illustrated in *Figure 15-1*, the induced draft firing condensing gas furnace is fired by an atmospheric burner assembly. An induced draft fan mounted at the flue outlet of the furnace draws the products of combustion across the furnace. The primary and secondary heat exchangers, which make up the first stage of the heat exchange, extract the sensible heat from the flue gases. The condensing heat exchanger, mounted beneath the primary and secondary heat exchangers, extracts the latent heat from the flue gases before they are power vented to the outside by a 2" (51 mm) PVC plastic vent pipe.

The pulse combustion condensing gas furnace utilizes pulse combustion, a resonant combustion process in which the fuel is burned in separate *pulses* rather than in a conventional continuously burning flame. As seen in *Figure 15-2*, the pulse combustion process begins when a small amount of air and gas is induced into a combustion chamber through *flapper valves* (Stage 1). The air and gas mixture is ignited by a spark plug, causing the first pulse (Stage 2). The resulting positive combustion pressure causes the flapper valves to close. This pressure relieves itself by forcing the products of combustion out of the combustion chamber and into the tail pipe (Stage 3). The length of the tail pipe is designed so that as the shock wave from the pulse reaches the end of the tail pipe it is reflected back to the combustion chamber. Meanwhile, a negative pressure is created in the empty chamber which allows the flapper valves to open again, admitting more gas and air (Stage 4). When the reflective wave re-enters the combustion chamber, the flame remnants of the previous pulse combustion ignite the new mixture causing a second pulse (Stage 5). We now have a sustained combustion process which is self-perpetuating since the ignition spark is no longer required. Each pulse of gas/air mixture is ignited at a rate of 60–70 times per second producing 1/4–1/2 Btu (0.07–0.15 W) per pulse combustion.

Figure 15-1: Duomatic Olsen Ultamax induced draft firing condensing gas furnace showing —

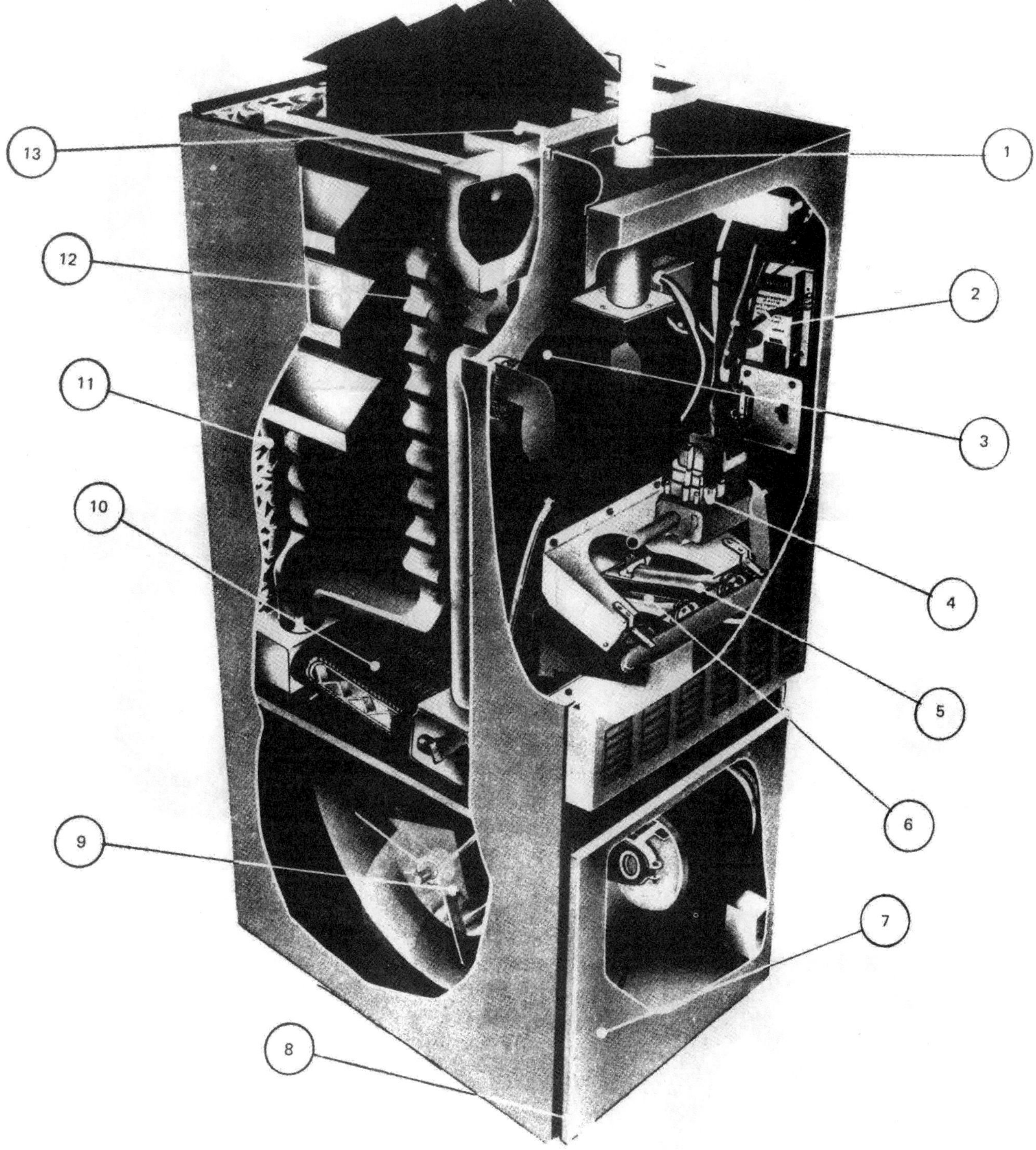

(1) plastic vent pipe
(2) IP ignition system
(3) ID fan
(4) gas valve having valve redundancy
(5) flame roll out switch
(6) atmospheric burner assembly
(7) fan compartment
(8) floor mounting
(9) two-speed fan
(10) condensing heat exchanger
(11) fibreglass insulation
(12) secondary heat exchanger
(13) primary heat exchanger

299

Figure 15-2: The pulse combustion process.

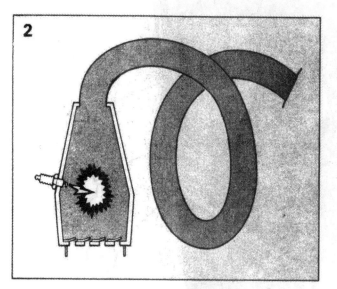

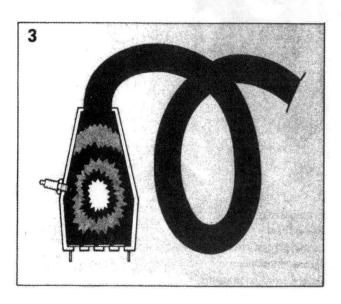

In a pulse combustion condensing gas furnace *(see Figure 15-3)* the products of combustion are forced across the furnace due to the high combustion pressure created by the pulse combustion process. *(See Figure 15-4.)* The first stage of heat exchange, in which sensible heat is extracted from the hot flue gases, consists of the combustion chamber, tail pipe and exhaust decoupler *(see Figure 15-5).* The second stage of heat exchange that involves extracting latent heat, is the condensing heat exchanger or condensing coil which is mounted below the exhaust decoupler and combustion chamber. The flue gases are finally vented under pressure to the outside by a 2" (51 mm) PVC plastic vent pipe.

The pulse furnace is classified as a *direct vent furnace* since the combustion system is totally sealed from the indoor environment. This closed system is completed by a second 2" (51 mm) PVC plastic pipe is used by bringing in combustion air directly from the outside.

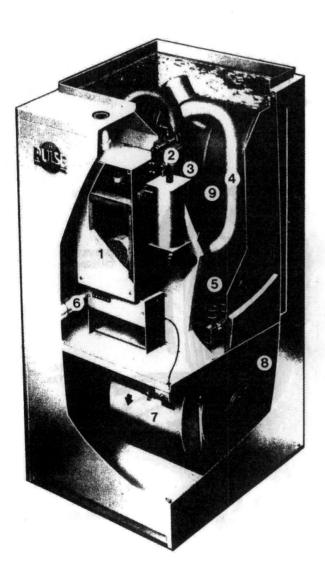

Figure 15-3: Lennox G14 pulse combustion condensing gas furnace showing—
(1) air intake, mixing valve and prepurge blower assembly
(2) gas valve
(3) combustion chamber
(4) tail pipe
(5) condensing heat exchanger or condensing coil
(6) flue vent pipe
(7) furnace fan or blower
(8) return air filter
(9) exhaust decoupler

Figure 15-4: Static pressure diagram illustrating pulse combustion.

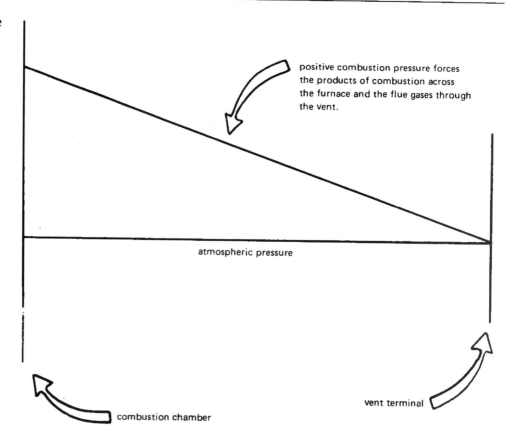

positive combustion pressure forces the products of combustion across the furnace and the flue gases through the vent.

atmospheric pressure

combustion chamber

vent terminal

Figure 15-5: Heat exchanger assembly of the Lennox pulse combustion condensing gas furnace.

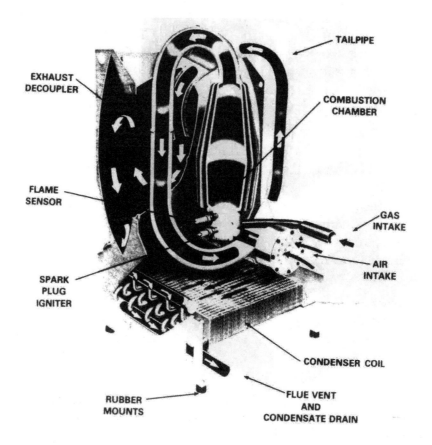

TAILPIPE

EXHAUST DECOUPLER

COMBUSTION CHAMBER

FLAME SENSOR

GAS INTAKE

AIR INTAKE

SPARK PLUG IGNITER

CONDENSER COIL

RUBBER MOUNTS

FLUE VENT AND CONDENSATE DRAIN

Induced Draft Firing Condensing Gas Furnace

Control System
An induced draft firing condensing gas furnace usually has the following control components (*Figures 15-6 and 15-7*):

1. *Ignition Control Module*
   A DSI, HSI or IP system utilizing the flame rectification method of flame detection. The ignition control module will often incorporate a purge timer giving a prepurge cycle prior to the ignition cycle. This is usually required for induced draft firing because of the restrictive nature of the furnace design.

2. *Fan (FS) and High Limited (LS) Control*
   A conventional fan and limit control.

3. *Low Speed Fan Switch LSFS)*
   An optional switch providing two speed fan operation.

4. *Control Relay (CR)*
   Allows the 24 volt thermostat circuit to energize the 110 volt induced draft fan circuit upon command from the room thermostat.

5. *Differential Pressure Switch (PS)*
   A dual function safety switch providing:

   i) An interlock between the ID fan and the combustion control circuit.

   ii) Protection against vent and heat exchanger blockage.

      The differential pressure switch is normally an open air switch that is actuated by a pressure differential created across the furnace when the induced draft fan is in operation. As illustrated in *Figure. 15-8*, its setting can be checked with an inclined U-tube or manometer.

      If the ID fan fails to start, a differential pressure cannot be established across the furnace and the switch will remain open preventing the burner circuit from being energized. Also, insufficient flue gas flow across the furnace caused by either restriction in the vent or the heat exchanger (i.e., condensate overflow in the condensing heat exchanger) will create a differential pressure below that of the switch setting and the switch will not close.

6. *Fan Compartment Door Switch (DS)*
   A switch that interlocks the fan compartment door with the burner control circuit. It ensures that the furnace will not operate if the fan door is open.

7. *Flame Rollout Switch (FRS)*
   A manual reset spillage or flame rollout switch that protects the furnace from flame rollout or excessive heating at the burner compartment.

Figure 15-6: Wiring schematic diagram of the Duomatic Olsen induced draft firing condensing gas furnace (see Figure 15-1).

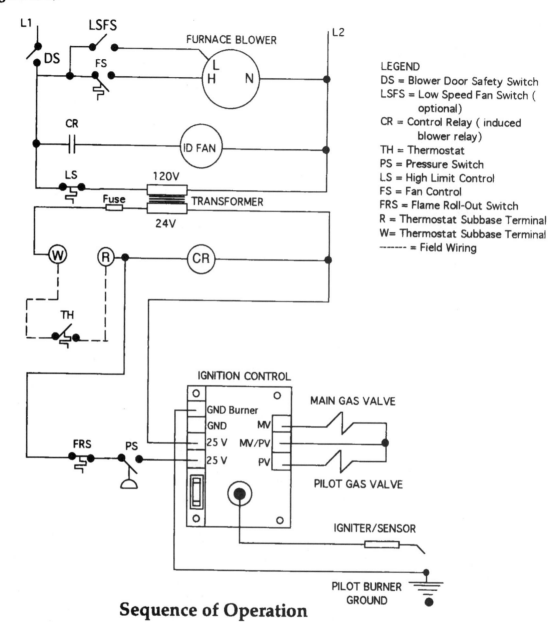

LEGEND
DS = Blower Door Safety Switch
LSFS = Low Speed Fan Switch (optional)
CR = Control Relay (induced blower relay)
TH = Thermostat
PS = Pressure Switch
LS = High Limit Control
FS = Fan Control
FRS = Flame Roll-Out Switch
R = Thermostat Subbase Terminal
W= Thermostat Subbase Terminal
------ = Field Wiring

Sequence of Operation

The following is the sequence of operation of the induced draft firing condensing gas furnace as illustrated in *Figures 15-1, 15-6 and 15-7*:

1. Thermostat calls for heat.
2. Control relay (induced draft blower relay) is activated.
3. Induced draft blower starts.
4. When induced draft blower reaches near full rpm, differential pressure switch closes.
5. 30 second prepurge timing sequence is activated by the ignition control module.

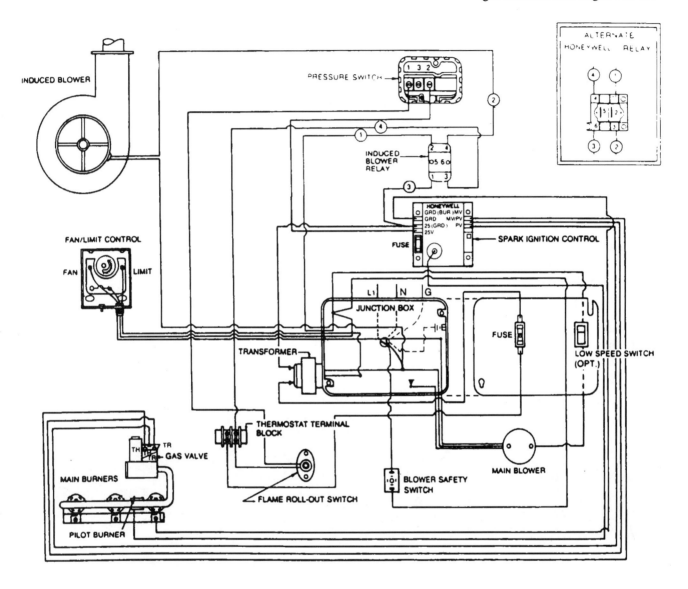

Figure 15-7: Pictorial wiring diagram of the Duomatic Olsen induced draft firing condensing gas furnace (see Figure 15-1).

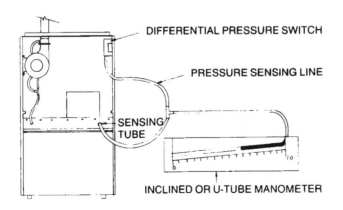

Figure 15-8: Checking the setting on the differential pressure switch with an inclined manometer.

6. When the 30 second prepurge cycle has finished, pilot valve opens and electrode spark begins.
7. When pilot flame is established, and proven, the spark will cease and the main valve opens.
8. Main burner lights.
9. System remains in this state until the call for heat is satisfied.
10. Thermostat opens.
11. Control relay and ignition module are de-energized. Main and pilot gas valves are closed and the induced draft blower begins to coast to a stop.
12. As the induced draft blower begins to slow down, the differential pressure switch opens.
13. The system remains idle until the next call for heat.

Figure 15-9: Installation of a typical induced draft firing condensing gas furnace showing required slope per foot and maximum support distance for the 2" (51 mm) plastic vent pipe as well as the location of the optional condensate neutralizer and gas connection.

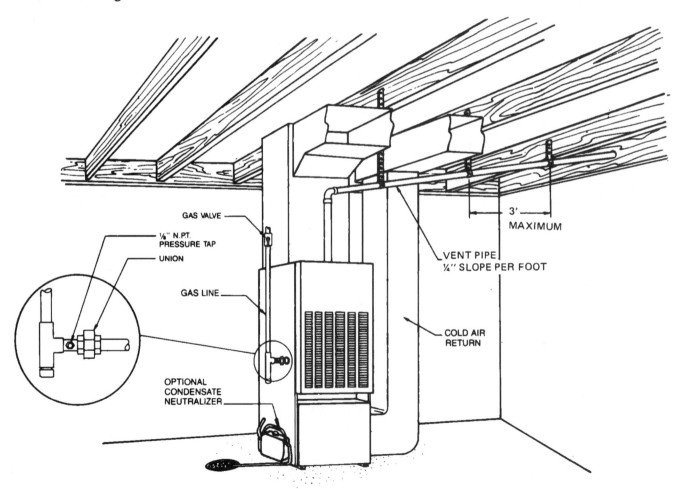

GAS VALVE

⅛" N.P.T. PRESSURE TAP

UNION

GAS LINE

OPTIONAL CONDENSATE NEUTRALIZER

3' MAXIMUM

VENT PIPE ¼" SLOPE PER FOOT

COLD AIR RETURN

Installation Requirements

The following is a summary of installation requirements pertaining to induced draft firing condensing gas furnaces.

Venting Material

The venting usually consists of schedule 40 PVC plastic pipe and fittings having a nominal diameter of 2" (51 mm). When assembling the vent, the surface of the plastic pipe should be cleaned with PVC primer/cleaner prior to the application of a PVC solvent cement, which is used for joining the connections. Finally, to ensure a tight vent, the joints are soap tested when the unit is running.

Vent Length

Maximum and minimum overall *equivalent vent length* must be adhered to when installing the vent. Keeping within the maximum and minimum equivalent vent lengths will ensure that the static pressure developed by the ID fan is not overcome by the effects of back pressure developed by gusts of wind at the vent terminal. If the maximum equivalent length is exceeded, then the furnace may experience erratic operation and nuisance shutdown due to the pressure switch tripping out.

Depending upon the furnace manufacturer, the maximum and minimum overall equivalent vent lengths are usually 60 feet (1830 cm) and 10 feet (305 cm) respectively. The overall equivalent vent length consists of straight vent pipe plus the resistance of the vent fittings as measured in equivalent length of straight pipe in which:

a)   2" (51 mm) 90° elbow is equivalent to 10 feet (305 cm) of 2" (51 mm) vent pipe.

b)   2" (51 mm) 45° elbow is equivalent to 5 feet (152 cm) of 2" (51 mm) vent pipe.

Running the Vent Inside the Building

The vent should be sloped upward from the furnace, usually 1/4" per running foot (2 cm/m), to allow for drainage of the condensate in the vent to the furnace. The vent should be adequately supported, usually every 3 feet (90 cm) with metal strapping to prevent sagging and vibration. *(See Figures 15-10 and 15-9.)* When the vent passes through an unheated space it must be insulated.

Figure 15-10: Vent support.

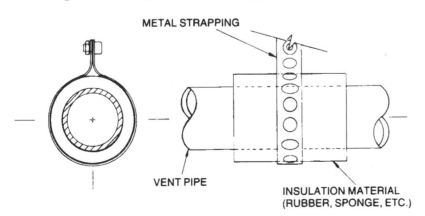

METAL STRAPPING

VENT PIPE

INSULATION MATERIAL
(RUBBER, SPONGE, ETC.)

Figure 15-11: Vent termination, illustrating through the wall venting associated with condensing gas furnaces (usually 1 foot (30 cm) dependent on local snow accumulation and code requirements).

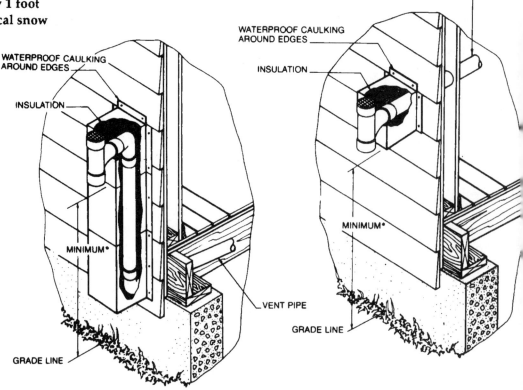

RISER TERMINAL   **STRAIGHT TERMINAL**

Vent Termination

As illustrated in *Figure 15-11*, factory supplied vent terminals provide effective outside termination for through the wall venting of the furnace.[1] It is important, when terminating the vent to the outside, that manufacturer's procedures and instructions are followed exactly. This will prevent nuisance shutdown and erratic furnace operation. When locating the vent terminal it should be:

1. Not less than 4 feet (120 cm) from building soffit.
2. Not less than 4 feet (120 cm) from an inside corner formed from two exterior walls.
3. On the sides of buildings which are not exposed to the prevailing winds.
4. Where it is accessible for maintenance and inspection.
5. Not less than 6 feet (180 cm) from a mechanical air supply inlet to a building.

---

[1] Through the wall venting is the preferred practice for venting the condensing furnace. However, in some cases this is not feasible. In such cases an existing chimney may be used, as long as it is not shared by any other appliance and a PVC vent pipe is run from the furnace, up the existing chimney to the factory supplied vent terminal.

6. Not less than the following from any building opening or combustion air supply inlet of another appliance:
   i) 12" (30 cm) for furnaces up to and including 100,000 Btuh,
   ii) 36" (90 cm) for furnaces exceeding 100,000 Btuh.
7. Not directly above a gas meter or service regulator and at least 6 feet (180 cm) from any regulator vent.
8. Not directly above a public walkway unless 7 feet (210 cm) above grade level.
9. Depending upon local snow accumulation and code requirements, 1 foot (30 cm) above the grade line.

Condensate Drainage and Neutralizer

The drain line should be a minimum of 1/2" (12.6 mm) flexible plastic tubing to allow sufficient drainage of the condensate. The drain line should be sloped a minimum of 1/4" per running foot (2 cm/m), downward from the furnace to the drain.

In certain installations, a floor drain may not be available or practical to use. *(See Figure 15-9.)* In these installations a condensate pump is usually available from the furnace manufacturer to drain the condensate. The condensate pump can be wired in parallel with the induced draft fan and is activated by the control relay. *(See Figure 15-6.)* If this is not a desirable arrangement, a float switch can be used to activate the condensate pump.

The condensate is mildly acidic and can be measured with a pH indicator. The pH scale is a measurement of acidity and/or alkalinity. As indicated in *Figure 15-13*, the condensate pH range is approximately 4 to 6. For comparison, pH levels of common liquids are: vinegar 2.4–3.4; wines 2.8–3.8; orange juice 3–4; and soft drinks 2–4. The concentration of the acidity of all these fluids including the condensate is very low and harmless. However, some localities may require that a condensate neutralizer be used in conjunction with the drain system. The neutralizer removes the acidic value of the condensate to neutralize it. The neutralizer is usually installed exterior to the furnace. *(See Figure 15-9.)* It is installed with an overflow to ensure continued furnace operation if it should become blocked. *(See Figure 15-12.)*

Figure 15-12: Drainage system.

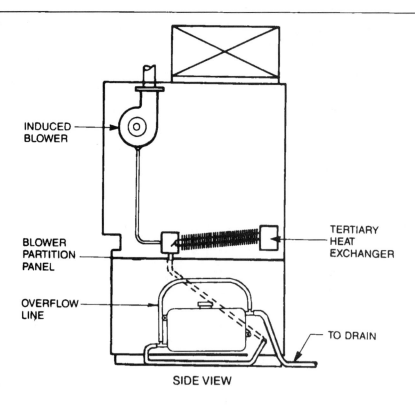

Figure 15-13: Condensate pH range.

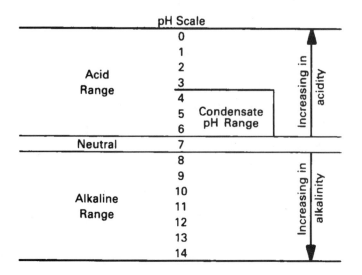

Service Analysis

The following is a service analysis for a typical induced draft firing condensing gas furnace as illustrated in *Figures 15-1, 15-6, and 15-7*.

SYMPTOM	CAUSE	REMEDY
Thermostat calling for heat induced draft blower not operating	No power (120 volt power supply to unit)	1. Ensure that the furnace disconnect switch is closed. 2. Ensure that breaker/fuse in furnace supply is closed. 3. Check for 120 V.A.C. at furnace. If there is voltage, check wiring connections, ensure that door switch in blower compartment is closed and that the limit switch is in closed position.
	No 24 V.A.C. power to control circuit.	1. Check for 24 V.A.C. on wire leads from transformer. 2. Check for a burnt fuse on the junction box cover; if fuse is burnt, replace. 3. Check thermostat circuit for a complete circuit.
	Relay or induced draft blower motor defective	1. With 120 V.A.C. power turned off - remove 120 V. leads from relay contact terminals. Isolate these wires and restore power. Check for continuity across the two relay terminals. If there is continuity, the induced draft blower motor should be checked. The thermal protector could be open, the motor should be allowed to remain idle for 5 to 10 minutes. Reconnect and apply power; if motor does not operate, replace with new motor. If there is no continuity through relay, replace relay.
Ignition control module does not activate	Prepurge Timer	There is a prepurge time delay of 30 seconds before ignition system is activated (i.e. Honeywell S860C).
	No power 24 V.A.C. supplied to ignition control module	1. Check for 24 V.A.C. on power terminals of the ignition control module. 2. If there is no voltage, ensure that the flame rollout switch is in the closed position by pressing the reset button. 3. Check for 24 V.A.C. between the common terminal on the pressure switch and the casing ground. If there is no voltage present then the flame roll-out switch is defective. To confirm this, jump out roll-out switch; voltage should be present between common terminal on pressure switch and the casing ground.

SYMPTOM	CAUSE	REMEDY
		4. Remove vacuum line to pressure switch and attach to an inclined manometer. If pressure reading is above setting then the pressure switch is defective. If the pressure reading is below setting then check the following: i) Remove vent at blower if reading goes above setting; then there is blockage in vent or vent is too long. ii) Check condensate drain line from induced draft blower: if level is above furnace blower partition panel, then condensate drain is blocked. (See Fig. 15-12). iii) Ensure that passes in the heat exchanger are clear; if clear then you have a defective induced draft blower assembly to replace. iv) Jump out pressure switch; ignition system should activate after prepurge. Replace faulty pressure switch. v) If replacement switch does not rectify problem, replace induced draft blower wheel. NOTE: Ensure that the maximum equivalent vent length does not exceed furnace manufacturer's specifications.
	Build-up of codsensate within induced draft blower	If unit is installed in an area where venting produces an excessive amount of condensate*, water may build-up in induced draft blower housing. Apply to furnace manufacturer for special vent drain assembly. *(Vent pipe installations, in unheated areas, or maximum vent length.)
	Burnt Fuse	If 24 V.A.C. present at 24V terminals on ignition control module, check that fuse on ignition control module is not burnt. If burnt, replace with same type and size.

SYMPTOM	CAUSE	REMEDY
No spark across ignition/sensor gap	Defective ignition control module	Pull ignition lead and check for spark at ignition control module ignition stud. (See Fig. 11-7) If no spark, replace control.
	Defective wires/connections in spark circuit	From above check, if spark is present, check for a crack in ceramic insulator, poor ignition cable, poor pilot grounding or the proper gap.
Pilot burner will not light	No gas supply	Ensure that all manual gas cocks are open, and that all gas piping is clear and unblocked. Ensure that wiring connections from the ignition control module to the gas control valve are proper and contacting.
	Defective ignition control module or gas control valve	Check for required voltage across gas valve terminals on the ignition control module; if voltage is present, replace gas control valve. If no voltage present, replace ignition control module. If ignition control module locks out, reset system.
Pilot burner cycles (on/off)	Check for proper condensate drainage	Ensure that condensate is draining properly from unit.
	Missing pilot sheild	Order sheilding pilot bracket (if applicable)
Spark does not stop when pilot lights	Faulty wiring	Check for continuity of ignition cable and ground wire.
	Pilot too low	Ensure that pilot flame covers electrode 3/8 - 1/2 inches (9.5 - 12.5 mm)
	Defective ignition control module	Replace module if above (electrode coverage) is sufficient.
Main burner will not light	Faulty wiring between ignition control module and gas control valve	Check all connections against wiring diagram to ensure that they are proper
	Faulty ignition control module or gas control valve	Check for 24V.A.C. across gas control valve terminals on ignition control module. If there is no voltage, replace ignition control module. If there is voltage, replace gas control valve.
Main burner shuts off before call for heat ends.	Faulty wiring	Check for continuity of the ignition cable and ground wire. (loose or bad connections may cause erratic shut down even though operation is normal at the time of check out)

313

SYMPTOM	CAUSE	REMEDY
	Defective ignition control module	Replace ignition control module.
System will not shut off when call for heat ends	Defective thermostat	Check to ensure that thermostat is operating properly. Replace if necessary.
	Defective ignition control module or gas control valve	Remove the (MV) valve lead at the ignition control module. If the valve closes, replace the ignition control module. If the valve remains open, replace the gas control valve.
Furnace not meeting the heating requirements of the building	Thermostat shutting off too soon	1. Adjust heat anticipator setting to that outlined in furnace installation instructions. 2. Ensure thermostat is positioned in a central location in the building and is not affected by heating ducts or exposure to sun
	Rating not properly adjusted according to rating plate instructions.	See specifications and adjustments in furnace manufacturer's operating manual.
	Furnace not properly sized for the building	Re-calculate heat loss according to method recommended by furnace manufacturer. The output of the furnace should be slightly in excess of the heat loss calculated for the building.
Induced draft blower will not shut off (thermostat open)	Relay contacts burned closed	Replace relay.

Pulse Combustion Condensing Gas Furnace

Unit Components

The Lennox G14 pulse combustion gas furnace employs control and burner components that are quite different from those of the induced draft firing furnace. The following is a list of the control and burner components found on the Lennox pulse furnace:

1. *Fan and Limit Control*
   The fan and limit has a sure start heater which is energized with the gas valve to close the fan control contacts after 30 to 45 seconds. The fan-off setting is factory adjusted to 90°F for a recommended off setting.

2. *Primary Control*
   The Lennox furnace employs both the Prestolite and Gas Energy primary controls (i.e., ignition control module). Both DSI systems are interchangeable and connect directly to a unit wiring harness. As such, either control will plug into and operate any Lennox pulse furnace without rewiring.

The primary control, either Prestolite or Gas Energy, has four main functions:

i) To initiate a prepurge cycle.
ii) To provide direct spark ignition to initiate combustion.
iii) To provide for flame sensing through the process of flame rectification.[2]
iv) To provide a post-purge cycle when the call for heat is satisfied. The ignition attempt sequence of the primary control provides five trials for ignition before locking out. The unit will usually ignite on the first attempt. *See Figure 15-16* for a normal ignition sequence. *Note:* nominal times are given for simplicity.

Proper gas/air mixture is required for ignition on the first attempt. If there is slight deviation, within tolerance of the unit, a second or third trial may be necessary for ignition. The control will lock out the system if ignition is not obtained within five trials. Reset after lock out requires only breaking and re-making the thermostat demand. See *Figure 15-17* for the ignition attempt sequence with retrials. *Note:* nominal timings are given for simplicity. Loss of combustion during a heating cycle is sensed through absence of flame signal thereby causing the control to lock out after five ignition retrials.

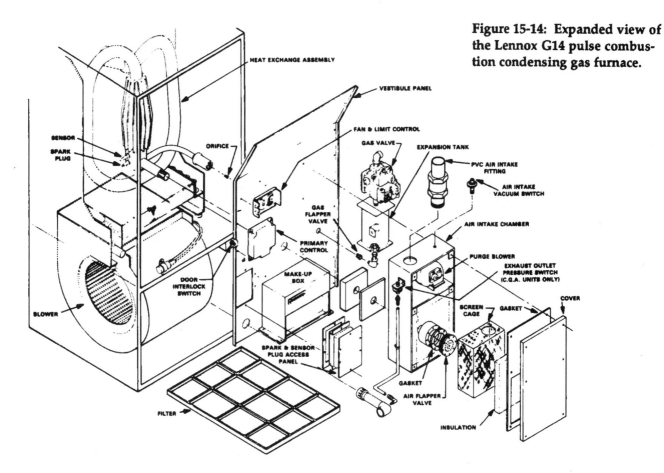

Figure 15-14: Expanded view of the Lennox G14 pulse combustion condensing gas furnace.

---

2 The flame signal for the Prestolite primary control is 3–5 microamps DC and for the Gas Energy primary control 25–35 microamps DC.

Figure 15-15: Prestolite and Gas Energy primary controls that are used on the Lennox G14 pulse combustion furnace.

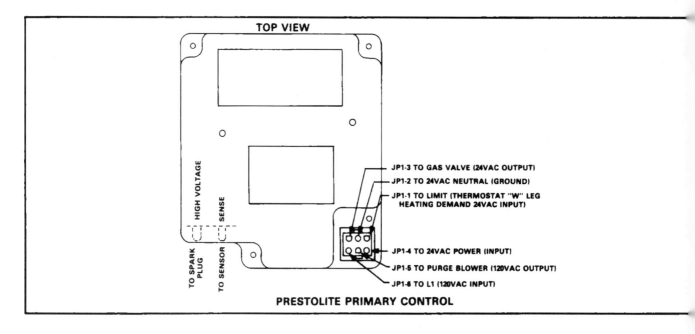

PRESTOLITE PRIMARY CONTROL

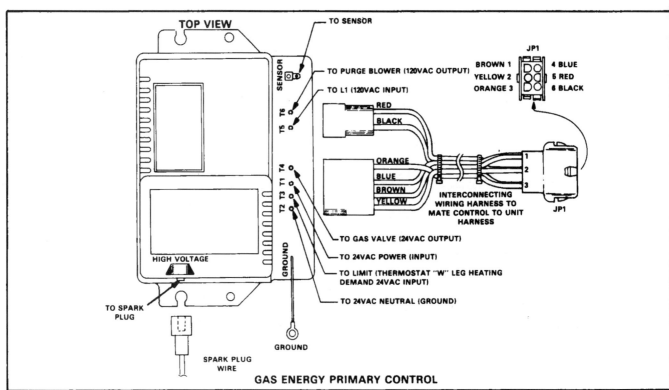

GAS ENERGY PRIMARY CONTROL

3. *Gas Valve and Expansion Tank*
   The gas control valve employs valve redundancy to ensure safety shut off. The expansion tank downstream of the gas valve *(see Figure 15-14)* absorbs any back pressure created during combustion to prevent damage to the gas valve diaphragm.

4. *Air Intake Vacuum Switch*
   A vacuum switch is mounted on top of the air intake chamber. See *Figure 15-14*. The switch is normally closed and remains closed under normal operating conditions. Obstructions or close-off of the air intake pipe cause the switch to open. When the switch opens, it breaks the heat demand circuit to shut down the unit. This is a safety shutdown function. The switch automatically resets when the restriction is removed from the air intake.

5. *Exhaust Outlet Pressure Switch*
   This pressure switch is mounted on the side of the air intake chamber, *(see Figure 15-14)*, and is connected to the exhaust outlet PVC elbow by a length of plastic tubing. The switch is normally closed and remains closed under normal operating conditions. Obstructions or close-off of the exhaust outlet pipe cause the switch to open. When the switch opens, it breaks the heat demand to shut down the unit. This is a safety shutdown function. The switch automatically resets when the restriction is removed from the exhaust outlet.

6. *Gas Intake Flapper Valve and Orifice*
   A union at the bottom of the expansion tank *(see Figure 15-14)*, provides for removal of the gas flapper valve assembly and access to the orifice. As illustrated in *Figure 15-18*, the flapper floats freely over the spacer and is opened against the clearance plate by incoming gas pressure. Back pressure from each combustion pulse forces the flapper against the valve body, closing off the gas supply. The single orifice is located downstream of the flapper valve and is sized specifically for each unit.

7. *Air Intake Chamber and Purge Blower*
   As illustrated in *Figure 15-14*, the air intake chamber houses the purge blower and air intake flapper valve assemblies. Air enters through the top inlet, passes through the purge blower and through the flapper valve to the combustion chamber. The entire air intake chamber is mounted on rubber isolators to eliminate vibration.
   The purge blower has a 120 volt motor and is powered only during the prepurge and post purge cycles. During combustion, the blower is not powered. However, air is drawn through the blower by negative pressure.

Figure 15-16

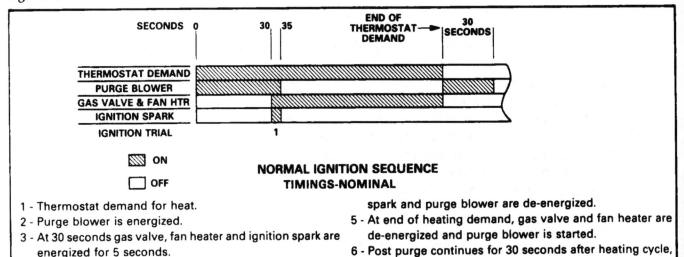

NORMAL IGNITION SEQUENCE
TIMINGS-NOMINAL

ON

OFF

1 - Thermostat demand for heat.
2 - Purge blower is energized.
3 - At 30 seconds gas valve, fan heater and ignition spark are energized for 5 seconds.
4 - When ignition occurs (sensed by flame rectification), the spark and purge blower are de-energized.
5 - At end of heating demand, gas valve and fan heater are de-energized and purge blower is started.
6 - Post purge continues for 30 seconds after heating cycle, then is de-energized.

Figure 15-17

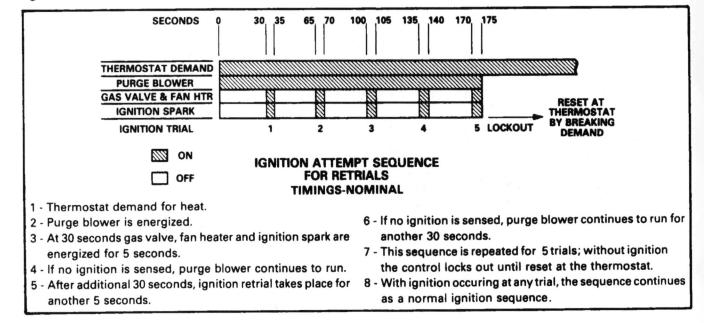

IGNITION ATTEMPT SEQUENCE
FOR RETRIALS
TIMINGS-NOMINAL

ON

OFF

1 - Thermostat demand for heat.
2 - Purge blower is energized.
3 - At 30 seconds gas valve, fan heater and ignition spark are energized for 5 seconds.
4 - If no ignition is sensed, purge blower continues to run.
5 - After additional 30 seconds, ignition retrial takes place for another 5 seconds.
6 - If no ignition is sensed, purge blower continues to run for another 30 seconds.
7 - This sequence is repeated for 5 trials; without ignition the control locks out until reset at the thermostat.
8 - With ignition occuring at any trial, the sequence continues as a normal ignition sequence.

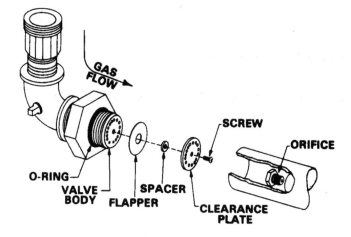

Figure 15-18: Gas intake flapper valve assembly.

8. *Air Intake Flapper Valve*

   The air intake flapper valve is similar to the gas flapper valve in operation. As illustrated in *Figure 15-19*, a flapper floats freely over a spacer between two plates. In actual operation, the flapper is forced against the clearance plate by the purge blower, thereby allowing air to enter the combustion chamber. Next, back pressure from combustion forces the flapper against the cover plate closing off the air supply. Finally, as negative pressure is created in the combustion chamber, the flapper is drawn to the clearance plate and air enters. The back pressure and negative pressure control the flapper valve with each combustion pulse once ignition has occurred.

9. *Spark Plug and Sensor*

   The spark plug and flame sensor are located on the lower left side of the combustion chamber. *(See Figure 15-14.)* Access to both is obtained through the special access panel located on the bottom left hand corner of the vestibule panel.

Figure 15-19: Air intake flapper valve assembly.

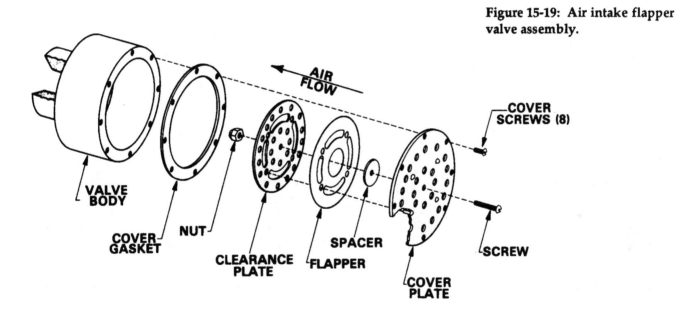

Sequence of Operation

The sequence of operation is illustrated in *Figure 15-20.*

Figure 15-20: Sequence of operation for the Lennox G14 pulse combustion condensing gas furnace.

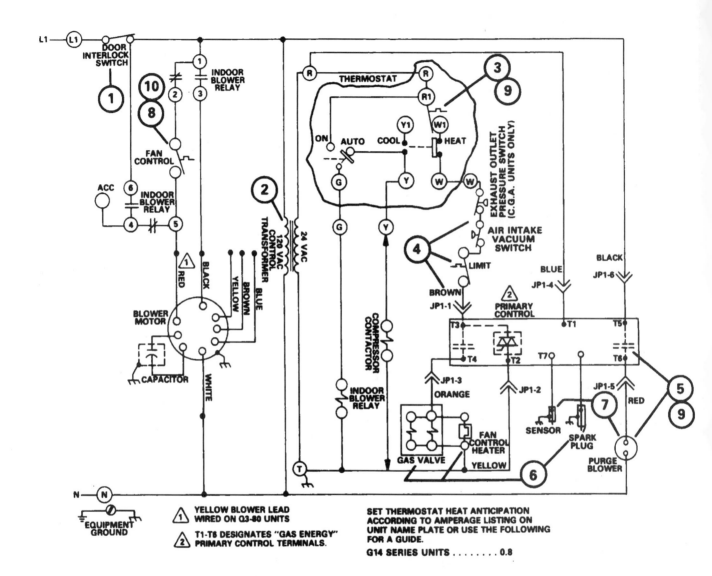

△1 YELLOW BLOWER LEAD WIRED ON Q3-80 UNITS

△2 T1-T6 DESIGNATES "GAS ENERGY" PRIMARY CONTROL TERMINALS.

SET THERMOSTAT HEAT ANTICIPATION ACCORDING TO AMPERAGE LISTING ON UNIT NAME PLATE OR USE THE FOLLOWING FOR A GUIDE.

G14 SERIES UNITS 0.8

1 - Line voltage feeds through the door interlock switch. Blower access panel must be in place to energize unit.

2 - Transformer provides 24 volt control circuit power.

3 - A heating demand closes the thermostat heating bulb contacts.

4 - The control circuit feeds from "W" leg through the exhaust outlet pressure switch (C.G.A. units only), the air intake vacuum switch (A.G.A. & C.G.A. units) and the limit control to energize the primary control.

5 - Through the primary control the purge blower is energized for approx. 30 sec. prepurge.

6 - At the end of prepurge the purge blower continues to run and the gas valve, fan control heater & spark plug are energized for approx. 8 seconds.

7 - The sensor determines ignition by flame rectification and de-energizes the spark plug and purge blower. Combustion continues.

8 - After approximately 30 to 45 seconds the fan control contacts close & energize the indoor blower motor on low speed.

9 - When heating demand is satisfied the thermostat heating bulb contacts open. The primary control is de-energized removing power from the gas valve & fan control heater. At this time the purge blower is energized for a 30 second post purge. The indoor blower motor remains on.

10 - When the air temperature reaches 90°F the fan control contacts open — shutting off the indoor blower.

Installation Requirements

1. Proper Installation Technique.

    In order to prevent any vibration from being transmitted by the building structure, the installation should be isolated. As illustrated in *Figure 15-21*, the following are devices that provide for isolation of the installation:

    1) Isolation mounting pads.
    2) Flexible boot supply air plenum.
    3) Flexible boot return air plenum.
    4) Flexible gas connector if acceptable by local code requirements.
    5) Gas supply piping centered in inlet hole.
    6) Isolation hangers.
    7) Electrical conduit isolated from ductwork and joists.
    8) Return air plenum insulated past first elbow.
    9) Supply air plenum insulated past first elbow.

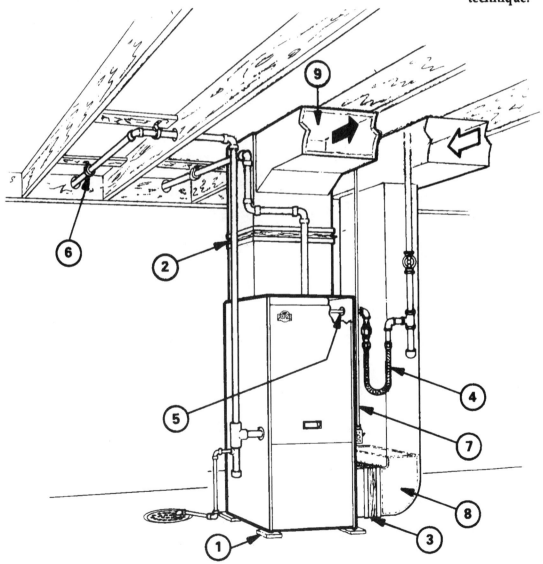

Figure 15-21 Proper installation technique.

2. General Intake/Exhaust Pipe Venting Requirements:

a) The intake and exhaust pipes can be installed with zero clearance to combustible materials. All piping joints must be tight and leakproof.

b) Suspend horizontal piping at a minimum of every 3 ft. (90 cm) using isolation hangers. Do not secure piping directly to joists or flooring.

c) Flue and intake length maximum is C.G.A. approved for 60 ft. (1830 cm) of straight pipe with four, 90° elbows. The minimum run length is 2 ft. (61 cm) with two 90° elbows.

d) The exhaust and intake termination should be in the same pressure zone (i.e., both open ends should exit on the same side of the house).

e) Where the exhaust is external to the building or passes through an unheated space, insulate that portion of the pipe with a minimum of 3/4" (2 cm) insulation, as required by climate conditions.

f) The exhaust and intake pipe must terminate as detailed in *Figure 15-22, 15-23 and 15-24.*

Figure 15-22

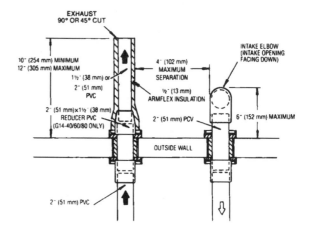

Top view wall termination air intake and exhaust 4" (102 mm) or less apart

Figure 15-23

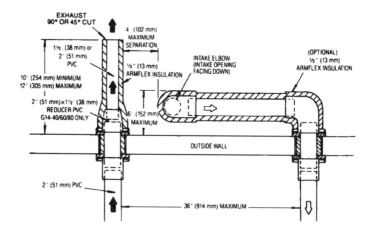

Top view wall termination air intake and exhaust more than 4" (102 mm) apart less than 36" (914 mm) apart

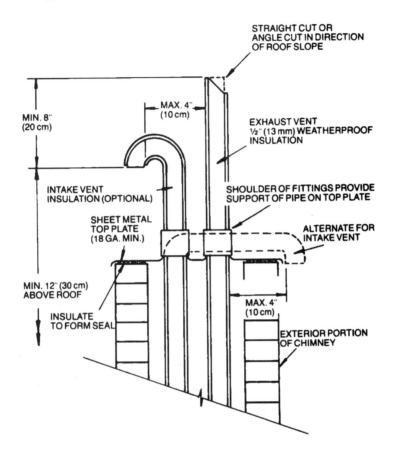

Figure 15-24

G14 VENTING IN EXISTING CHIMNEY

STRAIGHT CUT OR
ANGLE CUT IN DIRECTION
OF ROOF SLOPE

MAX. 4″
(10 cm)

MIN. 8″
(20 cm)

EXHAUST VENT
½″ (13 mm) WEATHERPROOF
INSULATION

INTAKE VENT
INSULATION (OPTIONAL)

SHOULDER OF FITTINGS PROVIDE
SUPPORT OF PIPE ON TOP PLATE

SHEET METAL
TOP PLATE
(18 GA. MIN.)

ALTERNATE FOR
INTAKE VENT

MIN. 12″ (30 cm)
ABOVE ROOF

INSULATE
TO FORM SEAL

MAX. 4″
(10 cm)

EXTERIOR PORTION
OF CHIMNEY

NOTE:
*Do not discharge exhaust gases directly into any
chimney or vent stack. If vertical discharge through an
existing unused chimney or stack is required insert
piping inside chimney until the pipe open end is above
top of chimney and terminate as illustrated. In any
exterior portion of chimney, the exhaust vent must be
insulated. An alternate method is to fill the chimney
cavity with vermiculite or equal to take advantage of its
acoustic and thermal properties.*

Electrical Installation Requirements

The electrical installation requirements are illustrated in *Figure 15-25*.

Figure 15-25

1 - Select fuse and wire size according to blower motor amps.
2 - Access holes are provided on both sides of cabinet to facilitate wiring.
3 - Install room thermostat according to instruction provided with thermostat.
4 - Install a separate fused disconnect switch near the unit so the power can be turned off for servicing.

5 - Complete wiring connections to equipment using provided wiring diagrams.
6 - Electrically ground unit in accordance with local codes, or in the absence of local codes in accordance with the CSA Standards.
7 - Seal unused electrical openings with snap-plugs provided.

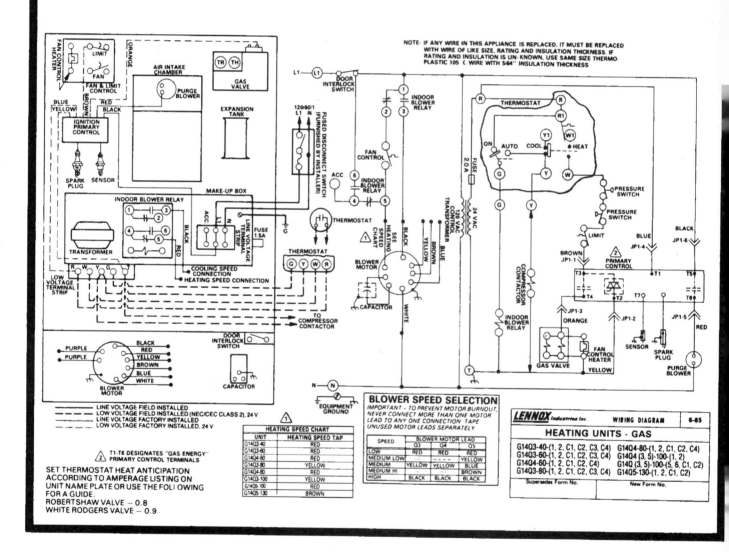

Assignment

1. Define the following terms:

   a) pulse combustion
   b) equivalent vent length
   c) direct vent furnace
   d) pH scale
   e) flapper valve
   f) ignition attempt sequence

2. Briefly describe the pulse combustion process.

3. Give the function for the following controls found on an induced draft firing condensing gas furnace: differential pressure switch; and door switch.

4. For the furnace illustrated in *Figure 15-6*, briefly describe:

   a) its sequence of operation
   b) how you would wire in a condensate pump
   c) how you would check a defective flame rollout switch
   d) how you would check a defective pressure switch
   e) a check to ensure that the drain is not blocked

5. Give the function(s) for the following controls and components found on the Lennox G14 pulse combustion furnace:

   a) primary control
   b) expansion tank
   c) air intake vacuum switch
   d) exhaust outlet pressure switch
   e) purge blower

6. Briefly describe the operating sequence of the Lennox G14 pulse furnace.

7. List the proper installation techniques associated with the Lennox pulse furnace.

8. Give the significance of the following figures:

   a) 1/4–1/2 Btu
   b) 30 seconds
   c) 1/4" per running foot (2 cm/m)
   d) 3 ft. (90 cm)
   e) 4 ft. (120 cm)
   f) 6 ft. (180 cm)
   g) 60 ft (1830 cm)
   h) 2 ft. (61 cm)
   i) 4" (10 cm)
   j) 5

9. Why is it important not to exceed the maximum equivalent vent length?

10. What are the factors that should be considered when locating the outside vent terminal?

Appendix I

Residential warm air systems

High-boy or up-flow forced air furnace

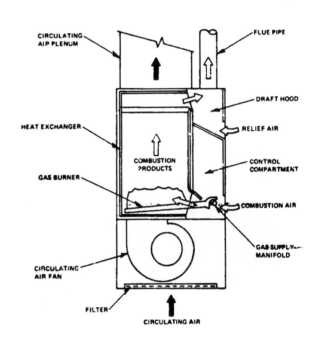

Low-boy forced air furnace

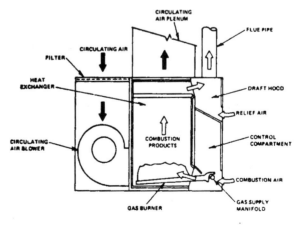

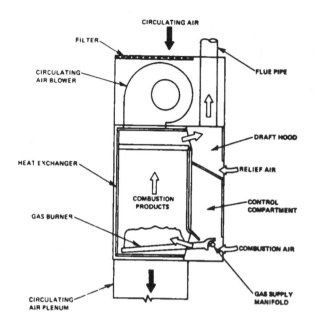

Counter (down) flow furnace

CIRCULATING AIR

FILTER

CIRCULATING AIR BLOWER

FLUE PIPE

DRAFT HOOD

HEAT EXCHANGER

RELIEF AIR

COMBUSTION PRODUCTS

CONTROL COMPARTMENT

GAS BURNER

COMBUSTION AIR

CIRCULATING AIR PLENUM

GAS SUPPLY MANIFOLD

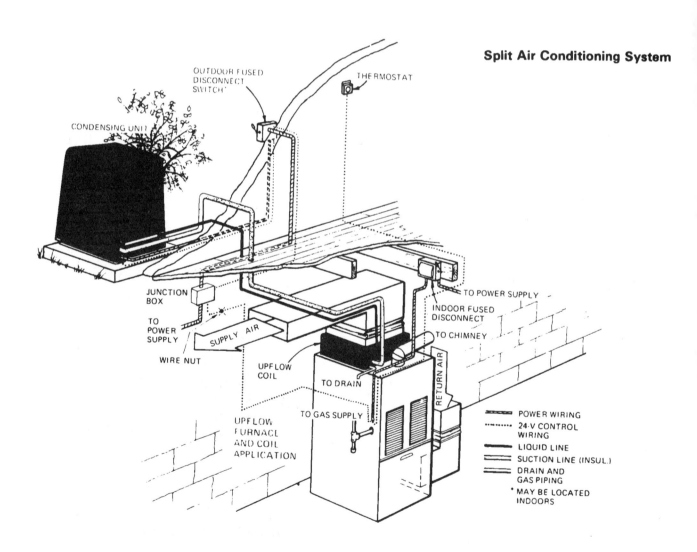

Split Air Conditioning System

OUTDOOR FUSED DISCONNECT SWITCH*

THERMOSTAT

CONDENSING UNIT

JUNCTION BOX

TO POWER SUPPLY

WIRE NUT

SUPPLY AIR

UPFLOW COIL

TO POWER SUPPLY

INDOOR FUSED DISCONNECT

TO CHIMNEY

RETURN AIR

TO DRAIN

UPFLOW FURNACE AND COIL APPLICATION

TO GAS SUPPLY

POWER WIRING

24-V CONTROL WIRING

LIQUID LINE

SUCTION LINE (INSUL.)

DRAIN AND GAS PIPING

* MAY BE LOCATED INDOORS

Floor furnace (space heater)

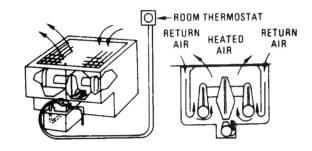

ROOM THERMOSTAT

RETURN AIR   HEATED AIR   RETURN AIR

Recessed Wall Heater

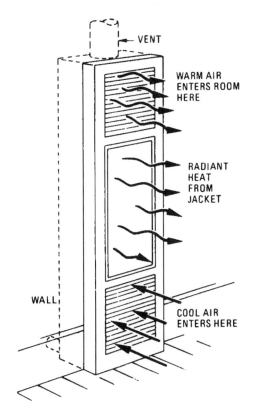

VENT

WARM AIR ENTERS ROOM HERE

RADIANT HEAT FROM JACKET

WALL

COOL AIR ENTERS HERE

Direct Vent Room Heater

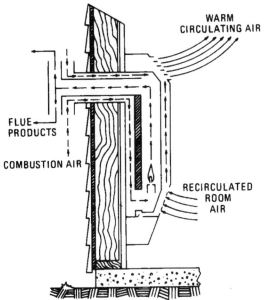

WARM CIRCULATING AIR

FLUE PRODUCTS

COMBUSTION AIR

RECIRCULATED ROOM AIR

Water systems

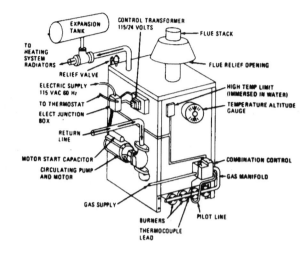

EXPANSION TANK

CONTROL TRANSFORMER 115/24 VOLTS

FLUE STACK

TO HEATING SYSTEM RADIATORS

FLUE RELIEF OPENING

RELIEF VALVE

ELECTRIC SUPPLY 115 VAC 60 Hz

HIGH TEMP LIMIT (IMMERSED IN WATER)

TO THERMOSTAT

TEMPERATURE ALTITUDE GAUGE

ELECT JUNCTION BOX

RETURN LINE

MOTOR START CAPACITOR

COMBINATION CONTROL

CIRCULATING PUMP AND MOTOR

GAS MANIFOLD

GAS SUPPLY

PILOT LINE

BURNERS

THERMOCOUPLE LEAD

Hydronic System

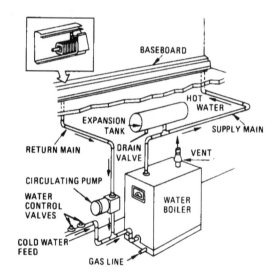

BASEBOARD

HOT WATER

EXPANSION TANK

SUPPLY MAIN

RETURN MAIN

DRAIN VALVE

VENT

CIRCULATING PUMP

WATER CONTROL VALVES

WATER BOILER

COLD WATER FEED

GAS LINE

330

Instantaneous type of water heater

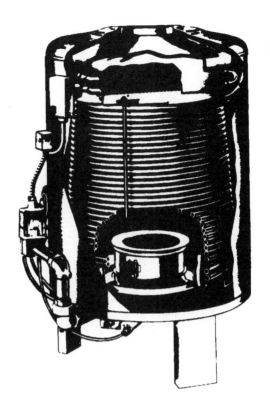

Two temperature water supply system employing an instantaneous water heater

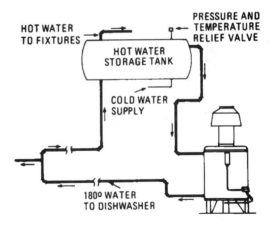

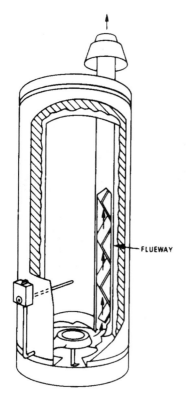

Domestic or residential size water heater having an offset flue (storage type)

Domestic or residential size hot water heater having a central flue (See Fig. 10-4)

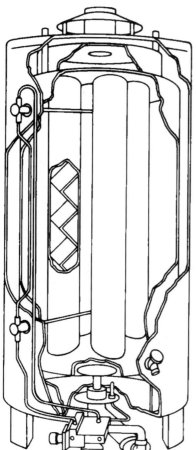

Commercial size hot water heater having multi flues (storage type)

Light commercial warm air systems

Horizontal forced air furnace

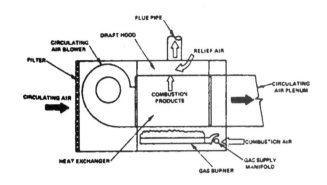

Heating and cooling unit, ventilator or roof top unit

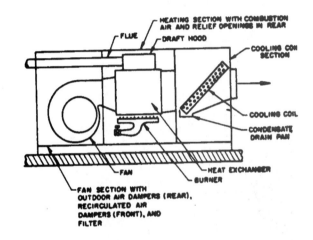

Duct furnace

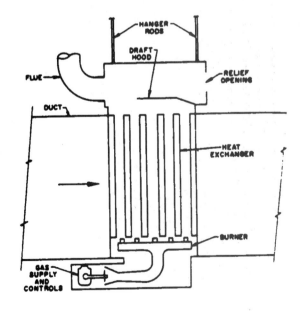

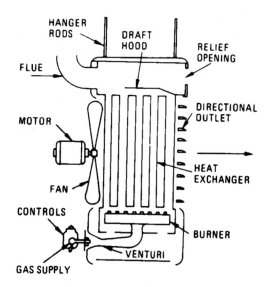

Unit heater

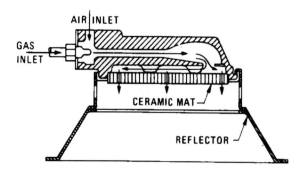

Infra red (radiant) heater

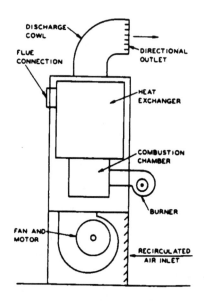

Floor mounted commercial/industrial size space heater

Direct-fired make-up air heating system

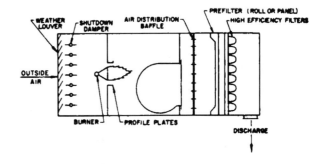

Portable Construction Heater

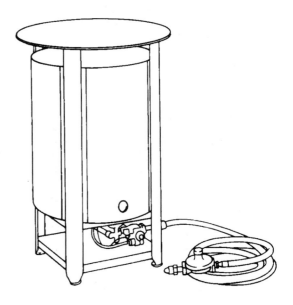

Appendix II

Useful tables and charts:

1) Dimensions of iron pipe fittings
2) Dimensional and capacity data for schedule 40 pipe
3) Number and letter sized drills
4) Metric units
5) Temperature conversion table
6) Conversion factors
7) Conversion table of feet head of water into pressure, per square inch
8) Comparative equivalents of liquid measures and weights

9. Combustion Efficiency
10 Combustion Efficiency Curves For Natural Gas And Fuel Oil.
11. Determining % Flue Loss With Propane Gas.
12. Orifice Sizing for LP Gases.

DIMENSIONS OF IRON PIPE FITTINGS

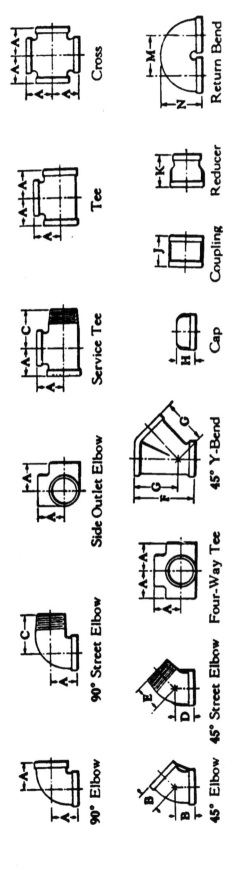

Cross · Return Bend · Tee · Service Tee · Reducer · Coupling · Cap · 90° Elbow · 90° Street Elbow · Side Outlet Elbow · 45° Elbow · 45° Street Elbow · Four-Way Tee · 45° Y-Bend

Size	Thread Engagement	A	B	C	D	E	F	G	H	J	K
1/8	1/4"	11/16	1/2	1	11/16	13/16			9/16	15/16	1
1/4	3/8"	13/16	3/4	1-3/16	5/8	15/16			5/8	1-1/16	
3/8	3/8"	15/16	13/16	1-7/16	11/16	1-1/16	2-1/8	1-7/16	3/4	1-3/16	1-1/8
1/2	1/2"	1-1/8	7/8	1-5/8	13/16	1-3/16	2-7/16	1-11/16	7/8	1-5/16	1-1/4
3/4	9/16"	1-5/16	1	1-7/8	15/16	1-5/16	2-13/16	2-1/16	1-1/16	1-1/2	1-7/16
1	11/16"	1-1/2	1-1/8	2-1/8	1-1/16	1-1/2	3-3/8	2-7/16	1-3/16	1-11/16	1-11/16
1-1/4	11/16"	1-3/4	1-5/16	2-7/16	1-1/4	1-11/16	4-1/16	2-15/16	1-1/4	1-15/16	2-1/16
1-1/2	11/16"	1-15/16	1-7/16	2-11/16	1-3/8	1-7/8	4-1/2	3-5/16	1-5/16	2-1/8	2-5/16
2	3/4"	2-1/4	1-11/16	3-1/4	1-11/16	2-1/4	5-7/16	4	1-7/16	2-1/2	2-13/16
2-1/2	15/16"	2-11/16	1-15/16	3-13/16	1-7/8	2-9/16	6-1/4	4-11/16	1-5/8	2-7/8	3-1/4
3	1"	3-1/8	2-3/16	4-1/2	2-1/8	3	7-1/4	5-9/16	1-3/4	3-3/16	3-11/16
3-1/2	1-1/16"	3-7/16	2-3/8	5-1/8	2-3/8	3-3/8			1-15/16	3-7/16	4
4	1-1/8"	3-3/4	2-5/8	5-11/16	2-1/2	3-3/4	8-7/8	6-15/16	2-1/16	3-11/16	4-3/8
5	1-1/4"	4-1/2	3-1/16	6-7/8					2-5/16	4-1/4	3-7/8
6	1-5/16"	5-1/8	3-7/16	8					2-9/16	4-3/4	4-3/8

RETURN BENDS

Size	M	N	Size	M	N
Close Pattern			**Open Pattern**		
1/2		1-3/4	1/2	1-1/2	1-7/8
3/4	1-1/4	2-3/16	3/4	2	2-1/4
1	1-1/2	2-1/2	1	2-1/2	2-5/8
1-1/4	1-3/4	2-13/16	1-1/4	3	3-3/16
1-1/2	2-3/16	3-3/16	1-1/2	3-1/2	3-5/8
2	2-5/8	3-7/8	2	4	4-3/8
Medium Pattern			2-1/2	4-1/2	4-15/16
1/2	1-1/4	1-5/8	3	5	5-9/16
3/4	1-1/2	1-15/16	4	6	6-11/16
1	1-7/8	2-1/4	**Wide Pattern**		
1-1/4	2-1/4	2-13/16	3/8	1-1/2	1-5/8
1-1/2	2-1/2	3-3/16	3/4	4	3-3/16
2	3	3-7/8	3/4	6	4-1/2
			1	6	4-1/2
			1-1/4	6	4-3/4
			1-1/2	6	5
			2	5	4-3/4
			2	6	5-5/16
			3	7-1/2	6-13/16
			3	8	6-13/16
			6	12	11-11/16

DIMENSIONAL AND CAPACITY DATA — SCHEDULE 40 PIPE

Diameter, Inches			Wall Thickness, In.	Cross-Sectional Area, Sq. In.			Weight per Foot, Lb.		
Nominal	Actual Inside	Actual Outside		Outside	Inside	Metal	Of Pipe Alone	Of Water in Pipe	Of Pipe and Water
⅛	0.269	0.405	0.068	0.129	0.057	0.072	0.25	0.028	0.278
¼	0.364	0.540	0.088	0.229	0.104	0.125	0.43	0.045	0.475
⅜	0.493	0.675	0.091	0.358	0.191	0.167	0.57	0.083	0.653
½	0.622	0.840	0.109	0.554	0.304	0.250	0.86	0.132	0.992
¾	0.824	1.050	0.113	0.866	0.533	0.333	1.14	0.232	1.372
1	1.049	1.315	0.133	1.358	0.864	0.494	1.68	0.375	2.055
1¼	1.380	1.660	0.140	2.164	1.495	0.669	2.28	0.649	2.929
1½	1.610	1.900	0.145	2.835	2.036	0.799	2.72	0.882	3.602
2	2.067	2.375	0.154	4.431	3.356	1.075	3.66	1.454	5.114
2½	2.469	2.875	0.203	6.492	4.788	1.704	5.80	2.073	7.873
3	3.068	3.500	0.216	9.621	7.393	2.228	7.58	3.201	10.781
3½	3.548	4.000	0.226	12.568	9.888	2.680	9.11	4.287	13.397
4	4.026	4.500	0.237	15.903	12.730	3.173	10.80	5.516	16.316
5	5.047	5.563	0.258	24.308	20.004	4.304	14.70	8.674	23.374
6	6.065	6.625	0.280	34.474	28.890	5.584	19.00	12.52	31.52
8	7.981	8.625	0.322	58.426	50.030	8.396	28.60	21.68	50.28
10	10.020	10.750	0.365	90.79	78.85	11.90	40.50	34.16	74.66
12	11.938	12.750	0.406	127.67	113.09	15.77	53.60	48.50	102.10
14	13.126	14.000	0.437	153.94	135.33	18.61	63.30	58.64	121.94
16	15.000	16.000	0.500	201.06	176.71	24.35	82.80	76.58	159.38
18	16.876	18.000	0.562	254.47	223.68	30.79	105.00	96.93	201.93
20	18.814	20.000	0.593	314.16	278.01	36.15	123.00	120.46	243.46

Nominal Dia., In.	Circumference, Inches		Sq. Ft. of Surface per Lineal Foot		Contents of Pipe per Lineal Foot		Lineal Feet to Contain		
	Outside	Inside	Outside	Inside	Cu. Ft.	Gal.	1 Cu. Ft.	1 Gal.	1 Lb. of Water
⅛	1.27	0.84	0.106	0.070	0.0004	0.003	2533.775	338.74	35.714
¼	1.69	1.14	0.141	0.095	0.0007	0.005	1383.789	185.00	22.222
⅜	2.12	1.55	0.177	0.129	0.0013	0.010	754.360	100.85	12.048
½	2.65	1.95	0.221	0.167	0.0021	0.016	473.906	63.36	7.576
¾	3.29	2.58	0.275	0.215	0.0037	0.028	270.034	36.10	4.310
1	4.13	3.29	0.344	0.274	0.0062	0.045	166.618	22.28	2.667
1¼	5.21	4.33	0.435	0.361	0.0104	0.077	96.275	12.87	1.541
1½	5.96	5.06	0.497	0.422	0.0141	0.106	70.733	9.46	1.134
2	7.46	6.49	0.622	0.540	0.0233	0.174	42.913	5.74	0.688
2½	9.03	7.75	0.753	0.654	0.0332	0.248	30.077	4.02	0.482
3	10.96	9.63	0.916	0.803	0.0514	0.383	19.479	2.60	0.312
3½	12.56	11.14	1.047	0.928	0.0682	0.513	14.565	1.95	0.233
4	14.13	12.64	1.178	1.052	0.0884	0.660	11.312	1.51	0.181
5	17.47	15.84	1.456	1.319	0.1390	1.040	7.198	0.96	0.115
6	20.81	19.05	1.734	1.585	0.2010	1.500	4.984	0.67	0.080
8	27.09	25.07	2.258	2.090	0.3480	2.600	2.878	0.38	0.046
10	33.77	31.47	2.814	2.622	0.5470	4.100	1.826	0.24	0.029
12	40.05	37.70	3.370	3.140	0.7850	5.870	1.273	0.17	0.021
14	47.12	44.76	3.930	3.722	1.0690	7.030	1.067	0.14	0.017
16	53.41	51.52	4.440	4.310	1.3920	9.180	0.814	0.11	0.013
18	56.55	53.00	4.712	4.420	1.5530	11.120	0.644	0.09	0.010
20	62.83	59.09	5.236	4.920	1.9250	14.400	0.517	0.07	0.008

NUMBER & LETTER SIZED DRILLS

NUMBER SIZED DRILLS

SIZE	DIA.-IN.	AREA - SQ. IN.
80	.0135	.000143
79	.0145	.000165
78	.0160	.000201
77	.0180	.000254
76	.0200	.000314
75	.0210	.000346
74	.0225	.000398
73	.0240	.000453
72	.0250	.000491
71	.0260	.000531
70	.0280	.000615
69	.02925	.000672
68	.0310	.000755
67	.0320	.000805
66	.0330	.000856
65	.0350	.000962
64	.0360	.001018
63	.0370	.001076
62	.0380	.001134
61	.0390	.001195
60	.0400	.001257
59	.0410	.001320
58	.0420	.001385
57	.0430	.00145
56	.0465	.00170
55	.0520	.00213
54	.0550	.00238
53	.0595	.00278
52	.0635	.00317
51	.0670	.00352
50	.0700	.00385
49	.0730	.00419
48	.0760	.00454
47	.0785	.00484
46	.0810	.00515
45	.0820	.00528
44	.0860	.00580
43	.0890	.00622
42	.0935	.00686
41	.0960	.00723

NUMBER SIZED DRILLS

SIZE	DIA. - IN.	AREA - SQ. IN.
40	.0980	.00755
39	.0995	.00777
38	.1015	.00810
37	.1040	.00850
36	.1065	.00893
35	.1100	.00950
34	.1110	.00968
33	.1130	.01002
32	.1160	.01055
31	.1200	.01130
30	.1285	.01298
29	.1360	.01452
28	.1405	.01550
27	.1440	.01629
26	.1470	.01697
25	.1495	.01755
24	.1520	.01812
23	.1540	.01863
22	.1570	.01935
21	.1590	.01985
20	.1610	.02039
19	.1660	.02162
18	.1695	.02258
17	.1730	.02348
16	.1770	.02461
15	.1800	.02542
14	.1820	.02603
13	.1850	.02685
12	.1890	.02805
11	.1910	.02865
10	.1935	.0294
9	.1960	.0302
8	.1990	.0311
7	.2010	.0316
6	.2040	.0327
5	.2055	.0332
4	.2090	.0343
3	.2130	.0356
2	.2210	.0384
1	.2280	.0409

LETTER SIZED DRILLS

SIZE	DIA.-IN.	AREA - SQ. IN.
A	.234	.0430
B	.238	.0440
C	.242	.0460
D	.246	.0475
E	.250	.0491
F	.257	.0519
G	.261	.0535
H	.266	.0556
I	.272	.0580
J	.277	.0601
K	.281	.0620
L	.290	.0660
M	.295	.0683
N	.302	.0716
O	.316	.0784
P	.323	.0820
Q	.332	.0866
R	.339	.0901
S	.348	.0950
T	.358	.1005
U	.368	.1063
V	.377	.1116
W	.386	.1170
X	.397	.1236
Y	.404	.1278
Z	.413	.1340

METRIC

1. Temperatures are expressed in degrees Celsius (°C).

2. Pressures are expressed in pascals (Pa), kilopascals (KPa) or megapascals (MPa).

3. Heat - the unit for quantity of heat is joule (J).

4. Heat capacity is expressed in joules per degree Celsius (J/°C).

5. Specific heat capacity is expressed in joules per kilogram degree Celsius (J/Kg°C).

6. Heat flow rate is expressed in joule per second (J/S) which is equal to one Watt (W).

7. Thermal Conductance (U factor) is expressed as Watt per square metre degree Celsius (W/m^2°C).

8. Length is expressed in metre (m), millimetere (mm) or centimetre (cm).

9. Area is expressed in square metres (m^2), square millimetres (mm^2) or square centimetres (cm^2).

10. Volume is expressed in cubic metres (m^3), cubic millimetres (mm^3) or cubic centimetres (cm^3) for solids and in litre (l) or millilitre (ml) for fluids or liquids.

11. Mass is expressed in grams (g), kilograms (Kg) or milligrams (mg).

12. Force due to gravity is expressed in newtons (n).

13. Velocity is epxressed in kilometres per hr. (Km/h) or metres per second (m/s).

14. Density is expressed in kilograms per cubic metre (Kg/M^3), grams per cubic centimetre (g/cm^3) on grams per cubic millimetre (g/mm^3) or in liquids it is expressed in grams per millilitre (g/ml) or grams per litre (g/l).

15. Energy is expressed in joule (J).

16. Frequency is expressed in hetz (Hz).

17. Power is expressed in Watts(W).

18. Electric charge is expressed in coulomb (c).

19. Electrical potential is expressed in volts(v).

20. Electric resistance is expressed in ohm (Ω).

21. Electric capacitance is expressed in farad (F).

TEMPERATURE CONVERSION TABLE

°C		°F
-17.8	0	32.0
-17.2	1	33.8
-16.7	2	35.6
-16.1	3	37.4
-15.6	4	39.2
-15.0	5	41.0
-14.4	6	42.8
-13.9	7	44.6
-13.3	8	46.4
-12.8	9	48.2
-12.1	10	50.0
-11.7	11	51.8
-11.1	12	53.6
-10.6	13	55.4
-10.0	14	57.2
- 9.44	15	59.0
- 8.89	16	60.8
- 8.33	17	62.6
- 7.78	18	64.4
- 7.22	19	66.2
- 6.67	20	68.0
- 6.11	21	69.8
- 5.56	22	71.6
- 5.00	23	73.4
- 4.44	24	75.2
- 3.89	25	77.0
- 3.33	26	78.8
- 2.78	27	80.6
- 2.22	28	82.4
- 1.67	29	84.2
- 1.11	30	86.0
- 0.56	31	87.8
0.0	32	89.6
0.56	33	91.4
1.11	34	93.2
1.67	35	95.0
2.22	36	96.8
2.78	37	98.6
3.33	38	100.4
3.89	39	102.2
4.44	40	104.0
5.00	41	105.8
5.56	42	107.6
6.11	43	109.4
6.67	44	111.2
7.22	45	113.0
7.78	46	114.8
8.33	47	116.6
8.89	48	118.4

°C		°F
9.44	49	120.2
10.0	50	122.0
10.6	51	123.8
11.1	52	125.6
11.7	53	127.4
12.2	54	129.2
12.8	55	131.0
13.3	56	132.8
13.9	57	134.6
14.4	58	136.4
15.0	59	138.2
15.6	60	140.0
16.1	61	141.8
16.7	62	143.6
17.2	63	145.4
17.8	64	147.2
18.3	65	149.0
18.9	66	150.8
19.4	67	152.6
20.0	68	154.4
20.6	69	156.2
21.1	70	158.0
21.7	71	159.8
22.2	72	161.6
22.8	73	163.4
23.3	74	165.2
23.9	75	167.0
24.4	76	168.8
25.0	77	170.6
25.6	78	172.4
26.1	79	174.2
26.7	80	176.0
27.2	81	177.8
27.8	82	179.6
28.3	83	181.4
28.9	84	183.2
29.4	85	185.0
30.0	86	186.8
30.6	87	188.6
31.1	88	190.4
31.7	89	192.2
32.2	90	194.0
32.8	91	195.8
33.3	92	197.6
33.9	93	199.4
34.4	94	201.2
35.0	95	203.0
35.6	96	204.8
36.1	97	206.6

°C		°F
36.7	98	208.4
37.2	99	210.2
37:8	100	212.0
43	110	230
49	120	248
54	130	266
60	140	284
66	150	302
71	160	320
77	170	338
82	180	356
88	190	374
93	200	392
99	210	410
100	212	413
104	220	428
110	230	446
116	240	464
121	250	482
127	260	500
132	270	518
138	280	536
143	290	554
149	300	572
154	310	590
160	320	608
166	330	626
171	340	644
177	350	662
182	360	680
188	370	698
193	380	716
199	390	734
204	400	752
210	410	770
216	420	788
221	430	806
227	440	824
232	450	842
238	460	860
243	470	878
249	480	896
254	490	914
260	500	932
266	510	950
271	520	968
277	530	986
282	540	1004

°C		°F
288	550	1022
293	560	1040
299	570	1058
304	580	1076
310	590	1094
316	600	1112
321	610	1130
327	620	1148
332	630	1166
338	640	1184
343	650	1202
349	660	1220
354	670	1238
360	680	1256
366	690	1274
371	700	1292
377	710	1310
382	720	1328
388	730	1346
393	740	1364
399	750	1382
404	760	1400
410	770	1418
416	780	1436
421	790	1454
427	800	1472
432	810	1490
438	820	1508
443	830	1526
449	840	1544
454	850	1562
460	860	1580
466	870	1598
471	880	1616
477	890	1634
482	900	1652
488	910	1670
493	920	1688
499	930	1706
504	940	1724
510	950	1742
516	960	1760
521	970	1778
527	980	1796
532	990	1814
538	1000	1832
543	1010	1850
549	1020	1868

INTERPOLATION FACTORS

°C		°F	°C		°F
0.56	1	1.8	3.33	6	10.8
1.11	2	3.6	3.89	7	12.6
1.67	3	5.4	4.44	8	14.4
2.22	4	7.2	5.00	9	16.2
2.78	5	9.0	5.56	10	18.0

Note:

The numbers in the center columns of Sheet Nos. A-10 through A-10-d refer to the temperature either in degrees Centigrade or Fahrenheit which it is desired to convert into the other scale. If converting from Fahrenheit degrees to Centigrade degrees, the equivalent temperature will be found in the left column; while if converting from degrees Centigrade to degrees Fahrenheit, the answer will be found in the column on the right.

Conversion Factors

1. LENGTH

1 in = 25.4 mm
1 in = 0.025 4 m
1 ft = 304.8 mm
1 ft = 0.304 8 m
1 yd = 914.4 mm
1 yd = 0.914 4 m
1 mile = 1.609 km
1 mile = 1 609.344 m

1 mm = 0.039 37 in
1 m = 1.094 yd
1 m = 3.28 ft
1 km = 0.621 4 mi

2. AREA

1 in2 = 645.2 mm2
1 in2 = 6.4516 cm2
1 ft2 = 929.030 cm2
1 yd2 = 0.836 127 m2

1 mm2 = 0.001 550 in2
1 m2 = 1.196 yd2

3. VOLUME — GAS VOLUME UNITS

1 cu in = .000 016 39 m 3
1 cu in = 0.016 39 dm3
1 cu ft = 0.028 316 m3
1 cu ft = 28.316 85 dm3
1 cu yd = 0.764 6 m3

1 m3 = 61 012.812 691 in3
1 dm3 = 61.023 74 in3
1 m3 = 35.31 ft3
1 dm3 = 0.035 31 ft3
1 m3 = 1.308 yd3

— LIQUID VOLUME UNITS

1 pt =0.568 261 litre
1 pt = 568.261 ml
1 qt = 1.136 522 litres
1 gal = 4.546 090 litres
1 gal = 4.546 090 dm3
1000 gal = 4.546 m 3
1 U.S. gal = 3.785 412 litres
1 U.S. gal = 3.785 412 dm3

1 ml = 0.001 760 pt
1 litre = 1.760 pt
1 litre = 0.879 877 qt
1 litre = 0.220 0 gal
1 litre = 61.023 74 in 3
1 m3 = 220.0 gal

Note: pints, quarts, and gallons are
Canadian unless otherwise noted.

4. PRESSURE

1 pound force per square inch (p.s.i.)(60°F) =
    6.895 kPa(15.55°C).
1 ounce force per square inch (02 f/in2)(60°F) =
    0.431 kPa(15.55°C).
1 inch water column (IN W.C.)(60°F) =
    0.249 kPa (15.55°C)(288.71K)
1 Pa = 0.145 x 103 p.s.i.
1 kPa =0.145 p.s.i.
1 kPa = 4.0 in W.C.
1 MPa = 145 p.s.i.
101.325 kPa is one standard atmosphere.

5. HEAT (ENERGY)

1 BTU = 1.055.06 J	1 J = 0.000 947 8 BTU
1000 BTU = 1.055 06 MJ	1 MJ = 947.813 BTU
1 Therm = 105.506 MJ	100 MJ = 0.947 813 Therm

6. HEAT RATE (POWER)

1000 Btu/h = 0.293 07 kW	1 kW = 3.600 MJ/h
1000 Btu/h = 1.055 06 MJ/h	1 kW = 3 412 Btu/h
1 hp = 745.699 W	1 kW = 1.341 hp
1 hp = 2.685 MJ/h	1 MJ/h =0.277 8 kW
	1 MJ/h = 947.8 Btu/h

7. CONCENTRATION

1 grain per cubic foot (gr) = 2.288 352 g/m3
           (ft3)
1 ounce per cubic foot (02) = 1.001 154 kg/m3
           (ft3)
1 pound per cubic foot (lb) = 16.018 46 kg/m3
           (ft3)

8. MASS

1 gr = 0.064 80 g	1 g = 0.035 27 oz
1 gr = 64.8 mg	1 g = 15.43 gr
1 oz = 28.35 g	1 kg = 2.205 lb
1 lb = 453.6 g	1 t = 2205 lb
1 lb = 0.453 6 kg	1 t = 0.984 long ton
	1 t = 1.012 3 short ton

1 long ton (2240 lb) = 1016 kg
1 long ton (2240 lb) = 1.016 t
1 short ton (2000 lb) = 907.185 kg
1 short ton (2000 lb) = 0.907 185 t

9. FLOW RATES — GAS

1ft3/h = 0.028 32 m3 h-1
1 m3-h-1 = 35.31 ft3.h-1
1 Btu/h = 0.293 071 W
1 Btu/h (ft3-h) = 0.037 259 9 MJ.m-3.h-1
1 ton/h (2000 lb) = 0.907 185 t/h (Mg.h-1)

10. RELATIVE DENSITY (SPECIFIC GRAVITY)

This is the ratio of the density of dry gas to that of dry air under the same conditions. As a ratio, it has no dimensions and remains the same in any system of units.

11. TEMPERATURE

CONVERSION FORMULAE

Temperature °C = (temperature °F - 32) x 5/9
Temperature °F = 9/5°C + 32

CONVERSION TABLE OF

FEET HEAD OF WATER INTO PRESSURE, PER SQUARE INCH

Feet Head	Lbs./Sq. In.	Feet Head	Lbs./Sq. In.	Feet Head	Lbs./Sq. In.
1	.43	60	25.99	2002	86.62
2	.87	70	30.32	225	97.45
3	1.30	80	34.65	250	108.27
4	1.73	90	38.98	275	119.10
5	2.17	100	43.31	300	129.93
6	2.60	110	47.64	325	140.75
7	3.03	120	51.97	350	151.58
8	3.40	130	56.30	400	173.24
9	3.90	140	60.63	500	216.55
10	4.33	150	64.96	600	259.85
20	8.66	160	69.29	700	303.16
30	12.99	170	73.63	800	346.47
40	17.32	180	77.96	900	389.78
50	21.65	190	83.29	1000	433.09

PRESSURE PER SQUARE INCH INTO FEET HEAD OF WATER

Lbs./Sq. In.	Feet Head	Lbs./Sq. In.	Feet Head	Lbs./Sq. In.	Feet Head
1	2.31	40	92.36	170	392.52
2	4.62	50	115.45	180	415.61
3	6.93	60	138.54	190	438.90
4	9.24	70	161.63	200	461.78
5	11.54	80	184.72	225	519.51
6	13.85	90	207.81	250	577.24
7	16.16	100	230.90	275	643.03
8	18.47	110	253.98	300	692.69
9	20.78	120	277.07	325	750.41
1C	23.09	125	288.62	350	808.13
15	34.63	130	300.16	375	865.89
20	46.18	140	323.25	400	922.58
25	57.72	150	346.34	500	1154.48
30	69.27	160	369.43	1000	2308.

COMPARATIVE EQUIVALENTS OF LIQUID MEASURES AND WEIGHTS

Measures and Weights for Comparison	Measure and weight equivalent of items in first columns						
	U.S. Gallon	Imperial Gallon	Cubic Inch	Cubic Foot	Cubic Metre	Litre	Pound
U.S. GALLON	1.	.833	231.	.1337	.00378	3.785	8.33
IMPRL. GAL.	1.20	1.	277.27	.1604	.00454	4.542	10.
CUBIC INCH	.0043	.00358	1.	.00057	.000016	.0163	.0358
CUBIC FOOT	7.48	6.235	1728.	1.	.02827	28.312	62.355
CUBIC METRE	264.17	.2200	61023.	35.319	1.	1000.	2200.54
LITRE	.12	.1	61.023	.0353	.001	1.	2.2005
POUND			27.72	.016	.00045	.454	1.

COMBUSTION EFFICIENCY

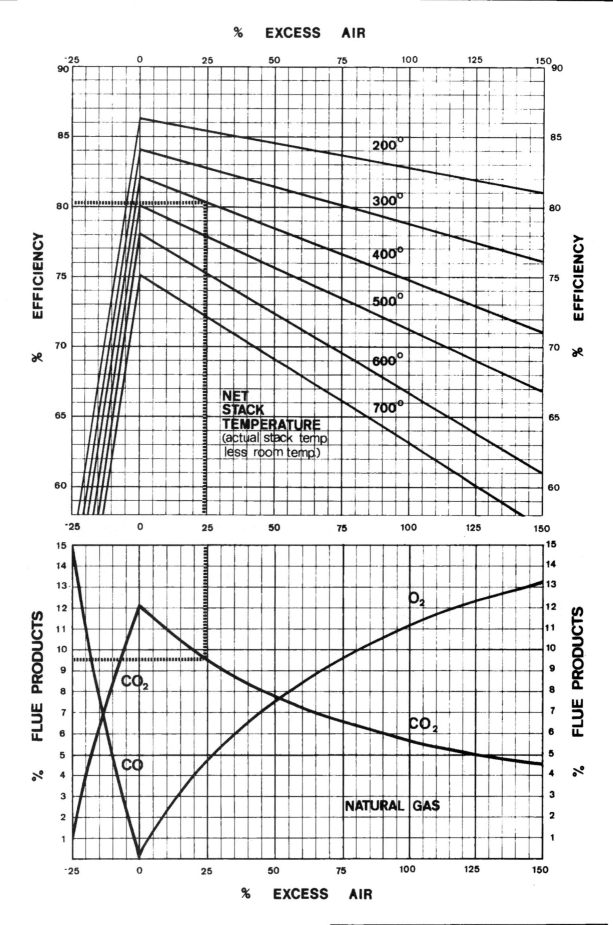

% EXCESS AIR

EFFICIENCY

% EFFICIENCY

200°
300°
400°
500°
600°
700°

NET STACK TEMPERATURE
(actual stack temp less room temp)

FLUE PRODUCTS

% FLUE PRODUCTS

O₂

CO₂

CO₂

CO

NATURAL GAS

% EXCESS AIR

COMBUSTION EFFICIENCY CURVES

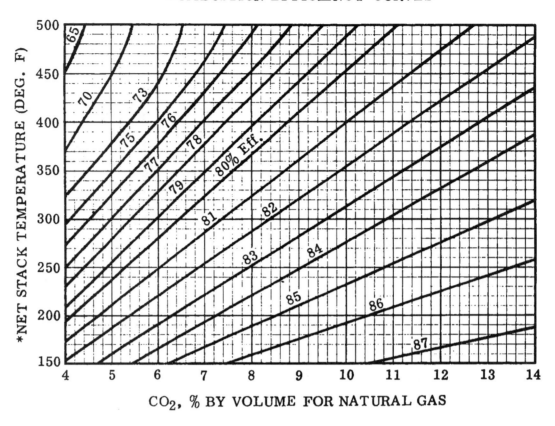

CO$_2$, % BY VOLUME FOR NATURAL GAS

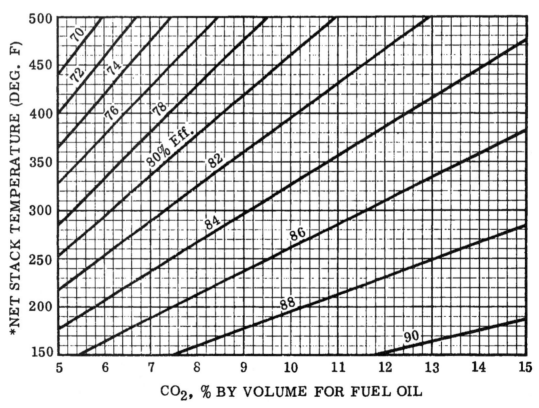

CO$_2$, % BY VOLUME FOR FUEL OIL

*NET = ACTUAL MINUS AMBIENT TEMPERATURE

	CO$_2$ IN FLUE GASES (%)																			
FLUE GAS TEMP. MINUS ROOM TEMP. °F (°C)	4.0	4.5	5.0	5.5	6.0	6.5	7.0	7.5	8.0	8.5	9.0	9.5	10.0	10.5	11.0	11.5	12.0	12.5	13.0	13.5
								FLUE LOSS (%)												
20 (11)	9.2	9.1	9.0	8.9	9.8	8.8	8.7	9.7	8.6	8.6	8.6	8.5	8.5	8.5	8.5	9.5	8.4	3.4	9.4	9.4
30 (17)	9.8	9.6	9.4	9.3	9.2	9.1	9.1	9.0	8.9	9.9	8.9	8.8	8.8	8.7	8.7	8.7	9.7	9.6	8.6	8.6
40 (22)	10.4	10.1	9.9	9.8	9.6	9.5	9.4	9.3	9.3	9.2	9.1	9.1	9.0	9.0	9.0	8.9	9.9	9.9	9.8	8.8
50 (28)	11.0	10.7	10.4	10.2	10.0	9.9	9.8	9.7	9.6	9.5	9.4	9.4	9.3	9.2	9.2	9.2	9.1	9.1	9.0	9.0
60 (33)	11.6	11.2	10.9	10.7	10.4	10.3	10.1	10.0	9.9	9.8	9.7	9.6	9.6	9.5	9.4	9.4	9.3	9.3	9.3	9.2
70 (39)	12.1	11.7	11.4	11.1	10.9	10.7	10.5	10.3	10.2	10.1	10.0	9.9	9.8	9.7	9.7	9.6	9.6	9.5	9.5	9.4
80 (44)	12.7	12.2	11.9	11.5	11.3	11.0	10.9	10.7	10.5	10.4	10.3	10.2	10.1	10.0	9.9	9.9	9.8	9.7	9.7	9.6
90 (50)	13.3	12.8	12.3	12.0	11.7	11.4	11.2	11.0	10.8	10.7	10.6	10.4	10.3	10.2	10.2	10.1	10.0	9.9	9.9	9.8
100 (56)	13.9	13.3	12.8	12.4	12.1	11.8	11.5	11.3	11.2	11.0	10.8	10.7	10.6	10.5	10.4	10.3	10.2	10.2	10.1	10.0
110 (61)	14.5	13.8	13.3	12.8	12.5	12.2	11.9	11.7	11.5	11.3	11.1	11.0	10.9	10.7	10.6	10.5	10.5	10.4	10.3	10.2
120 (67)	15.1	14.4	13.8	13.3	12.9	12.5	12.3	12.0	11.8	11.6	11.4	11.3	11.1	11.0	10.9	10.8	10.7	10.6	10.5	10.4
130 (72)	15.7	14.9	14.2	13.7	13.3	12.9	12.6	12.3	12.1	11.9	11.7	11.5	11.4	11.2	11.1	11.0	10.9	10.8	10.7	10.6
140 (78)	16.3	15.4	14.7	14.2	13.7	13.3	13.0	12.7	12.4	12.2	12.0	11.8	11.6	11.5	11.4	11.2	11.1	11.0	10.9	10.8
150 (83)	16.9	15.9	15.2	14.6	14.1	13.7	13.3	13.0	12.7	12.5	12.3	12.1	11.9	11.7	11.6	11.5	11.4	11.2	11.1	11.0
160 (89)	17.5	16.5	15.7	15.0	14.5	14.1	13.7	13.3	13.0	12.8	12.6	12.3	12.2	12.0	11.8	11.7	11.6	11.5	11.3	11.2
170 (94)	18.0	17.0	16.2	15.5	14.9	14.4	14.0	13.7	13.4	13.1	12.8	12.6	12.4	12.2	12.1	11.9	11.8	11.7	11.6	11.5
180 (100)	18.6	17.5	16.7	15.9	15.3	14.8	14.4	14.0	13.7	13.4	13.1	12.9	12.7	12.5	12.3	12.2	12.0	11.9	11.8	11.7
190 (106)	19.2	18.1	17.1	16.4	15.7	15.2	14.7	14.3	14.0	13.7	13.4	13.2	12.9	12.7	12.6	12.4	12.2	12.1	12.0	11.9
200 (111)	19.8	18.6	17.6	16.8	16.1	15.6	15.1	14.7	14.3	14.0	13.7	13.4	13.2	13.0	12.8	12.6	12.5	12.3	12.2	12.1
210 (117)	20.4	19.1	18.1	17.3	16.6	16.0	15.5	15.0	14.6	14.3	14.0	13.7	13.5	13.3	13.0	12.9	12.7	12.5	12.4	12.3
220 (122)	21.0	19.7	18.6	17.7	17.0	16.3	15.8	15.3	14.9	14.6	14.3	14.0	13.7	13.5	13.3	13.1	12.9	12.8	12.6	12.5
230 (128)	21.6	20.2	19.1	18.1	17.4	16.7	16.2	15.7	15.3	14.9	14.6	14.3	14.0	13.8	13.5	13.3	13.2	13.0	12.8	12.7
240 (133)	22.2	20.7	19.5	18.6	17.8	17.1	16.5	16.0	15.6	15.2	14.8	14.5	14.3	14.0	13.8	13.6	13.4	13.2	13.0	12.9
250 (139)	22.8	21.3	20.0	19.0	18.2	17.5	16.9	16.4	15.9	15.5	15.1	14.8	14.5	14.3	14.0	13.8	13.6	13.4	13.3	13.1
260 (144)	23.4	21.8	20.5	19.5	18.6	17.9	17.2	16.7	16.2	15.8	15.4	15.1	14.8	14.5	14.3	14.0	13.8	13.6	13.5	13.3
270 (150)	24.0	22.3	21.0	19.9	19.0	18.3	17.6	17.0	16.5	16.1	15.7	15.4	15.1	14.8	14.5	14.3	14.1	13.9	13.7	13.5
280 (156)	24.6	22.9	21.5	20.4	19.4	18.6	18.0	17.4	16.9	16.4	16.0	15.6	15.3	15.0	14.8	14.5	14.3	14.1	13.9	13.7
290 (161)	25.2	23.4	22.0	20.8	19.9	19.0	18.3	17.7	17.2	16.7	16.3	15.9	15.6	15.3	15.0	14.7	14.5	14.3	14.1	13.9
300 (167)	25.8	23.9	22.5	21.3	20.3	19.4	18.7	18.1	17.5	17.0	16.6	16.2	15.8	15.5	15.2	15.0	14.7	14.5	14.3	14.1
310 (172)	26.4	24.5	23.0	21.7	20.7	19.8	19.1	18.4	17.8	17.3	16.9	16.5	16.1	15.8	15.5	15.2	15.0	14.7	14.5	14.3
320 (178)	27.0	25.0	23.5	22.2	21.1	20.2	19.4	18.7	18.2	17.6	17.2	16.8	16.4	16.0	15.7	15.5	15.2	15.0	14.8	14.6
330 (183)	27.6	25.6	23.9	22.6	21.5	20.6	19.8	19.1	18.5	17.9	17.5	17.0	16.7	16.3	16.0	15.7	15.4	15.2	15.0	14.8
340 (189)	28.2	26.1	24.4	23.1	21.9	21.0	20.1	19.4	18.8	18.2	17.8	17.3	16.9	16.6	16.2	15.9	15.7	15.4	15.2	15.0
350 (194)	28.8	26.7	24.9	23.5	22.4	21.4	20.5	19.8	19.1	18.6	18.0	17.6	17.2	16.8	16.5	16.2	15.9	15.6	15.4	15.2
360 (200)	29.4	27.2	25.4	24.0	22.8	21.7	20.9	20.1	19.5	18.9	18.3	17.9	17.5	17.1	16.7	16.4	16.1	15.9	15.6	15.4
370 (206)	30.0	27.7	25.9	24.4	23.2	22.1	21.2	20.5	19.8	19.2	18.6	18.2	17.7	17.3	17.0	16.7	16.4	16.1	15.9	15.6
380 (211)	30.6	28.3	26.4	24.9	23.6	22.5	21.6	20.8	20.1	19.5	19.9	18.4	18.0	17.6	17.2	16.9	16.6	16.3	16.1	15.8
390 (217)	31.2	28.8	26.9	25.3	24.0	22.9	22.0	21.2	20.4	19.8	19.2	18.7	18.3	17.9	17.5	17.1	16.8	16.5	16.3	16.0
400 (222)	31.8	29.4	27.4	25.8	24.5	23.3	22.3	21.5	20.8	20.1	19.5	19.0	18.5	18.1	17.7	17.4	17.1	16.8	16.5	16.2
410 (228)	32.5	29.9	27.9	26.3	24.9	23.7	22.7	21.8	21.1	20.4	19.8	19.3	18.8	18.4	18.0	17.6	17.3	17.0	16.7	16.5
420 (233)	33.1	30.5	28.4	26.7	25.3	24.1	23.1	22.2	21.4	20.7	20.1	19.6	19.1	18.6	18.2	17.9	17.5	17.2	16.9	16.7
430 (239)	33.7	31.0	28.9	27.2	25.7	24.5	23.5	22.5	21.7	21.0	20.4	19.9	19.4	18.9	18.5	18.1	17.8	17.4	17.2	16.9
440 (244)	34.3	31.6	29.4	27.6	26.2	24.9	23.8	22.9	22.1	21.4	20.7	20.1	19.6	19.2	18.7	18.4	18.0	17.7	17.4	17.1
450 (250)	34.9	32.1	29.9	28.1	26.6	25.3	24.2	23.2	22.4	21.7	21.0	20.4	19.9	19.4	19.0	18.6	18.2	17.9	17.6	17.3
460 (256)	35.5	32.7	30.4	28.6	27.0	25.7	24.6	23.6	22.7	22.0	21.3	20.7	20.2	19.7	19.2	18.8	18.5	18.1	17.8	17.5
470 (261)	36.2	33.2	30.9	29.0	27.4	26.1	24.9	23.9	23.1	22.3	21.6	21.0	20.5	20.0	19.5	19.1	18.7	18.4	18.0	17.7
480 (267)	36.9	33.8	31.4	29.5	27.9	26.5	25.3	24.3	23.4	22.6	21.9	21.3	20.7	20.2	19.8	19.3	18.9	18.6	18.3	19.0
490 (272)	37.4	34.4	31.9	29.9	28.3	26.9	25.7	24.6	23.7	22.9	22.2	21.6	21.0	20.5	20.0	19.6	19.2	18.8	18.5	18.2
500 (278)	38.0	34.9	32.4	30.4	28.7	27.3	26.1	25.0	24.1	23.3	22.5	21.9	21.3	20.8	20.3	19.8	19.4	19.1	18.7	18.4
510 (283)	38.6	35.5	32.9	30.9	29.2	27.7	26.4	25.4	24.4	23.6	22.8	22.2	21.6	21.0	20.5	20.1	19.7	19.3	18.9	18.6
520 (289)	39.3	36.0	33.5	31.3	29.6	28.1	26.8	25.7	24.7	23.9	23.1	22.4	21.8	21.3	20.9	20.3	19.9	19.5	19.2	18.8
530 (294)	39.9	36.6	34.0	31.8	30.0	28.5	27.2	26.1	25.1	24.2	23.4	22.7	22.1	21.6	21.0	20.5	20.1	19.7	19.4	15.0

DETERMINING % FLUE LOSS WITH PROPANE GAS

LP-Gases
(Btu Per Hour at Sea Level)

	Propane	Butane
Btu per Cubic Foot =	2,500	3,175
Specific Gravity =	1.53	2.00
Pressure at Orifice, Inches Water Column =	11	11
Orifice Coefficient =	0.9	0.9

For altitudes above 2,000 feet, first select the equivalent orifice size at sea level from Table 6.

Drill Size (Decimal or DMS)	Gas Input, Btu Per Hour For:	
	Propane	Butane or Butane-Propane Mixtures
.008	500	554
.009	641	709
.010	791	875
.011	951	1,053
.012	1,130	1,250
80	1,430	1,590
79	1,655	1,830
78	2,015	2,230
77	2,545	2,815
76	3,140	3,480
75	3,465	3,840
74	3,985	4,410
73	4,525	5,010
72	4,920	5,450
71	5,320	5,900
70	6,180	6,830
69	6,710	7,430
68	7,560	8,370
67	8,040	8,910
66	8,550	9,470
65	9,630	10,670
64	10,200	11,300
63	10,800	11,900
62	11,360	12,530
61	11,930	13,280
60	12,570	13,840
59	13,220	14,630
58	13,840	15,300
57	14,550	16,090
56	16,990	18,790
55	21,200	23,510
54	23,850	26,300
53	27,790	30,830
52	31,730	35,100
51	35,330	39,400
50	38,500	42,800
49	41,850	45,350
48	45,450	50,300
47	48,400	53,550
46	51,500	57,000
45	52,900	58,500
44	58,050	64,350
43	62,200	69,000
42	68,700	76,200
41	72,450	80,200
40	75,400	83,500
39	77,850	86,200
38	81,000	89,550
37	85,000	94,000
36	89,200	98,800
35	95,000	105,300
34	97,000	107,200
33	101,000	111,900
32	105,800	117,000
31	113,200	125,400
30	129,700	143,600
29	145,700	163,400
28	154,700	171,600
27	163,100	180,000
26	169,900	187,900
25	175,500	194,600
24	181,700	201,600
23	186,800	206,400
22	193,500	214,500
21	198,600	220,200
20	203,700	225,000
19	217,100	241,900
18	225,600	249,800

Appendix III

Service and trouble shooting check list:

1) General points to keep in mind when testing powerpile systems (750 M.V. specifically).
2) Service tips and methods of trouble shooting for powerpile systems (750 M.V. specifically).
3) Examples of heating equipment and the types of controls usually applied on each.
4) Possible venting problems, causes, and remedies.
5) Causes, conditions, and corrections for delayed ignition and pilot outage (samples).
6) Central heating — possible problems, causes, and remedies.
7) Common problems in heating systems.
8) Conditions, causes, and corrections for common water heater complaints.

GENERAL POINTS TO KEEP IN MIND WHEN TESTING POWERPILE SYSTEMS (750 M.V. SPECIFICALLY)

THERMOSTATS - Usually up to 10 m.v. drop (without heat anticipation)

- Usually up to 100 m.v. drop (with heat anticipation)

(Round Honeywell T.S. 86 draws 125 m.v.)

LIMITS - Usually up to 10 m.v. drop

WIRING - Loss or drop 50 m.v. or less (in excess of thermostat or limit

reading) usually acceptable. (test taken at valve)

- Poor connection can cause high readings

VALVES - Usually up to 135 m.v. drop

- Test

- pilot is off

- jumper limit and thermostat circuits at valve (closed test)

- place test leads on valve coil terminals (across valve coil)

- light pilot or make circuit

- valve should open by time meter reads 135 m.v. (approximately)

<u>LOCATING VALVE</u> (except general controls B63Y)
<u>COIL</u>
- 1. Disconnect all wiring from valve except one powerpile lead

- 2. Touch other powerpile lead terminal to various valve terminals
  until valve opens

    - the two terminals being touched at that time are the valve
      coil terminals

- 3. If valve does not open:
    - disconnect the original powerpile lead left on the valve
    - install other powerpile lead on its original terminal
    - repeat (2) above

<u>GENERAL POINTS TO KEEP IN MIND WHEN TESTING POWERPILE SYSTEMS</u>

<u>Pilotstat</u> - Usually 160 m.v. or less.

- Test.

    - Jumper limit and thermostat circuit at valve.
      (Closed test.)
    - Place test leads on powerpile terminals on valve (usually).
    - Turn pilot off.
    - Pilotstat should not drop out until reading is less than
      160 m.v.

<u>Powerpile</u> - Open Circuit.

    - Usually 500 m.v. approximately to 800 m.v. approximately.
    - Test.

        - Open circuit at some point.
        - Install test leads on powerpile terminals, on
          valve (usually).
        - Reading should be in above range.

                    OR

        - Disconnect powerpile leads from valve.
        - Install test leads on powerpile leads.
        - Take reading.

- Closed circuit.

    - Usually 225 m.v. approximately and up.
    - Test.

- Leave circuit closed.

- Jumper limit and thermostat circuits usually.

- Install test leads on powerpile terminals on valve

- Reading should be as above.
- Pilots must be proper to obtain required powerpile operation

- flame enveloping 3/8" to 1/2" of powerpile hot junction area

- stable, proper characteristics

SERVICE TIPS AND METHODS OF TROUBLE SHOOTING FOR POWERPILE SYSTEMS
(750 M.V. Specifically)

PILOT MUST
- Envelope 3/8" to 1/2" of powerpile tip, be stable, not be effected by drafts, and have proper flame characteristics (shown in Baso book).
- Cartridge type powerpiles should have steady flame at least half way up cartridge.

Thermostat Closed Test
- Test at thermostat 10 M.V. (without heater), 100 M.V. (with heater).
- The round Honeywell TS 86 draws 125 M.V.
- If readings are in excess of these mentioned, then service or replace thermostat.

Limit Closed Test
- Test at limit 10 M.V.
- If in excess of 10 M.V., service or replace unit.

Wiring Closed Test
- When testing limit or thermostat at valve, reading should not exceed those noted in the first two tests by more than 50 M.V. If they are in excess of 50 M.V., check for poor connections or poor wire size.

Valve Closed Test
- Jumper thermostat and limit at valve.
- Place test leads across valve coil.
- Valve should open when meter reads 135 M.V. If it doesn't, service or replace unit.

Pilotstat Closed Test
- Connect meter on P & P terminals.
- Jumper thermostat and limit at valve.
- Turn pilot off, pilotstat should not drop out until reading is lower than 160 M.V. If it does, service or replace pilotstat or wire lead.
- Tighten spade connector 1/4 turn past finger tight, clean with cardboard (business card).

Powerpile
- Remove jumper from thermostat and limit, making a closed circuit.
- Main burner should operate for 5 minutes.
- Connect tester leads across the valve coil.
- Providing all other components are operating properly, the reading obtained should be 10 M.V. avove the valve opening reading, or 10 M.V. above the pilotstat "drop out" reading. If not, repair or replace powerpile.

Locating Valve Coil
- Disconnect all wiring from valve top except one powerpile lead.
- Jumper other powerpile lead to various terminals until the valve opens.
- If the valve does not open, place powerpile lead on the other powerpile terminal and repeat jumpering process.
- Opening of valve indicates valve coil.

Examples of Heating Equipment and the types of Controls usually applied on each.

TYPE OF SYSTEM	TYPE OF EQUIPMENT	TYPES OF CONTROLS (USUALLY)
Gravity Warm Air	– Furnace	TH. S.P. H.L.
	– Room Heater	TH. S.P. F.C.
	– Floor Furnace	TH. S.P.
	– Sealed Combustion Chamber Heater	TH. S.P.
	– Recessed Heater	TH. S.P. H.L.

Forced Warm Air	– Furnaces
	   – Standard
	   – Horizontal
		TH. S.P. H.L. F.C.

	– Down Flow N.B.UPPER H.L. ON DOWN FLO – MANUAL RESET.	TH. S.P. 2 H.L. F.C.
	– Unit Heaters	TH. S.P. H.L. F.C.
Hot Water Gravity	– Boilers – Section Type – Closed and Open Systems	TH. S.P. H.L. L.W.C.O. (L.L.)
Hot Water Forced	– Boilers – Section Type – Coil Type	TH. S.P. H.L. P.C. L.W.C.O. (L.L.)
Steam	– Res./or Light Comm. Section Type	TH. S.P. H.L. L.W.C.O. P.T. L.L.

N.B. EXPLANATION OF ABBREVIATIONS

Thermostat	TH	Pump Control	PC
High Limit	HL	Low Water Cut Off	LWCO
Fan Control	FC	Pressuretrol	PT
Safety Pilot	SP	Low Limit	LL

352

POSSIBLE VENTING PROBLEMS, CAUSES AND REMEDIES

The following is a list of incorrect venting conditions or problems and example causes and remedies for the problems.

INCORRECT CONDITION OR PROBLEM	POSSIBLE CAUSE	REMEDY

(1) Incorrect Combustion. Flue products remaining in combustion chamber area.	- Poor draft
	  - cold
	  - blockage in flue passage
	  - wrong size
	  - incorrectly installed
	  - deteriorated or incorrect
	  - poor air replacement
		- Relocate vent or insulate products.
		- Clear, clean.
		- Correct size.
		- Install correctly.
		
		- Replace.
		
		- Correct air for ventilation.

(2) Spillage of combustion products at draft hood relief opening.	- Down draft - Blocked flue - Wrong size connector, diverter or vent - Incorrectly installed vent, connector or diverter - Poor draft - see (1) Causes	- Check installation and termination. - Clear, clean. - Resize. - Re-install. - See (1) Remedy.

(3) Condensation	- Flue products cooling below Dew Point (127°)
	  - point at which water vapor in flue gases turns to liquid
	  - poor draft
	    - see (1) and (2) Causes
	- Vent in cold area
		
		- See (1) and (2) Remedy
		
		- Insulate products or relocate vent.

(4) Wet plaster and/or dampness.	- See (2) and (3) - Faulty or dirty appliance combustion chamber	- As in (2) and (3). - See procedure for cracked combustion chamber. - See procedure for cleaning dirty and/or sooted combustion chambers.
(5) Deteriorated vent connector, vent, or chimney.	- See (3) - Incorrect materials for appication.	- See (3). - Correct.

CAUSES, CONDITIONS AND CORRECTIONS FOR DELAYED IGNITION AND PILOT OUTAGE (SAMPLES)

CAUSES	CONDITIONS/REASONS	CORRECTIONS
Pilot Position		
- Too far from main burner.	- Design, bracket loose.	- Reposition as per specs.
- Too close to main burner.	- Bracket broken.	- Reposition as per specs.
	- Main burner deterioration.	
- Condensation falling on pilot.	- Condensation dripping from cold metal.	- Reposition as per specs.
		- Check flue passage for obstruction.
Pilot Size		
- Flame too large (impingement).	- Burner out of adjustment.	- Adjust gas.
	- Corrosion, carbon and CO.	
- Flame too small.	- Dust.	- Clean primary air hole
- Flame luminous.	- Plugged orifice.	and/or orifice.
- Flame blowing.	- Noisy.	- Adj. gas and/or air.
Input and Manifold Pressure		
- Input or pressure too great.	- Blowing.	- Adjust pressure, check/adj orifice.
- Input or pressure too little.	- Low flame.	- Adjust pressure, check/adj orifice.
Air for Combustion		
- Insufficient primary air.	- Luminous flame.	- Increase primary air.
- Insufficient secondary air.	- CO produced.	- Increase secondary air.
- Insufficient air for ventilation and venting.	- Floating flames.	
	- Draft hood spillage.	- Proper sized openings for air infiltration.
Restricted vent or flues		
- Recirculation of products of combustion.	- Floating, luminous flames.	- Clean or remove restrictions.
- Products of combustion not being vented.		- Check proper vent size.
Excessive draft through the combustion chamber.		
- Boiler and sections not properly sealed.	- Blowing pilot flame out.	- Reduce draft (if appropriate).

CAUSES	CONDITIONS/REASONS	CORRECTIONS
- Cracked heat exchanger (forced air).	- Blowing pilot flame away from main burner. - Pilot flame blowing away from thermocouple (pilot outage).	- Seal. - New chamber or new furnace
High Ambient Heat - Not enough secondary air.	- Candling of pilot flame - M.V. drop due to lack of heat differential between hot and cold junctions. - Cooling of bi-metal, burner shuts off on safety.	- Check input. - Check flue passages. - Check secondary air circulation.
Improper burner alignment.	- Improper gas injection. - Insufficient primary air inspiration. - Improper combustion. - Burner extinction. - Carbon.	- Align burners correctly with manifold, orifice and heating sections of appliance.
Bleed line from automatic valve. - Plugged.	- Valve does not open. - Opens too slowly.	

- Improperly positioned.	- Heats thermal elements
	  - blows pilot from safety.
		- Check for:
		  - proper position.
		  - proper size.
		- Clean or replace.

Poor combustion	- Obstructed, plugged and/or dirty burner and/or ports.	- Clean and/or clear burner and/or ports. - Drill undrilled ports. - Adjust for proper flame characteristics. - Clean flue passage.

CAUSES, CONDITIONS AND CORRECTIONS FOR DELAYED IGNITION AND PILOT OUTAGE (cont'd.)

CAUSES	CONDITIONS/REASONS	CORRECTIONS
Thermocouple and		
Electromagnet		
– Weak output.	– Valve will not open on demand.	– Clean or adjust pilot.
– Weak magnet.	– Safety drops out.	– Check MV circuit.
		– Replace thermocouple or magnet if necessary.
Bi-Metal		
– Burnt out.	– Safety drops out.	– Properly position.
– Weak.	– Valve not opening.	– Check condition.
– Out of adjustment.		– Clean or adjust pilot flame.
– Out of position.		– Adjust timing.
		– Replace bi-metal if necessary.
		– Clamp firmly in place.
		– Adjust timing.
Electricity or Wiring		
Faulty	– Not operating.	– Check supply voltage.
	– Erratic operation.	– Supply correct.
	– Blowing fuses.	– Check all connections.
		– Check load amps.
		– No shorts.

CENTRAL HEATING POSSIBLE PROBLEMS, CAUSES AND REMEDIES

POSSIBLE PROBLEMS	SEE POSSIBLE CAUSES AND REMEDIES
High Operation Cost	1, 2, 3, 4, 5, 6, 11, 15, 18, 21, 29, 30, 41.
High Temperature Cut-Off	10, 23, 27, 28, 29, 30, 39, 41.
Dirt From Furnace	20, 21, 29.
High Basement Temperature	15, 22, 27, 28, 29.
Pilot Goes Out	8, 9, 18, 24, 25, 26, 42, 43.
Too Much Heat	1, 12, 15, 17, 30, 38.
Soot	1, 4, 6, 18, 19, 20, 21.
Condensation	2, 20, 21, 42, 44.
Blows Cold Air	27, 39.
Floating Flame	6, 18, 21, 42.
Burns In Mixer	2, 3, 18, 19, 35, 42.
Odors - Fumes	1, 2, 4, 5, 9, 20, 21, 35, 42, 44.
Noisy	1, 2, 3, 4, 6, 8, 9, 18, 19, 27.
Cycling On And Off	1, 2, 8, 9, 11, 12, 14, 17, 25, 27, 31.
Not Enough Heat	2, 8, 9, 10, 11, 12, 14, 16, 17, 18, 19, 21, 23, 24, 27, 28, 29, 30, 32, 38, 41.
No Heat	5, 7, 8, 13, 14, 16, 17, 23, 24, 25, 29, 31, 32, 34, 37, 40, 43.
Blowing Fuses	31, 33, 45.

POSSIBLE CAUSES AND REMEDIES

1.	Maximum input too high	- Decrease size of orifice/pressure.
2.	Maximum input too low.	- Increase size of orifice/pressure.
3.	Primary air too much.	- Adjust air shutter.
4.	Primary air too little.	- Adjust air shutter/clean burner.
5.	Secondary air too much.	- Adjust)
6.	Secondary air too little.	- Adjust) Where applicable.
7.	Safety pilot too high.	- Adjust.
8.	Safety pilot too low.	- Adjust/clean.
9.	Safety pilot timed too closely.	- Adjust or replace.
10.	Thermostat differential too great.	- Adjust or replace.
11.	Thermostat differential too little.	- Adjust or replace.

POSSIBLE CAUSES AND REMEDIES

12.	Thermostat heater element wrong or loose.	- Adjust, repair or replace.
13.	Power failure - transformer fuse out.	- Replace fuse.
14.	Short circuit in thermostat wiring.	- Repair.
15.	Gas valve sticks open.	- Clean, repair, or replace.
16.	Gas valve sticks closed.	- Clean, repair or replace.
17.	Short circuit in gas valve.	- Repair or replace.
18.	Unstable gas pressure, defective regulator.	- Clean leak limiter or replace regulator.
19.	Wrong size burner ports - burner ports clogged.	- Clean or replace.
20.	Crack or leak in body or section.	- Replace.
21.	Chimney too small or plugged.	- Clean or replace.
22.	Limit control set too high or defective.	- Adjust or replace.
23.	Limit control set too low or defective.	- Adjust or replace.
24.	Thermocouple not hot enough or inoperative.	- Adjust pilot, reposition thermocouple, or replace thermocouple.
25.	Pilot too close to burner.	- Reposition.
26.	Too much draft.	- Reposition vent assembly.
27.	Fan speed not right.	- Adjust.
28.	Fan running in reverse.	- Change direction of rotation.
29.	Filter clogged.	- Clean or remove.
30.	Hot and cold air duct not well balanced.	- Suggest balancing.
31.	Bad wiring connections.	- Repair.
32.	Faulty gas valve.	- Replace.
33.	Motor amperage too high.	- Replace.
34.	Open circuit in valve coil.	- Replace.
35.	Bleed line plugged or restricted.	- Clean or replace.
36.	Dirt under valve seat.	- Clean.
37.	Open circuit in thermostat.	- Clean or replace.
38.	Thermostat out of calibration.	- Calibrate.
39.	Defective fan control or out of adjustment.	- Adjust or replace.

40. Thermostat too close to heat source.   - Remove heat source.

41. Insufficient return air.   - Rectify.

42. Main burner out of adjustment or dirty.   - Clean, adjust.

43. Pilot out of adjustment or dirty.   - Clean, adjust.

44. Vent problem.   - Rectify.

45. Motor start switch out.   - Replace.

COMMON PROBLEMS IN HEATING SYSTEMS

PROBLEM LOCATION	SYMPTOMS	CAUSES	CORRECTION
Wiring	- Erratic operation - Not heat - Blows fuses - Not enough heat	- Loose connections - Motor amperage too high - Improper wire size - Improper wiring - Shorts	Repair or replace
Pressure	- Pilot outage - Late ignition - High bills	- Defective appliance regulator - Defective service regulator - Plugged vent or leak limiter	Clean, adjust or replace
Gas Valve	- Not heat - Erratic operation - Noisy - Passes gas when closed	- Open circuit in valve coil - Bleed line plugged - Dirt under valve seat N.B. Also See Wiring or Pressure above.	- Replace - Clean - Clean
Thermostat	- No heat - Undershoots room temperature - Overshoots room temperature burner short cycles	- Open circuit in Thermostat Out of calibration Heat anticipator out of adjustment or wrong rating	- Clean or replace - Adjust or replace heater plug
High Limit	- No heat - Room temperature too low - Bonnet temperature too high	- Defective control - Limit setting too low - Limit seeting too high	- Replace - Adjust or replace

COMMON PROBLEMS IN HEATING SYSTEMS (cont'd.)

PROBLEM LOCATION	SYMPTOMS	CAUSES	CORRECTION
Heating Medium (Air/ Water)	– Furnace/boiler operates off high limit – Not enough heat	Blower speed incorrect Insufficient return air/water Pump not working Air registers covered or closed Radiator fins dirty	– Adjust – Check registers or radiators – Customer to replace – Check out/or clean
	– One or more rooms too cold	– System needs balancing N.B. See section High Limit above	– Partially close dampers on short runs, open on long runs
Hot Water	– Water pressure regulator, dumps water on every burner cycle	– Cushion tank full of water	– Drain and refill
Millivolt Systems	– No heat – Valve opens only if tapped with heavy object – Erratic operation	See Electrical Trouble Shooting Chart	

COMMON PROBLEMS IN HEATING SYSTEMS (cont'd)

PROBLEM LOCATION	SYMPTOMS	CAUSES	CORRECTION
Fan/Pump Control	- Blows cold air	- Defective or out of adjustment	- Replace or adjust
	- Circulates cold water	- Defective or out of adjustment	- Replace or adjust
	- Burner shuts down on high limit	- Defective or out of adjustment	- Replace or adjust
		N.B. See also <u>High Limit</u> above	
Draft Condition	- Improper combustion	Incorrect primary air adjustment	
	- Incorrect neutral pressure point	Incorrect secondary air adjustment	- Adjust - Check CO_2 (Conversion Burners only
	- Spillage at diverter	Blockage or down draft in chimney	- Clean or repair
	- Pilot outage		
	- High bills	Vent to cold	
	- Poor efficiency	Incorrect input	- Adjust
	- Fumes and/or carbon in home	Primary air out of adjustment	- Adjust
	- Occupants complain of headaches		
	- Condensation in home	Incorrect vent size	
		N.B. Any or all of these causes could apply to any one of symptoms.	

CONDITIONS, CAUSES AND CORRECTIONS FOR COMMON WATER HEATER COMPLAINTS.

CONDITION	CAUSE	CORRECTION
- No Hot Water	- Pilot Outage - Defect Safety - Pilot Dirty - Pilot out of adjustment	- Test Control - replace if necessary - Clean - Adjust
- Not Enough Hot Water	- Heater Overdrawn (not large enough) - Input too low - Leaky faucets - Dip tube split or rotted off - Thermostat set too low - Thermostat out of calibration - Cold water mixing with hot - through faulty shower valve	- Refer to Sales - Adjust - Inform customer - Replace or refer to contractor - Re-set temperature and inform customer - Recalibrate - Inform customer

- Relief Valve Blows on
Temperature
	- Thermostat out of
	calibration
	- Dirt under thermostat
	seat
	- Temperature stacking
	within tank
	(High recovery water
	heater)
	- Input too high
		- Recalibrate
		
		- Clean
		
		- Check and adjust the
		following:
		  - input
		  - pressure
		- Temperature
		N.B. - if not corrected
		temperature may be
		lowered by 10°. Adjust.

CONDITIONS, CAUSES AND CORRECTIONS FOR COMMON WATER HEATER COMPLAINTS. (cont'd.)

CONDITION	CAUSE	CORRECTION
- Relief Valve Drips	- pressure setting too close to main pressure	- old relief valve - replace - new relief valve - check with supervisor before adjusting pressure setting
	- spring corroded	- replace relief valve
	- seat defective	- replace relief valve
- Floating Fire Soot	- primary air opening plugged or closed	- vacuum clean flue passages - adjust primary air
	- down draft at chimney	- check stack height
	- blockage	- remove blockage
- Rusty Water	- corrosion inside tank	- refer to Sales
	- rusty pipes	- drain regularly - plumber
- Rumbling	- sediment in bottom of tank	- flush tank - plumber
	- air bubbles	N.B. - follow local procedure

Appendix IV

General check list for equipment installation and maintenance:

1) General check list for gas furnace installation and maintenance.
2) General check list for gas water heater installation and maintenance.
3. General Check List For Residential No Heat Call.

General check list for gas furnace installation and maintenance

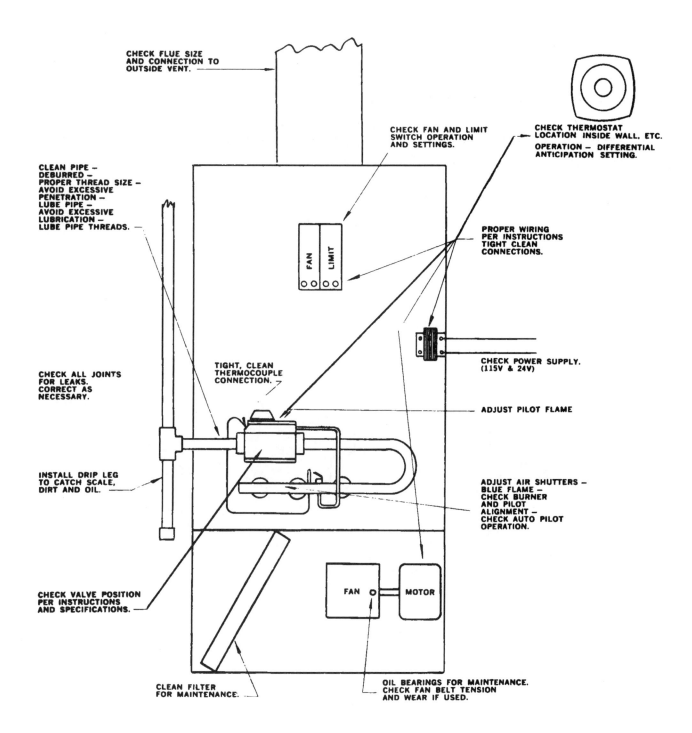

CHECK FLUE SIZE AND CONNECTION TO OUTSIDE VENT.

CHECK FAN AND LIMIT SWITCH OPERATION AND SETTINGS.

CHECK THERMOSTAT LOCATION INSIDE WALL, ETC.

OPERATION — DIFFERENTIAL ANTICIPATION SETTING.

CLEAN PIPE — DEBURRED — PROPER THREAD SIZE — AVOID EXCESSIVE PENETRATION — LUBE PIPE — AVOID EXCESSIVE LUBRICATION — LUBE PIPE THREADS.

PROPER WIRING PER INSTRUCTIONS TIGHT CLEAN CONNECTIONS.

FAN

LIMIT

CHECK ALL JOINTS FOR LEAKS. CORRECT AS NECESSARY.

TIGHT, CLEAN THERMOCOUPLE CONNECTION.

CHECK POWER SUPPLY. (115V & 24V)

ADJUST PILOT FLAME

INSTALL DRIP LEG TO CATCH SCALE, DIRT AND OIL.

ADJUST AIR SHUTTERS — BLUE FLAME — CHECK BURNER AND PILOT ALIGNMENT — CHECK AUTO PILOT OPERATION.

CHECK VALVE POSITION PER INSTRUCTIONS AND SPECIFICATIONS.

FAN   MOTOR

CLEAN FILTER FOR MAINTENANCE.

OIL BEARINGS FOR MAINTENANCE. CHECK FAN BELT TENSION AND WEAR IF USED.

General check list for gas water heater installation and maintenance

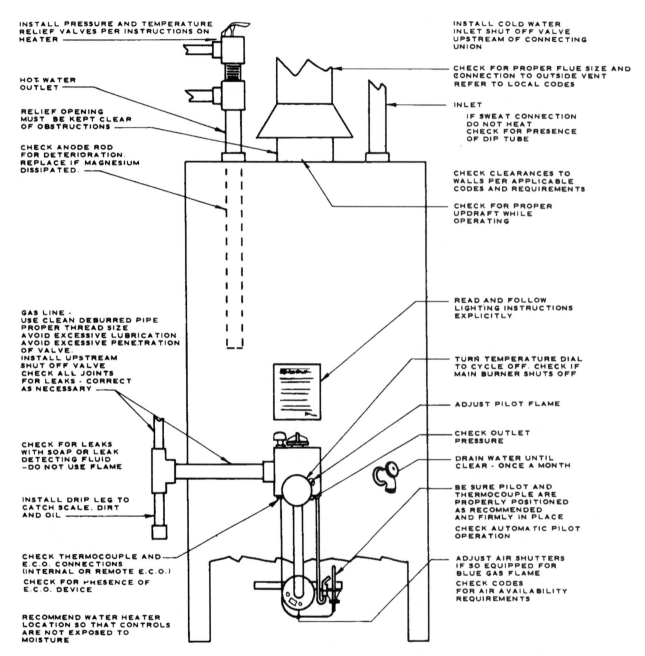

INSTALL PRESSURE AND TEMPERATURE RELIEF VALVES PER INSTRUCTIONS ON HEATER

HOT WATER OUTLET

RELIEF OPENING MUST BE KEPT CLEAR OF OBSTRUCTIONS

CHECK ANODE ROD FOR DETERIORATION. REPLACE IF MAGNESIUM DISSIPATED.

GAS LINE - USE CLEAN DEBURRED PIPE PROPER THREAD SIZE AVOID EXCESSIVE LUBRICATION AVOID EXCESSIVE PENETRATION OF VALVE. INSTALL UPSTREAM SHUT OFF VALVE CHECK ALL JOINTS FOR LEAKS - CORRECT AS NECESSARY

CHECK FOR LEAKS WITH SOAP OR LEAK DETECTING FLUID -DO NOT USE FLAME

INSTALL DRIP LEG TO CATCH SCALE, DIRT AND OIL

CHECK THERMOCOUPLE AND E.C.O. CONNECTIONS (INTERNAL OR REMOTE E.C.O.) CHECK FOR PRESENCE OF E.C.O. DEVICE

RECOMMEND WATER HEATER LOCATION SO THAT CONTROLS ARE NOT EXPOSED TO MOISTURE

INSTALL COLD WATER INLET SHUT OFF VALVE UPSTREAM OF CONNECTING UNION

CHECK FOR PROPER FLUE SIZE AND CONNECTION TO OUTSIDE VENT REFER TO LOCAL CODES

INLET IF SWEAT CONNECTION DO NOT HEAT CHECK FOR PRESENCE OF DIP TUBE

CHECK CLEARANCES TO WALLS PER APPLICABLE CODES AND REQUIREMENTS

CHECK FOR PROPER UPDRAFT WHILE OPERATING

READ AND FOLLOW LIGHTING INSTRUCTIONS EXPLICITLY

TURN TEMPERATURE DIAL TO CYCLE OFF. CHECK IF MAIN BURNER SHUTS OFF

ADJUST PILOT FLAME

CHECK OUTLET PRESSURE

DRAIN WATER UNTIL CLEAR - ONCE A MONTH

BE SURE PILOT AND THERMOCOUPLE ARE PROPERLY POSITIONED AS RECOMMENDED AND FIRMLY IN PLACE CHECK AUTOMATIC PILOT OPERATION

ADJUST AIR SHUTTERS IF SO EQUIPPED FOR BLUE GAS FLAME CHECK CODES FOR AIR AVAILABILITY REQUIREMENTS

SET TEMPERATURE DIAL PER CUSTOMER NEEDS – RECOMMEND MODERATE TEMPERATURE SETTING FOR LONGER LIFE. EXPLAIN TO HOMEOWNER, IF AVAILABLE, THAT TEMPERATURE DIAL IS ADJUSTABLE AND SHOULD BE USED TO MEET VARYING CONDITIONS AND REQUIREMENTS.

TAKE TIME TO EXPLAIN OPERATION AND MAINTENANCE TO CUSTOMER, IF AVAILABLE.

GENERAL CHECK LIST FOR RESIDENTIAL NO HEAT CALL

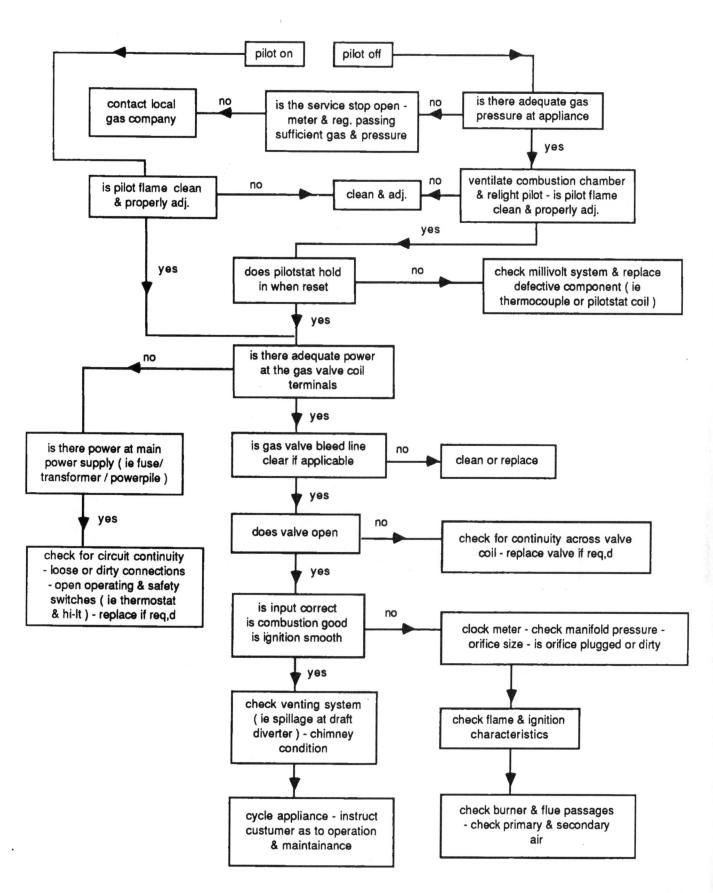

Appendix V

Figure 1: Two psig copper tubing system.

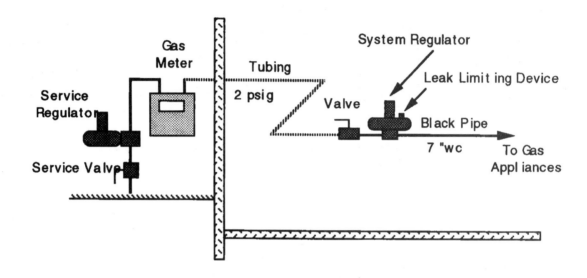

To reduce the cost of multi-unit residential[1] and light commercial gas installations, special 2 psig (14k Pa) copper tubing systems, see *Figure 1*, are being considered by the gas industry. The copper tubing is sized at a much higher allowable pressure drop[2] giving a significant reduction is the gas supply line size *(see Table 1)*.

As shown in *Figure 1*, the 2 psig copper tubing system must be equipped with a *system regulator*. The regulator will reduce the 2 psig supply pressure to the conventional 7"wc houseline pressure required by the gas appliances. The system regulator is like the service regulator in that it is a pounds/inch regulator having a positive shut off. The system regulator for the 2 psig tube system does not require the following if it is equipped with a ball check leak limiting device orificed for 1 cfh (7.8 cm^3/s):

[1] Townhouses and commercial plazas.

[2] The maximum allowable pressure drop for gas lines systems having a supply pressure at or over 2 psig (14 kPa) is 75% of the supply pressure. For the 2 psig copper tube system the maximum allowable pressure drop is 1.5 psig (10 kPa). Most provincial codes have tube sizing tables for the 2 psig system giving allowable pressure drops of 1 psig (7 kPa) and 1.5 psig

i) either full internal or line relief valve,
ii) regulator vent line and relief valve vent line terminating outdoors.

Table 1 is the tube sizing table for a 2 psig copper tubing system having a 1 psig (7 kPa) allowable pressure drop.

Maximum Capacity of Semi - Rigid Tubing in cfh for a Gas Pressure of 2.0 psig and a Pressure Drop of 1.0 psig (Based on a 0.60 Relative Density Gas)

Outside Diameter (Inch)	Equivalent Length of Tubing, Feet													
	10	20	30	40	50	60	70	80	90	100	125	150	175	200
3/8	233	160	127	110	96	88	81	76	71	67	39	54	49	46
1/2	481	330	264	227	201	182	168	156	146	138	123	111	102	95
5/8	978	672	537	462	409	371	341	317	298	281	249	226	207	193
3/4	1709	1175	938	808	716	648	597	555	520	492	436	395	363	338
7/8	2425	1667	1331	1145	1015	919	847	787	738	698	619	560	515	479

Maximum Capacity of Semi - Rigid Tubing in m3/h for a Gas Pressure of 14 kPa and a Pressure Drop of 7 kPa (Based on a 0.60 Relative Density Gas)

Outside Diameter (Inch)	Equivalent Length of Tubing, Metres													
	3	4	5	6	8	10	12	15	20	25	30	40	50	60
3/8	6.64	5.69	5.04	4.56	3.92	3.46	3.14	2.80	2.38	2.11	1.90	1.64	1.45	1.32
1/2	13.72	11.70	10.40	9.42	8.09	7.14	6.48	5.77	4.92	4.35	3.93	3.38	2.99	2.72
5/8	27.91	23.85	21.17	19.15	16.45	14.53	13.18	11.74	10.01	8.83	7.99	6.88	6.09	5.52
3/4	48.79	41.73	37.01	33.48	28.77	25.40	23.05	20.53	17.50	15.48	13.96	12.03	10.65	9.66
7/8	69.19	59.17	52.49	47.48	40.80	36.03	32.69	29.11	24.81	21.96	19.80	17.06	15.10	13.69

The following is tube/pipe sizing example of a typical 2 psig copper tubing system:

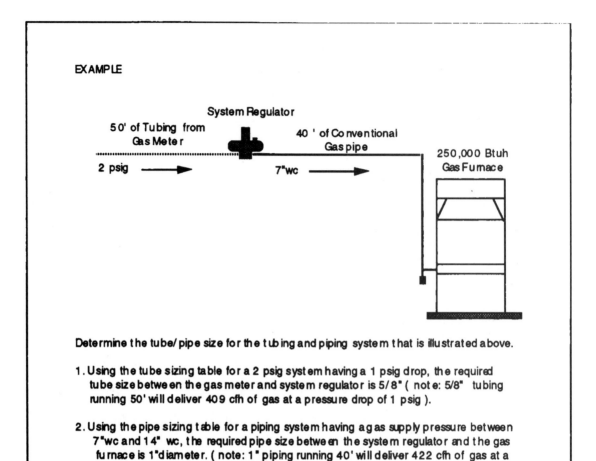

EXAMPLE

System Regulator

50' of Tubing from Gas Meter

40 ' of Conventional Gas pipe

2 psig →

7"wc →

250,000 Btuh Gas Furnace

Determine the tube/pipe size for the tubing and piping system that is illustrated above.

1. Using the tube sizing table for a 2 psig system having a 1 psig drop, the required tube size between the gas meter and system regulator is 5/8" (note: 5/8" tubing running 50' will deliver 409 cfh of gas at a pressure drop of 1 psig).

2. Using the pipe sizing table for a piping system having a gas supply pressure between 7"wc and 14" wc, the required pipe size between the system regulator and the gas furnace is 1"diameter. (note: 1" piping running 40' will deliver 422 cfh of gas at a pressure drop of 1 " wc.

Appendix VI

CONTROL SWITCHES

Temperature Actuated

Flow Actuated

Liquid Level Actuated

Pressure Actuated

Moisture Actuated

STEP DOWN CONTROL TRANSFORMER

IGNITION TRANSFORMER

SOLENOID (VALVE)

OVERLOAD(BIMETAL)

CIRCUIT BREAKER

ELECTRICAL CONNECTION

Crossover (no connection)

Connection

JUNCTION PLUG (WIRING HARNESS)

BATTERY

CAPACITOR

FUSE

Cartridge type

Fuse link

GROUND

System   Equipment

Schematic symbols used with schematic wiring diagrams

SWITCHES

Single-pole, single-throw   Double-pole, single-throw

Single-pole, double-throw   Double-pole, double-throw

RESISTORS & HEATERS

Fixed resistor   Variable resistor   Thermal heater element

LIGHT

     ★ = indicates colour

SINGLE PHASE ELECTRIC MOTOR

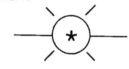

RELAYS

Control Relay   Time Delay Relay

Coil = ———(CR)———

Normally open contact =   1CR1*   —||—

Normally closed contact =   1CR2**   —\|—

Coil = ———(TDR)———

Normally open contact =   1TDR1   —||—

Normally closed contact =   1TDR2   —\|—

*1CR1 = 1 st contact belonging to 1 st relay coil
**1CR2 = 2 nd contact belonging to 1 st relay coil

Schematic symbols used with schematic wiring diagrams

Glossary

The following terms are associated with the use of natural gas:

100% Pilot Protection: A pilot safety shut off system where both main burner gas supply and pilot gas supply are protected against pilot failure.

100% Safety Shut Off: See 100% pilot protection.

A Vent: Masonry chimney, steel chimney and factory built chimney.

Absolute Pressure: A pressure measurement of a gas from a perfect or complete vacuum.

AC: Alternating Current

Adjustable Orifice: An orifice equipped with an adjustable needle inside the orifice spud that can vary the gas discharge or flow rate through the orifice.

Aerated Pilot: A pilot that develops a rather sharp, intense blue flame as a result of the premixing of air and gas.

AFUE: Annual fuel utilization efficiency.

Air Switch: An interlock that proves air flow as established by a burner fan or a furnace induced draft fan.

Allowable Pressure Drop: The maximum pressure drop that can be imposed on a gas line as established by an installation code.

Annual Fuel Utilization Efficiency: See seasonal efficiency.

Appliance Regulator: A pressure regulator that reduces the upstream houseline pressure to the required downstream manifold pressure at the burner.

Atmospheric Burner: A burner which uses the energy in a gas stream or jet to induce air at atmospheric pressure to be mixed with the gas.

Atmospheric Pressure: The pressure of our atmosphere exerted on the earth's surface.

Automatic Control Valve: See control valve.

Automatic Ignition System: A combustion control system that automatically establishes the source of ignition upon each call for heat.

Automatic Safety Vent Limiting Device: A regulator accessory consisting of a ball check that permits free inhalation of the regulator for fast regulator-diaphragm response, but automatically limits escaping gas to safe limits should a diaphragm rupture. This device gives sensitive response even at low inlet pressure.

Automatic Vent Damper: An energy conservation device located at the appliance draft diverter outlet which is designed to prevent building air migration to the outside during the appliance off cycle.

B Vent: Double wall metal vent connector.

Barometric Draft Control: See draft regulator.

Barometric Pressure: See atmospheric pressure.

Base Pressure: The pressure at which the gas meter is calibrated.

Bellows Meter: See diaphragm meter.

BH Vent: Stainless steel, thermoplastic and PVC plastic vent used for special venting systems associated with high efficiency gas appliances.

Blower Compartment Door Switch: A switch that interlocks the furnace blower compartment door with the combustion control circuit (i.e., ignition control).

Blue Flame: See Bunsen flame.

Btu: British thermal units; the amount of heat energy that will raise one pound of water through one degree Fahrenheit (°F).

Btuh: Btu per hour.

Building Line Pressure: See houseline pressure.

Building Line: See gas supply line.

Bunsen Flame: A blue flame as a result of some premixing of air and fuel which takes place prior to the combustion process.

Burner Assembly: An assembly of individual burners that are mounted from a common manifold within the burner compartment of the appliance.

Burner Head: The part of the burner that contains the burner ports.

Burner Mixing Tube: The burner tube that directs the gas/air mixture to the burner port(s).

Burner Port: The burner opening that discharges the gas or gas/air mixture to be burned.

Burner: A device that is used to burn a fuel.

BW Vent: Oval double wall metal vent connector.

C Vent: Single wall metal vent connector.

Cap Orifice: A multiple orifice designed to give either natural gas or propane gas operation.

Carbon Dioxide (CO_2): A product of combustion that is found in every combustion process (perfect, complete and incomplete combustion).

Carbon Monoxide (CO): A toxic gas generated by the incomplete combustion of the gas.

Carbonizing Flame: See rich flame.

Category I Vented Appliance: An appliance which operates with a non-positive vent pressure and with a flue or vent loss not less than 17%.

Category II Vented Appliance: An appliance which operates with a non-positive vent pressure and with a flue or vent loss less than 17%.

Category III Vented Appliance: An appliance which operates with a positive vent pressure and with a flue or vent loss not less than 17%.

Category IV Vented Appliance: An appliance which operates with a positive vent pressure and with a flue or vent loss less than 17%.

CF: Cubic feet.

CFH: Cubic feet per hour.

Chimney Liner: A clay-tile or metal liner that is inserted into a chimney.

Chimney: A masonry or steel vent that conveys the appliance flue gases to the outside.

Clocking The Burner Input: A method of determining the burner Btuh input by timing the meter test dial.

Closed Circuit Test: A test that determines the voltage drop across the power unit (i.e., pilotstat coil) and indicates if the coil is adequately energized to hold the safety shut off valve in the open position.

Combination Control Valve: A control valve where all of the necessary control components (i.e., regulator, pilotstat control valve operator, etc.) are provided in one body assembly.

Combustion Air: Air that is required to give effective gas appliance operation. It is the air required for the combustion of the gas, draft control dilution and ventilation.

Combustion Chamber: A chamber, within the appliance, that contains the burner firing.

Combustion Efficiency: The efficiency of the appliance as determined by appliance Btuh output divided by the appliance Btuh input.

Combustion Gas Analyzer: An instrument that determines the percentage of carbon dioxide and oxygen in the appliance flue gases.

Combustion Testing: The quantitative sampling of combustion products together with the taking of the flue gas temperature to determine the appliance combustion efficiency.

Combustion: The rapid combination of a fuel with oxygen resulting in the release of heat.

Complete Combustion: The complete burning of the fuel; however, excess air (oxygen) is found in the flue gases as a result of an initial air supply greater than that required for perfect combustion to insure that all of the fuel is burned.

Condensation: The process of the water vapour in the flue gases condensing into a liquid as a result of excessive cooling of the flue gases.

Constant Pilot: See continuous pilot.

Consumption Dials: Meter dials that measure gas consumption over a period of time for billing purposes.

Continuous Pilot: A pilot that is on all of time whether the main burner is on or off.

Control Valve: The gas control valve, sometimes referred to as the automatic control valve, functions to open or energize when the thermostat calls for heat and to close or de-energize when the demand for heat has been satisfied.

Conversion Burner: A gas burner used to convert a heating appliance that was originally designed for another fuel such as coal or oil.

Cross over igniters: Igniter ports that allows an ignition flame to bridge the individual burners of a burner assembly.

DC: Direct Current

Delayed Ignition: A condition where the burner flame is not immediately ignited.

Dew Point Temperature: The temperature at which water vapour would begin to condense out of the flue gases.

Diagnostic Light: A light found on an ignition control module that is used to trouble shoot the system through a coded flash sequence.

Diaphragm Meter: A gas meter which uses an arrangement of flexible bellows to measure the volume of gas.

Diaphragm Valve: A valve that is powered by gas pressure as the primary force for opening and closing the valve. The valve can be operated electrically by opening and closing a small bleed line through the actions of a small electrical operator. The diaphragm valve opens and closes in response to the opening and closing of the bleed line. Both internal and external bleed line types of diaphragm valves are available. External bleed valves require porting of the bleed gas to a location near a constant burning pilot for internal bleed models, bleed gas is ported back into the valve outlet or manifold.

Differential Pressure Switch: A normally open air switch that is actuated by a pressure differential created across the furnace when the induced draft is in operation.

Dilution Air: Room air that is drawn through the relief opening of the appliance draft control.

Direct Spark Ignition (DSI): An automatic ignition system in which the burner flame is directly ignited by an ignition spark upon each call for heat.

Direct Vent Appliance: An appliance in which the appliance combustion zone or burner compartment is sealed from the indoor environment and combustion air and the products of combustion are drawn from and exhausted to the outdoors.

Dirt Pocket: See drip pocket.

Downdraft: The movement of outside air down through the appliance venting system as a result of either insufficient combustion air supplied to the appliance or inappropriately placed outside vent location.

Draft Control: A mechanical device located in the appliance venting system that regulates or controls the draft condition in the combustion zone of the appliance.

Draft Diverter: See draft hood.

Draft Hood: A fixed draft control that establishes a neutral overfire draft condition in the combustion zone of a natural draft appliance.

Draft Regulator: A draft control that is designed to regulate the desired draft condition in the appliance combustion zone.

Draft: The flow of combustion products and/or air through the appliance and the appliance venting system.

Drilled Port Burner: A cast iron burner having a series of drilled holes as the burner ports.

Drip Pocket: A piping arrangement, consisting of a tee, nipple and cap, located at the bottom of a drop line designed to trap moisture and dirt that may be in the gas line.

Drop Line: The part of a branch line that drops down to the appliance and is fed by an overhead supply line.

Drop Out Test: A test that determines the minimum voltage drop across the power unit (i.e., pilotstat coil) that will just hold it in.

Drop Valve: A manual shut off valve located in the drop line.

ECO: See energy cut-off.

Energy Cut-Off: A temperature high limit switch that is wired in series with the thermocouple and the power unit inside the thermostatic control valve. It is calibrated to open and take control at a temperature range above the thermostat control range. Both main and pilot gas are thereby shut off when this limit is reached.

Equivalent Length of Pipe: The resistance of pipe fittings and valves equated in equivalent length of straight pipe of the same diameter.

Equivalent Vent Length: Consists of straight vent pipe plus the resistance of the vent fittings (i.e., elbows) as measured in equivalent length of straight pipe.

Excess Air: Air that is found as a combustion product of the gas as a result of an air supply that is above the theoretical amount.

Extinction Pop: The act of the flame flashing back into the burner port when the burner is turned off.

Extra Low Voltage: Voltage of 1 volt or less.

Fan Assisted Appliance: An appliance in which an induced draft fan pulls the products of combustion across the appliance. However, the induced draft fan does not create a positive vent pressure. The appliance relies on the buoyant effects of the hot flue gases to vent them to the outside.

Fan Assisted Burner: A burner equipped with a burner fan to supply the air for combustion with sufficient air pressure to just over come the resistance of the burner.

Fixed Orifice: An orifice that is designed to give a fixed amount of gas discharge or flow rate.

Flame Characteristics: The flame characteristics are the color, shape and intensity of the flame.

Flame Conductivity: The process of air and gas molecules between the flame sensor (i.e., the flame rod) and the grounded area of the burner head become ionized allowing the flame to conduct an electrical current.

Flame Current: The resulting current flowing through a detected flame as established by an automatic ignition control system.

Flame Establishing Period: See trial for ignition time.

Flame Failure Response Test: A test that determines the time for the power unit or pilotstat coil to drop out, placing the system in a safety shut down condition.

Flame Failure Response Time: Time it takes the ignition control module to react to the presence or absence of the flame.

Flame Lifting: The act of the flame lifting off the burner port.

Flame Rectification: The process of the flame current flowing mostly in one direction because of the size difference between the flame sensor and ground areas.

Flame Rod: A metal rod that is exposed in the flame to function as an electrode in a flame detection circuit.

Flame Roll-Out Switch: A manual reset thermal limit required to protect the appliance combustion air opening (i.e., burner's secondary air inlet pouch) from excessive heat and flame roll out.

Flame Roll-Out: The act of the burner flame rolling out of the appliance combustion chamber when the appliance starts.

Flame Safeguard Protection: A system of flame protection where the main burner flame cannot be established if the pilot flame is not present to ignite the main flame.

Flame Sensor: The component of an automatic ignition system that senses the flame.

Flame Signal: See flame current.

Flame Speed: The speed at which the flame front moves towards the air/gas mixture issuing from the burner port.

Flame Spreader: See flame target.

Flame Target: A flame baffle.

Flame Temperature: The temperature of a flame that occurs at perfect combustion.

Flash Back: The act of the flame flashing back into the burner port.

Flexible Connector: Flexible tubing designed to connect portable gas appliances to rigid gas piping.

Flue Collar: The part of the appliance to which the vent connector or draft hood is connected.

Flue Gas Analysis: Determining the combustion process by the quantitative measurement of carbon dioxide, oxygen and carbon monoxide in the flue gases.

Flue Gases: The combustion gases that are produced from the combustion of the gas with air, namely carbon dioxide, water vapour, nitrogen and oxygen (as a result of excess air).

Flue Losses: The heat that is absorbed by the flue gases that is lost up the appliance vent.

Flue: An enclosed passage that is designed to convey hot flue gases.

Forced Draft Burner: A burner equipped with a burner fan to supply the air for combustion with sufficient air pressure to overcome the resistance of the burner and the appliance.

Gas Main: The main gas line supplying gas to customers along a city street.

Gas Outlet: The termination of the gas piping near or at the location of an appliance or a proposed appliance.

Gas Pressure Regulator: A pressure regulating device that maintains a constant downstream pressure regardless of variations in flow rate and upstream pressure.

Gas Service: The gas line that conveys gas from the gas main to the customer's premises.

Gas Supply Line: The main interior building line that supplies gas to the various appliances within the building.

Gauge Pressure: A pressure measurement taken by a pressure gauge in which zero is calibrated at local atmospheric pressure.

Glow Coil: A high resistance wire that becomes very hot when an electrical current is applied across it, hot enough to provide an assured source of pilot ignition—sometimes referred to as hot wire ignition.

GND: An electrical ground.

Gravity Venting: See natural draft venting.

Gross Stack: Temperature: The temperature at the appliance stack upstream from the appliance draft control.

Grounded Area: The grounded part of a flame sensing circuit of an ignition control system.

Hard Flame: See lean flame.

Heat Content: See heating value.

Heating Value: The amount of heat energy released by a measured amount of the gas during the combustion process.

High Efficiency Condensing Furnace: A furnace that raises the steady state efficiency by condensing the hot flue gases, thus capturing their latent heat of condensation.

High Efficiency Non-Condensing Furnace: A furnace that raises the steady state efficiency by operating with a low stack temperature that is just above that which will induce condensation of the flue gases.

Hot Surface Ignition (HSI): An automatic ignition system in which the burner flame is ignited by a hot surface igniter upon each call for heat.

Houseline Pressure: The pressure at the outlet of the gas meter.

Hydraulic Control System: A non electric control system that uses a temperature sensitive fluid and flexible bellows to open and close a control valve.

Ignition Activation Period: A feature of a hot surface ignition system that allows the igniter to remain on for a short period after burner flame has been established.

Ignition Control Module: The main component of an automatic ignition system that controls system operations.

Ignition Temperature: The temperature at which the combustible mixture of the gas and air will initiate and maintain the combustion reaction.

Incinerating Pilot: Is a variation of the aerated type of pilot. In this type of pilot, the primary air is drawn through a tube or air duct which passes around the pilot flame incinerating any lint or dust that could be in the primary air.

Incomplete Combustion: Occurs when fuel is not completely burned due to insufficient air supply.

Indicating Dial: A 100 cu. ft. dial found on commercial meters that gives accuracy to the first consumption dial.

Induced Draft Appliance: An appliance equipped with an induced draft fan which pulls the products of combustion across the appliance and power vents them to the outside.

Induced Draft Fan: A fan located in the venting system that mechanically establishes a draft.

Induced Draft Firing Appliance: See induced draft appliance.

Induced Draft: A mechanical draft that is established by an induced draft fan located in the appliance vent downstream from the appliance combustion zone.

Integrated Furnace Control: An expanded automatic ignition control that contains a microprocessor that governs all of the furnace operations.

Interlock: A safety control switch that proves an equipment function such as an air switch that proves burner fan motor operation.

Intermittent Pilot (IP)—Ignition System: An automatic ignition system in which the burner flame is ignited by a pilot flame that is established, usually by an ignition spark, upon each call for heat.

Intermittent Pilot: A pilot that is established upon each the call for heat; ignites the main burner flame and remains on throughout the burner on period.

Interrupted Pilot: A pilot that is established upon each call for heat; ignites the main burner flame and is automatically shut off after the main burner flame is well established.

L Vent: Similar to type B vent, however made from greater heat and corrosion resistant material required for the venting of oil burning appliances.

Latent Heat: Heat absorbed or given off by a substance without changing its temperature when the substance changes its physical state.

Lean Flame: A flame that has too much air and insufficient fuel. It is a small, very sharp intense blue flame.

Limit Control: See limit switch.

Limit Switch: A safety control switch that establishes the safe operating limits for a heating system (i.e., a high temperature safety limit switch).

Limits of Flammability: The upper and lower percentages of gas in the air/gas mixture that will support combustion.

Lock Out Module: See lock out timer.

Lock Out Timer: A component that can convert an automatic ignition system having non 100% safety shut off to one having 100% safety shut off.

Lock Up Pressure: See static pressure.

Lock-out or Safety Shut-off: The process of the ignition control module shutting down upon failure to establish flame during the ignition cycle. A manual reset is required to restart the control.

Low Voltage: 24 volts

Luminous Flame: See rich flame.

m^3/h: Cubic metres per hour.

m^3: Cubic metres

Manifold Pressure: The pressure at the gas burner downstream of all control valves.

Manometer: A U shaped water filled tube that measures gas pressure in inches of water column.

Mechanical Draft: A draft that is established by a mechanical means such as an induced draft fan.

Microamperes: 1,000,000 microamperes = 1 ampere

Millivolt System: A gas control system where the power supply is provided by a thermopile.

Millivolt: 1000 millivolts = 1 volt

Minimum Pilot Test: See pilot turndown test.

Mono Port Burner: A burner having a single burner port.

Multiple Port Burner: A burner having multiple burner ports.

MV: Millivolt

Natural Draft Appliance: An appliance in which a draft hood establishes a neutral overfire draft condition within the combustion zone or burner compartment of the appliance; and, natural draft is required to vent the flue gases to the outside.

Natural Draft Burner: A burner that is not equipped with a mechanical device, such as a burner fan, for supplying the air for combustion.

Natural Draft Venting: A venting system that relies on natural draft to remove the products of combustion to the outdoors.

Natural Draft: Draft that is established by the difference in weight (buoyancy) between the hot flue gases and the surrounding cooler

Negative Overfire Draft: A negative draft condition that is established by a draft regulator in the combustion zone of an appliance.

Net Stack Temperature: The actual temperature rise of the flue gases across the appliance and is obtained by subtracting the room temperature from the appliance stack temperature.

Neutral Flame: See perfect flame.

Neutral Overfire Draft: A neutral draft condition that is established by a fixed draft control in the combustion zone of a natural draft appliance.

Neutralizer: A device used by condensing furnaces that neutralize the acidity of the condensate.

Nitrogen N_2: An inert gas found in the products of combustion of the gas. In its free state it constitutes approximately 80% of the earth's atmosphere.

Non 100% Safety Shut Off: See non 100% pilot protection.

Non Aerated Pilot: A pilot that develops a rather lazy, soft blue flame as a result of no premixing of air and gas.

Non 100% Pilot Protection: A pilot safety shut off system where only the main burner gas supply is protected against pilot failure.

Off Cycle Losses: The losses incurred by the appliance when it is not operating (i.e., firing).

Open Circuit Test: A test that determines the full voltage output from a thermocouple.

Orifice Spud: A brass plug or cap containing an orifice.

Orifice: A small opening through which gas can be discharged.

Oxidizing Flame: See lean flame.

Oxygen (O_2): A gas that constitutes approximately 20% of the earth's atmosphere. It is a necessary component in the combustion of the gas.

Partial Premixing: A combustion system in which some of the air required for the combustion process is partially premixed with the fuel prior to the combustion process.

Pascal (Pa): A metric unit of pressure in which 6895 Pa = 1 psi.

Perfect Combustion: The complete burning of the fuel with the exact amount of air (i.e., theoretical or ideal air supply) for the combustion process.

Perfect Flame: A flame which has sufficient intensity to give flame stability. Its color is blue, however, it is not a brilliant blue or as intense as the lean or hard flame.

pH: A scale that is used to measure the acidity of an acid.

Pilot Generator: Pilot burner and thermopile as a package unit.

Pilot Turndown Test: A test to ensure that a pilot that will just hold in the pilotstat will provide effective ignition of the main gas within 4 seconds.

Pilotstat Coil: See power unit.

Pilotstat: A pilot safety shut off device that is energized by the thermocouple.

Pipe Dope: A compound designed to provide a sealant for threaded pipe and fittings.

Piping Extension: A piping arrangement, consisting of a tee, nipple and cap, located at the end of a supply line designed to provide for the future extension of the supply line.

Power Unit: The electromagnetic coil in the pilot safety shut-off device that is energized by the thermocouple.

Power Venter: See induced draft fan.

Powerpile: See thermopile.

Prepurge: A feature of the ignition control module that allows the operation of an induced draft fan or burner fan to purge the appliance combustion chamber during the period between the thermostat's initial call for heat and the beginning of the module's ignition cycle.

Primary Air: The air that is premixed with the fuel prior to the combustion process.

Primary Control: See ignition control module.

Products of Combustion: The products resulting from the perfect combustion of the gas.

Proven Pilot: A pilot that is supervised by an automatic ignition control system which senses the presence of the pilot before allowing gas supply to the main burner.

PSI: Pounds per square inch.

Pulse Combustion: A resonant combustion process in which the fuel is burned in separate pulses rather than in a conventional con

Recycling: The process of the ignition control module repeating the ignition sequence upon lost of flame detection during the burner's running cycle.

Reducing Flame: See rich flame.

Relative Density: See specific gravity.

Remote Reset: Resetting the ignition control module by turning down the room thermostat to interrupt the 24 volt power supply to the module.

Required Air /Gas Ratio: The required amount of air needed to achieve the perfect combustion of 1 cu. ft. of the gas.

Retry: A feature of the ignition control module that allows the control to repeat the ignition sequence if the burner flame is undetected after the first try for ignition.

Ribbon Port Burner: A burner that has a continuous opening down each side of the burner head creating the appearance of a ribbon.

Rich Flame: Is a flame in which there is too much fuel and not enough air. It is a soft, rather large floating yellowish flame.

Riser: Same as a drop line except it conveys the gas up to an appliance.

Rotary Meter: A gas meter which uses an arrangement of rotating impellers to measure the volume of gas.

Safe Start Check: The feature of an ignition control module that prevents it from starting if it is experiencing a real or simulated flame condition prior to the call for heat.

Safety Shut Off Device: A device that interrupts gas supply to the burner in the event of ignition source failure (i.e., pilot flame failure).

Safety Shut Off Valve: A valve that interrupts gas supply to the burner in the event of ignition source failure (i.e., pilot flame failure).

Safety Switch Timing: See trial for ignition time.

Seasonal Efficiency: The overall annual efficiency of the appliance as recorded from the sum of the firing cycles (i.e., steady state efficiency) minus the off cycle losses.

Secondary Air: Air that is mixed with the fuel at the point of combustion and which surrounds the flame to ensure the complete combustion of the fuel.

Sensible Heat: The addition or removal of heat which results in a change in temperature.

Service Regulator: A regulator located at the gas meter inlet that reduces the upstream gas service line pressure in pounds per square inch to 7"wc houseline pressure at the meter outlet.

Slotted Port Burner: The burner is equipped with elongated slots either running across or along the full length of the burner head.

Snap-Acting Control: A non electric control system that employs a snap disc that converts the inherent modulating control action of the system to a on-off action.

Solenoid Valve: A quick opening/quick closing electric valve that is actuated by a solenoid coil.

Spark Igniter: The spark igniter consists of an inner electrode (insulated rod) and an outer ground electrode that may be a normal electrode or the top of the burner. The tip of the spark electrode extends into the path of the main burner gas, arcing the ignition spark across the spark gap thereby igniting the main flame.

Special Venting Systems: Venting systems associated with high efficiency appliances where the appliance manufacturer specifies a specific type of venting such as stainless steel, thermoplastic or PVC plastic vent.

Specific Gravity: The weight of a gas as compared to the weight of air.

Spillage Susceptible Appliances: Natural draft and fan assisted appliances that are susceptible to spillage due to an insufficient draft condition established in the vent system.

Spillage: The process of the flue gases exiting at the appliance draft control relief opening as a result of insufficient draft or a blocked vent.

Stack Losses: See flue losses.

Standing Pilot: See continuous pilot.

Static Pressure: The pressure in a gas line in which no flow is taking place.

Steady State Efficiency: The efficiency of the appliance as determined by appliance Btuh output divided by the appliance Btuh input when the appliance has been firing for some time and all of the operating conditions are at a steady state (i.e., flue gas temperature rise across the appliance).

Surge Arrester: A regulator accessory that induces soft lighting, controls flame roll out and maintains pilot flame stability. The surge arrester is mounted in the regulator vent boss and causes the regulator to open slowly and close normally.

System Control Module: See ignition control module.

Target Pilot: In this type of pilot burner design the gas stream is discharged through a pilot orifice thereby entraining air in the opening. The resulting air/gas mixture will burn against a target type of hood that is located a short distance from the pilot orifice. The target hood functions to direct the pilot flame, helping to determine the flame pattern as well as protecting the flame from drafts.

Terminal Block Connection: A terminal block located in the thermocouple circuit that allows a limit switch to be wired in series with the power unit or pilotstat coil.

Test Dials: 1/2, 1, 2 and 5 cu. ft. meter dials that are used to determine cfh capacity through the meter.

Theoretical Air: See required air/gas ratio.

Thermocouple: A thermal electric device consisting of two dissimilar metals joined together at two junctions. If one of the junctions is heated, there will be created between the junctions a DC(direct current) voltage. The amount of DC voltage produced is determined by the temperature difference between the two junctions.

Thermopile: A thermal electric device consisting of thermocouples wired in series. The voltage output from the thermopile is the collective output of the individual thermocouples.

Thermostatic Control Valve: A non electric control unit that combines both the temperature control and valve functions.

Trial for Ignition Time: Maximum time allowed the ignition control module to establish flame upon burner start up from a call for heat

Turndown Range: The range between the maximum and minimum Btuh firing rates.

Turndown Ratio: Maximum Btuh firing rate/minimum Btuh firing rate.

U-Tube: See manometer.

UA: Microamperes

Ultimate % CO_2: The maximum percentage of carbon dioxide that is obtainable in the fuel gases which only occurs at perfect combustion.

Valve Redundancy: A control valve equipped with two in line valves that operate together giving added protection against valve failure.

Vent Connector: That portion of a venting system that conveys the appliance flue gases from the appliance to the chimney or vent.

Vent Limiting Orifice: A regulator accessory that allows equal limits of inhalation and exhalation of air from the upper diaphragm chamber within the regulator. In the event that the diaphragm does rupture, the leakage is limited to less than 1 cfh at 7" wc gas pressure.

Vent Safety Switch: A thermally activated safety limit switch located at the appliance draft control that protect the appliance from spillage.

Vent: The vertical portion of a venting system that conveys the appliance flue gases to the outside.

Venting System: The system employed by the appliance to vent its products of combustion to the outdoors.

Venturi Tube: See burner mixing tube.

Watt: A metric unit of heat input rate in which 1 watt = 3.413 Btuh.

"WC: Inches of water column.

Working Pressure: The pressure in a gas line in which flow is taking place within the gas line.

Yellow Flame: A flame in which there is no premixing of the air with the gas, resulting in a flame that is yellow in color.

Yellow Tipping: The yellowing of the burner flame as the primary air supply is reduced.

Zero Overfire Draft: See neutral overfire draft.

Index

O

Off Cycle Losses 287

P

Partial Premixing 153
Pascal 15
Pilot
    as a relay 192
    as a separate valve 190
    as a valve component 193
    automatic 183
    burner service analysis 190
    coil 176
    generator 175
    location 188
    protection
        100% 183
        non 100% 183
    turndown test 190
    types
        aerated 184
        incinerating 185
        non - aerated
        target 185**Pilotstat**

Pipe
    branch outlet 72
    coating 70
    dope 70
    identification 75
    minimum size 75
    sizing
        determining factors 82
        multiple appliance installation 87
        single appliance installation 86
    support 71
    tape 71
    vertical chase 73
Piping
    concealed 67, 73
    extension 67
    fittings 68
    location 72
    material 69
    prohibited practice 71
Power Unit Coil 176
Power Ventors 126
Prepurge 219, 250
Pressure
    absolute 22
    atmospheric 22
    barometric 22
    building line 25
    definition 14
    differential switch 303
    drop
        allowable 82
        definition 21
        determining 24
    gauge 22
    gauge
        Bourdon tube 26
        water filled manometer 26
    houseline 25
    inside buildings 75
    lock up 24
    manifold 25
    measurement 25
    static 24
    switch 291
    units 24
    working 24

R

Recycling 219, 250
Regulator (gas pressure)
    analysis of operation 53
    operating elements 52
    sizing 60
    types
        appliance 53
        accessories 58
        component of a combination
          control valve 55
        field servicing 60
        high capacity 55
        low capacity 55
        outlet pressure adjustment 55
    service
        available features 58
        operating components 58
        positive shut off 60
Relative Density 2
Remote Dial Application 207
Remote Reset 219
Retry 219, 250
Rod and Tube Temperature Sensing 207

S

Safe Start Check 219
Safety Shut-off 219
Snap-acting Control 207
Spark Igniter 221
Specific Gravity 2
System Control Module 220

T

Temperature
    dew point 92
    flue gas rise 274
    ignition 3, 8